## Date Due

| | | |
|---|---|---|
| 29 54 | | |
| 10 54 | | |
| | | |

# THE *Natural History* OF *Mammals*

THE *Natural History*

TRANSLATED FROM THE FRENCH
*by H. M. Parshley*

NEW YORK: 1954:
*Alfred A. Knopf*

*by François Bourlière*

OF *Mammals*

L. C. catalog card number: 52–12183

THIS IS A BORZOI BOOK,
PUBLISHED BY ALFRED A. KNOPF, INC.

FIRST AMERICAN EDITION

Originally published in France as
VIE ET MOEURS DES MAMMIFÈRES,
copyright 1951, by Payot, Paris

"*My* work on the species question
*has impressed me very forcibly with the importance of all such works as your intended one, containing what people are pleased generally to call trifling facts. These are the facts which make one understand the working or economy of nature.*"

**CHARLES DARWIN**

*Letter to L. Jenyns, October 12, 1845.*

# Preface
## to the American Edition

THIS translation into English of my book on mammals (*Vie et mœurs des mammifères*, Paris, 1951) has been revised and brought up to date to make it a more comprehensive and more nearly worldwide introduction to field mammalogy. New drawings and photographs have been added, and I hope that they will increase the usefulness of the book.

The bibliography has been enlarged, but it is not intended to be exhaustive. I have selected titles by authors in various countries, wishing to avoid scientific provincialism, and at the same time I have chosen studies representative of the main trends of modern zoological research in the field.

It is a privilege to express my thanks to the many persons who have helped me in the preparation of this edition in English. Among them I may name my friend Richard Pough, Curator of Conservation and Preservation of Natural Resources in the American Museum of Natural History, without whose assistance this book would probably never have been published, and the late Professor H. M. Parshley of Smith College, who undertook the task of translating the original French text and of working out with me the numerous additions and revisions. I gratefully acknowledge also my indebtedness to the individuals and institutions that have aided me in gathering the supplementary drawings and photographs: namely, P. Barruel (Paris), Dr. M. Eisentraut (Frankfurt), Prof. P. P. Grassé (Paris), Robert Hainard (Geneva), Prof. H. Hediger (Basel), Dr. R. Verheyen (Brussels), the New York Zoological Society, and the Marine Studios, Marineland, Florida. Finally, I wish to express my thanks to Alfred A. Knopf, Inc., and to Mr. Philip Vaudrin in particular, for the courteous consideration they have shown me and for the care they have bestowed on the book.

**FRANÇOIS BOURLIÈRE**

*Laboratoire de Biologie Médicale,*
*Faculté de Médecine, Paris,*

# *Introduction*

OF all animals the mammals are probably the most familiar to us. Among them we find the earliest and most valued auxiliaries of man, those domesticated hoofed animals which have played a determining role in the history of civilization and still remain of great importance in the world economy of today. Other species have become our daily companions, and still others have made themselves uninvited guests in our homes and cities. Certain species are prized game animals, whereas others, often labeled "injurious," may be hunted down to the point of extinction.

Besides, since the rise of the experimental sciences, it is the mammals that have furnished the majority of laboratory animals; most of the researches in physiology, experimental medicine, and comparative psychology during the last fifty years have been carried out mainly on a few species of rodents and carnivores.

It might then be supposed that this multiplicity of contacts between the mammals and man would have brought with it a better knowledge of their biology; it would indeed be logical for the various aspects of their life to be better known to us than those of birds, fishes, or certain groups of insects. Unfortunately this is true only in part. Certainly the domesticated species and the laboratory rodents have been studied in great detail, and that biological reagent *par excellence*, the white rat, for example, has served as the subject matter of thousands of publications. This, however, has not much advanced our knowledge of the life of wild mammals—all those which live outside the artificial conditions of domestication or captivity. Moreover, many laboratory biologists have a regrettable tendency to apply to mammals in general, including the primates to which we ourselves belong, the conclusions drawn from their observations on the cat, the dog, the guinea pig, the white rat, or the mouse. Has not, for example, a whole school of experimental psychologists somewhat confused animal psychology with the study of the behavior of the white rat? Such excesses were inevitable once the biologist ceased to be a naturalist, and laboratory experimentation was no longer accompanied by observation in the field. They are no less dangerous to the progress of our knowledge than they are for the conclusions, practical or philosophical, that some will draw from them.

The study of *ethology* (the habits) and of *ecology* (the relations of individuals and of populations with their environment) is therefore of great theoretical and practical importance. It alone will inform us regarding the normal modes of life of the various species, their reactions throughout their vital cycles, and their numerous and remarkable adaptations. It allows us to take account of the great differences, at once morphological, physiological, and psychological, that exist between the different groups, and in some measure serves as an antidote against oversimplification and premature generalization.

Unfortunately the observation of mammals in nature is a delicate matter; most small species are nocturnal, and all display caution and shyness toward the observer. To obtain results of interest requires much ingenuity and patience—and sometimes luck. The study of birds in the field is much easier, and here probably lies one of the major causes of the neglect of the mammals by many naturalists.

During the last twenty years, however, the enthusiasm of a few outdoor mammalogists has increased our knowledge considerably. Thanks to them, many problems have been solved and others—formerly unsuspected—have been posed to challenge the sagacity of research workers. Most of their works, unfortunately, have been published in specialist journals of difficult accessibility and many of them have thus remained unknown to the average naturalist. It is not uncommon even today, therefore, to see articles on mammals which, from the ethological and ecological point of view, could have been written a half century ago.

In the absence of a general synthesis of mammalian ethology and ecology—which would be at present as premature as unwise—the lack of any broad survey of the existing state of our knowledge constitutes an evident gap. It is this gap that I have attempted to fill with this book, limiting myself to the chief problems and to the best known aspects of this vast subject. I have not endeavored to write a manual, still less a treatise on the biology of mammals, but rather a plain introduction to the comparative ethology and ecology of wild mammals. I am quite aware of the imperfections and shortcomings of this work, the aim of which is rather to furnish basic information than to give answers to problems whose solutions depend largely upon future researches. Yet I hope that, such as it is, it will be of service and will guide the beginner through the existing maze of the literature.

I have not considered it necessary to rehearse here the

fundamental concepts of anatomy, taxonomy, and physiology, which, I assume, are familiar to the reader. If, however, he should feel the need of refreshing his memory in these matters, he will find all the essential information in certain of the works cited at the end of this volume. Nor have I considered it necessary to grapple with the problems of genetics, speciation, and geographical distribution. These questions have formed the subject, during the last ten years, of several excellent books.[1]

I have asked my friend Paul Barruel—whose artistic talent is in every way equal to his competence as a naturalist—to make a series of drawings that have freed my text from much arid descriptive matter. I wish to express my sincere gratitude to him. In addition I have been able to reproduce a number of photographs owing to the kindness of Professor Hediger and of the following institutions: the American Museum of Natural History (New York); the United States Fish and Wildlife Service (Washington); *l'Institut des Parcs nationaux du Congo Belge* (Brussels); and *les Expéditions polaires françaises* (Paris). It is my pleasant duty to express here my thanks to them.

[1] Especially: E. Mayr, *Systematics and the Origin of Species* (New York: 1942); and the works of Allee *et al.*, Cuenot, Dobzhansky, Huxley, and Simpson.

# Contents

# Contents

# Illustrations

# Illustrations in the Text

THE *Natural History* OF *Mammals*

### CHAPTER I

# Locomotion

THE mammals have colonized all environments in the course of their evolution. They abound not only in the various terrestrial habitats but in addition some of them have become successfully adapted to aquatic and aerial life. We should not be surprised, therefore, to find among them a great variety of means of locomotion, which can be grouped under three principal heads: walking, swimming, and flying. But nature does not recognize rigid classifications, and it is possible, as we know, to walk, swim, and fly in many ways. In the following pages we shall examine some of the methods most commonly used.

Unhappily our knowledge of this chapter in mammalian biology is particularly meager. There exist a considerable number of works on the structural adaptation of recent and fossil species to different types of locomotion, and on their evolution in time. But we are much more poorly informed on the mechanics of movement in the living animal and on the physiological adaptations to running, diving, or flight. Much remains to be done on this subject, and close observation in the field, accompanied by well-directed experimentation, may well open new horizons for us.

### TERRESTRIAL LOCOMOTION

THE method most frequently practiced by the great majority of land mammals is four-footed, or quadrupedal, locomotion. The mechanics of the normal quadrupedal *walk*, found in the majority of hoofed animals and members of the cat family and the dog family, may be schematized as follows:

In the walk, the animal raises the two diagonally opposite feet, for example the anterior right and the posterior left; it advances them while the other diagonal pair supports and propels the body forward. The animal then replaces on the ground the feet it has advanced and raises the other two

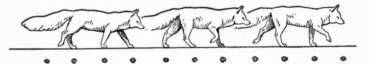

FIG. 1: *Typical "diagonal" gait of fox. Only one half of a stride is represented; the other is symmetrical.*

(fig. 1). According to the relative length of legs and trunk, the hind foot falls in the print of the front foot, behind it, or in front of it. Likewise, in accordance with the width of the body and the length of the legs, the footprints of one side fall on the same line as those of the other side or on parallel lines more or less widely separated.

Certain species, such as the giraffe, brown bear, or camel, exhibit normally a different type of co-ordination of the members, called *pacing*. In this case it is the legs of the same side that are moved simultaneously and not those of one or the other diagonal. Thus, while the two feet of the left side are on the ground, the two feet of the right side are raised, and just when the latter are put down the others are raised (fig. 2). The gait here has a peculiar character, and the legs of the same side move in a parallel fashion. Pacing may also be observed in young or old individuals of species

FIG. 2: *A giraffe pacing. Drawn from photographs by the author.*

that do not practice it ordinarily. It is, for example, the first gait of colts.

In the *trot,* the legs of one diagonal throw the body simultaneously, and between the instants of support by one diagonal or the other there is a period of suspension.

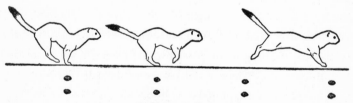

FIG. 3: *Gallop of the ermine.*

The *gallop* is a succession of leaps. In the simplest cases, such as that of the ermine (fig. 3), the animal throws itself by means of the hind legs, extends its body in the air, and lands on the front feet; it immediately shifts the hind feet forward in order to support itself upon them, and then the cycle begins again. Thus the feet are set down more or less in a quadrangle, the hind feet in front of the forefeet. In the hares the forefeet are set down one after the other, then the hind ones touch the ground simultaneously (fig. 4). Lastly, many species place their four feet successively, the hind ones, however, remaining always more separated and making contact with the ground more nearly synchronously than do the front feet.

FIG. 4: *Gallop of the hare, showing succession of positions of contact with the ground.*

The maximum speed attained by wild mammals at a gallop is considerable and can be maintained for rather long periods of time. Table 1 gives some examples furnished by reliable observers. In most cases these speeds have been determined by using an automobile, keeping the car abreast of the animal running on a course parallel with the road. The cheetah, or hunting leopard of India, appears to be the swiftest of all mammals. In full gallop an individual can reach 45 miles an hour two seconds after starting! At full speeds cheetahs are faster than the swiftest greyhounds, attaining rates of 60 to 70 miles an hour. Although we have to do here, of course, with extreme speeds that the animal cannot maintain for long, there is a record of a cheetah covering more than 700 yards in 20 seconds—a rate of slightly more than 71 miles an hour. It is obvious from all this that a trained cheetah is admirably suited to the hunt.

**Table 1.** *Maximum running speeds of some land mammals. (In part after Howell)*

SPECIES/SPEEDS IN MILES PER HOUR

| | |
|---|---|
| *Camel* 9–10 | *Roan antelope* 30–35 |
| *Sheep* 11 | *Hare* 35–45 |
| *Banteng* 11 | *Springbok* 35–60 |
| *Kouprey* 15–18 | *Cape hartebeest* 40 |
| *Wild rabbit* 20–25 | *Mountain zebra* 40 |
| *African elephant* 15–25 | *Spotted hyena* 40 |
| *Black rhinoceros* 28 | *Coyote* 40 |
| *Wolf* 28 | *Grant's gazelle* 40–50 |
| *Wart hog* 30 | *Thomson's gazelle* 50 |
| *Giraffe* 28–32 | *Wildebeest* 50 |
| *Jackal* 35 | *Lion* 50 |
| *Indian wild ass* 30–32 | *Cheetah* 65–70 |
| *Cape buffalo* 35 | |

LOCOMOTION OF PINNIPEDS ON LAND. The seals and related aquatic mammals returning to the land for only a short time each year exhibit all the intermediate stages between typical quadrupedal walking and an awkward creeping in which their rudimentary limbs no longer take any part.

The Falkland sea lion still uses its four limbs after the fashion of an ordinary mammal, but the soft tissues and tail extend so far toward the ankle joints that at each step the hindquarters as a whole are swung forward. Its gait can become rapid if the animal is excited, and on a pebbly beach an adult male can "run" as fast as a man (Hamilton). The enormous southern elephant seal of the subantarctic islands uses only its front legs in traveling on land. "The fore flippers are spread out at the side with the palms on the ground and the fore part of the body is raised by them and hitched forward. At the same time that the fore part is being raised, the back is curved upwards, so that the hind flippers are drawn up slightly nearer, and as the front flippers hitch

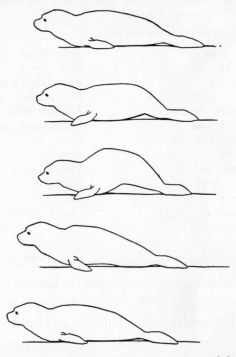

FIG. 5: *Successive stages in the progress of an adult earless seal. Walking consists in a series of forward hitchings. In part after Harrison Matthews.*

forward, the back is straightened, and the body is pushed forward from the pelvic region" (Matthews). These massive creatures, however, can attain a maximum speed of 5 miles an hour and may stray up to 700 yards from the shore. Weddell's seal, a typically antarctic species wintering under the ice pack, has forelegs so small that they do not

*Storing of food. Here an oribi antelope has been killed and placed in a tree by a leopard,* Panthera pardus. *Photograph by G. F. de Witte, taken at Lusinga, Belgian Congo, in January 1948. Courtesy of the* Institut des Parcs nationaux du Congo Belge.

Breathing-hole of a Weddell's seal in the Antarctic ice pack, Adélie Land. Photograph by Harders. Courtesy of the Expeditions polaires françaises.

Resting and sleeping position of a lesser horseshoe bat. Photograph by Ernst Krause. Courtesy of Dr. M. Eisentraut.

even touch the ground when the animal is out of the water. Progression on land then becomes essentially a creeping motion in which the pelvic and pectoral regions are drawn alternately forward.

In the gray seal of the European seas these different types of locomotion are successively used as the individual grows. On the first day the young seal tries to walk on its four feet; it advances its forelegs one after the other and drags its body forward while its hind legs attempt to push. On the second day all systematic use of the hind legs is given up and little by little the front legs become synchronized in their movements; they are extended forward together to afford support to the animal so that it can draw its body forward. This method of locomotion persists until about the tenth day, at which point the young seal has become so fat that the front feet are no longer strong enough to accomplish propulsion by themselves. From now on the animal moves along on its belly (fig. 5) by alternately jerking forward the pectoral and pelvic regions (J. L. Davies).

BIPEDAL WALKING. Certain quadrupeds are able in special circumstances to maintain a bipedal attitude for a few steps. Some stags, for instance, fight in this position, and Waller's gazelle stands up on its hind legs to browse on foliage (fig. 6). But these are exceptional cases among the non-primates.[1]

The bipedal walk of the anthropoids (fig. 8) is altogether different, as witness this vivid description of it in the case of a lar gibbon: "Having mounted the large limb, the animal may stand semi-erect with its hands and arms held

[1] Certain armadillos (fig. 7) and pangolins can on occasion walk on the hind legs with the aid of the tail.

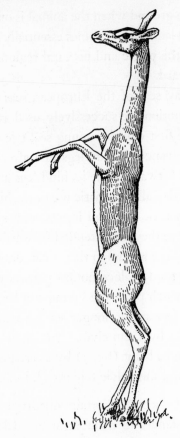

FIG. 6: *Erect bipedal posture of Waller's gazelle browsing on foliage. Based on photographs by Priemel.*

out from its sides and with the elbows and wrists flexed. The legs, too, will be only partially straightened and the trunk will be inclined slightly forward. As the gibbon progresses on the limb, its pelvis rotates markedly as one foot is placed directly before the other. . . ." (Carpenter). This manner of progression is not, however, the most frequent under

FIG. 7: *Bipedal walking in an armadillo,* Priodontes gi-ganteus. *Drawn from a photograph from Grassé,* Traité de zoologie, *Vol.* XVII.

natural conditions, and brachiation, or locomotion by means of the arms, is the rule.

Chimpanzees and gorillas are also only partially bipedal. They rarely stand quite upright, and when walking gener-ally touch their knuckles to the ground with the digits ex-tremely flexed (fig. 9). Man alone is completely bipedal, al-though the pelvis of the fossil Australopithecinæ of South Africa gives us reason to suppose that these primates had as erect a posture as our own.

LEAPING. Along with normal walking, quadrupedal or bipedal, we find in certain mammals a very peculiar progres-sion by leaps in which the tail plays an important part.

The clearest example of it is afforded by the Australian kangaroos (family Macropodidæ). When they walk slowly, the step may be analyzed as follows: The animal, being sup-ported partly on its forelegs and partly on its tail, first raises its hind legs together; then, in a second movement, it is supported on its hind feet, while its forefeet and its tail are raised. The kangaroos, then, really use five members in walking. When the animal accelerates its gait, it employs only the powerful extension of its hind legs, and, during the

FIG. 8: *Bipedal walk of the black gibbon,* Hylobates concolor. *Drawn from a photograph by Suschitzky.*

leap, the tail acts as a counterbalance and is held quite horizontal. So moving, the forester kangaroo can attain a speed of 25 miles an hour, the "peaks" approaching 29 or 30. At a slow pace the leaps may be from about 4 to 6 feet, but they rapidly lengthen with increased speed, and a large animal will cover 26 feet in one bound. Leaps up to nearly 40 feet have been reported. These extreme performances are probably attained only on an especially favorable terrain. It is worth noting that the tail of these large kangaroos has a very special structure: the hemal processes of the vertebræ are

FIG. 9: *Bipedal walk of the chimpanzee. Note how the animal uses the support of its front limbs.*

much flattened; the lower surface of the organ is well supplied with fatty tissue, and the intervertebral muscles are well developed.

Among the rodents a whole series of species normally move about by means of successive leaps or hops. Some, like the spring haas of South Africa, walk on four feet when they are not disturbed and leap by means of their hind legs only when they are frightened. It is the same with the North American jumping mouse. The jerboas of the Old World, on the other hand, generally use only their hind legs in locomotion, and their hind feet are the longest in comparison to the forefeet known among leaping mammals (fig. 10). The

FIG. 10: *Bipedal walk of the northern three-toed jerboa. After a photograph by Serebrennikov.*

tail, likewise, is proportionately very long. The lesser Egyptian jerboa when unhurried walks bipedally, with alternate movements of the hind limbs, the front feet being used to sift through the sand in search of food. When rapid, this animal's locomotion takes the form of a series of lengthy bipedal leaps during which the long tail serves as a balancing organ. The kangaroo rats of western North America, in addition to a bipedal walk used only when the animal is feeding or traveling a short distance, move mostly by long bipedal hops in the manner of the jerboas (fig. 11). When moving slowly, the Merriam kangaroo rat occasionally uses

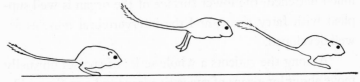

FIG. 11: *Rapid bipedal locomotion of the Merriam kangaroo rat. Redrawn from Bartholomew and Caswell.*

quadrupedal hopping. Its hind legs supply the chief propulsive force, lifting the body forward and upward, but the forefeet support the body weight as the hind legs are drawn forward.

That very peculiar primate, the tarsier of the Malay Archipelago, often moves by leaps, although it is strictly a tree-dwelling form. As with the jerboas, it is the action of the hind legs that accomplishes locomotion, and in both species the tibia and fibula are united distally. One difference is, however, to be noted: in the tarsier it is the tarsal bones and not the metatarsals that are elongated, doubtless so as not to hinder the grasping action of the fingers. Photographs at five thousandths of a second, recently made at the National Zoological Park in Washington, have made it possible to analyze these movements. This little animal, weighing hardly 85 grams when adult, commonly makes leaps of about 6 feet during which it can rise to a height of 2 feet. Before it lands, the tail, held horizontally up to that point, is quickly raised over the back, while the paws are held out to absorb the shock (fig. 12).

ARBOREAL LOCOMOTION. A number of mammalian species spend their entire lives in trees, descending to the ground only rarely, or accidentally. This is true not only of certain monkeys and apes but also of many rodents and arboreal marsupials in tropical regions. Their methods of locomotion would be most interesting to study in detail and offer an almost unexplored field for research.

The techniques of arboreal locomotion would all seem to be more or less directly derived from the techniques of walking, but in some details they show interesting adaptations to a particular environment.

Mounting a tree trunk or a tropical vine by alternate grasping with the hand and foot of one or the other diagonal seems to be a method often used by some monkeys and even by certain species with powerful claws, the three-toed anteater, or tamandua, for example.

FIG. 12: *The leap of the tarsier at the outset. The animal has just left the ground and is rising, its tail extended. After a photograph at ⅕.₀₀₀ of a second by E. P. Walker.*

Some animals climb by alternate movement of the limbs of one side and then of the other, a method that is usually marked by slower progression. Others climb by successive holds, first by the front limbs and then by the hind ones. This method is common among squirrels when they climb a tree trunk, and it has been aptly remarked that in this case "the progress up a tree is essentially a gallop, the fore and hind feet being used alternately in pairs" (Hatt).

In nature, however, the technique of climbing can vary in the same species according to the character of the holds and the way the animal clings to its support. Species with prehensile fingers can grasp the support when it is not too big, as do most of the arboreal primates. Species with well-developed nails (squirrels, tamanduas, etc.) cling by means of their claws when this is at all possible. Other species (bears, sloths, koalas, etc.) literally embrace the support with their limbs and progress more slowly. Possession of a prehensile tail greatly facilitates arboreal locomotion, and certain New World monkeys, such as the spider monkeys, use at once the hands, arms, and tail to make contact with supports when they leap from one tree to another. The

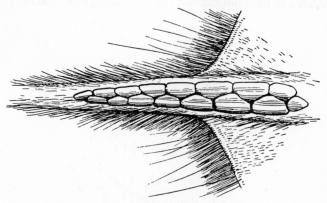

FIG. 13: *Scales on the underside of the tail of a flying squirrel,* Anomalurus, *which serve as an "antiskid" device. From Grassé,* Traité de zoologie, *Vol. XVII.*

scales (fig. 13) beneath the tail of certain flying squirrels of Africa act as an "antiskid" device when the animals land on tree trunks. Among devices for clinging to the support should be mentioned also the adhesive disks of the tarsier's paws.

How animals descend tree trunks is a topic that deserves methodical study. It would appear that species with prehensile fingers, and also those which embrace the support with their limbs, generally descend with the head up. Squirrels, on the other hand, descend head downward (fig. 14), clinging by means of their claws and ordinarily using the four feet independently.

BRACHIATION. Certain monkeys of arboreal habit, such as gibbons and spider monkeys, have a special mode of progression that has been called brachiation. It corresponds in a way to the bipedal walk, but here it is the front limbs that are used in locomotion, not the hind ones. One and the same

FIG. 14: *A squirrel descending a tree trunk, head down. The animal clings to the bark by means of its claws.*

species, for instance the lar gibbon, can moreover use bipedal walking or bimanual brachiation according to whether it is progressing on the ground or in the trees. Carpenter believes that in their customary forest environment the gibbons he observed in Siam move about mostly by brachiation; walking on the ground is practiced only rather exceptionally—in 10 per cent of cases, he estimates.

The mechanism of this two-handed locomotion is simple. First one hand, say that of the right arm, grasps a branch and draws the body forward; then the body oscillates on the pivot made by the right hand, and the hand of the extended

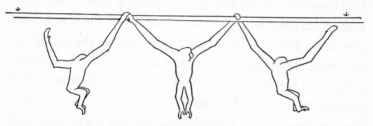

FIG. 15: *Brachiation as performed by the lar gibbon. Drawn from a photograph.*

left arm lays hold on another branch (fig. 15). The gibbon advances rapidly in this way, being able to cover 10 feet in a single swing. If the animal goes from one branch to another that is a little farther away, a short glide occurs between holds.

Such a mode of locomotion is correlated with an extraordinary freedom of motion of the shoulder joint, far greater than that characteristic of man.

The red spider monkey of Panama normally moves about by walking on all fours on large branches, its long tail curved over its back. These monkeys use brachiation only in passing from one branch to another, and they show no hesitation in making impressive leaps, which may reach a length of 38 feet. During the leap the four legs and the prehensile tail are kept outspread to check the fall and to increase the chances of coming in contact with branches. Spider monkeys have been observed letting themselves fall vertically 20 to 25 feet from one branch to another of the same tree.

### AQUATIC LOCOMOTION

SWIMMING BY LAND MAMMALS. Most strictly terrestrial mammals are capable of swimming, if need arises, or at least of keeping themselves at the surface of the water. Species as far from being aquatic as the hare or the European hedgehog sometimes take to the water voluntarily and, under greater compulsion, are able to cross a small stream when pursued. Most of the Muridæ—mice and their allies—do the same, and among the Mustelidæ the ermine, the polecat, and the mink are excellent swimmers. The hamster inflates its cheek pouches with air before taking to the water. The European mole can swim without apparent fatigue for several hundred yards, and the American star-nosed mole can do likewise. The latter has even been seen swimming beneath the ice in winter in small ponds and "sculling" with its tail.

Most ungulates, or hoofed animals, and carnivores can cross small stretches of water. An American black bear, for example, has been observed to swim for five miles! (Cahalane.) That wild boars can cross arms of the sea of considerable size is attested to by the fact that a number of them reached the French island of Oléron after having crossed at least a mile of salt water. The Texas armadillo is also a good swimmer, but if the stream is narrow it simply walks across on the bottom.

Many monkeys have no fear at all of the water and swim with ease. Rhesus macaques normally swim across small streams, and in the experimental colony established on Santiago Island, Puerto Rico, it is not uncommon to see them bathing on the seashore. The lar gibbon, on the other hand, seems incapable of co-ordinated limb movements when placed in water; the fur very soon becomes wet, and experiment has shown that this animal can not even keep itself at the surface for one minute. Gorillas and chimpanzees appear equally incapable of swimming.

In these land species it seems that swimming motions do not differ essentially from those of walking. The problem deserves closer study, however, especially in the case of monkeys.

Even bats are able to keep themselves at the surface. In a recent work, Olof Ryberg cites a whole series of previous observations and adds some new ones that are very convincing. It now appears certain that species like Daubenton's bat, which customarily pursue insects close to the water, can take flight again after having remained some moments at the surface. The fish-eating bat of tropical America does the same.

SWIMMING IN AMPHIBIOUS AND AQUATIC MAMMALS. It is well known that beavers, otters, muskrats, and water rats normally take to the water. The American beaver, when swimming, keeps nine tenths of the body under water, and the front legs, folded back under the chest, are not used; only the hind legs (fig. 16), moving together, propel the animal. The beaver is capable, moreover, of "sculling" at a slow rate of speed, using its tail alone, but this behavior would seem much less frequent than in the muskrat.

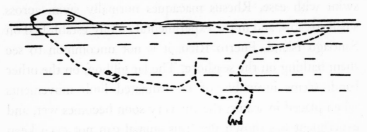

FIG. 16: *Swimming position of the American beaver. After Grinnell, Dixon, and Linsdale.*

The sea otter of the north Pacific comes ashore only on very rare occasions and moves about on land very awkwardly. These otters rest and sleep while floating on their backs, preventing drift by occasional strokes of their tails. They swim on the belly, like fresh-water otters, only when in a hurry; otherwise they always move about on their backs, their four feet in the air, propelled by slow sideways movements of their tails.

Seals use co-ordinated movements of their rudimentary appendages for locomotion in water. But very great differences exist according to the species concerned and their adaptation, more or less nearly complete, to the marine environment. In the Falkland sea lion the front flippers alone are used at slow speeds, in a rowing manner. When the animal wishes to increase its speed it brings its hind limbs into play. The southern elephant seal, on the contrary, never uses its front limbs, which remain pressed against its body while the posterior limbs propel the animal. The same is true of Weddell's seal; the two hind feet are pressed one against the other by their palmar surfaces, with the fingers widely separated for maximum extension of the webs. This whole apparatus is set in motion by regular lateral undulations that enable the animal to maintain a cruising speed of 7 knots (Bertram).

With the cetaceans and sirenians—whales and sea cows —locomotion is accomplished by oscillations of the tail and the flippers in a vertical plane. But tail and flukes move out of phase, the flukes leading the tail by a quarter of a wavelength (Parry). The results obtained by this mode of propulsion are very remarkable: a maximum speed of 15 knots is common in the cetaceans, and blue whales have been observed to swim at speeds of 20 knots for 10 minutes and 14.5 knots for two hours.

SUBMERSION AND ITS MECHANISM. Naturally all the aquatic mammals are capable of distinctly longer submersion than the land species. While the dog has not been ob-

**Table 2.** *Maximum duration of submersion of some amphibious and aquatic mammals. (In part after Irving)*

SPECIES/MAXIMUM SUBMERSION OBSERVED, IN MINUTES

| | |
|---|---|
| *Muskrat* 12 | *Fin whale* 30 |
| *Southern elephant seal* 12 | *Blue whale* 49 |
| *American beaver* 15 | *Sperm whale* 75 |
| *Common seal* 15 | *Greenland right whale* 80 |
| *Florida manatee* 16 | *Bottlenose whale* 120 |

served to remain under water more than 4 minutes and 25 seconds and the white rat more than 3 minutes and 6 seconds, it is quite otherwise with many amphibious and purely aquatic mammals. See Table 2.

Although it is possible that some of the extreme figures given in this table reflect inaccurate observations, it is none the less certain that sirenians, pinnipeds, and cetaceans can bear much longer immersion than land mammals.

Furthermore, these animals dive to considerable depths, as the observations of Scholander and of Laurie demonstrate. Young seals can go down to 240 feet, and the fin whale commonly plunges or "sounds" to depths varying from 275 to 1,150 feet. The sperm whale very probably reaches 3,000 feet!

By what mechanisms can they, as air-breathing vertebrates, endure such prolonged periods without oxygen and return from such great depths without the occurrence of gas bubbles in the bloodstream? Only within the last ten years have the researches of physiologists begun to afford satisfactory answers to this curious problem.

First some negative statements: The resistance of diving mammals to lack of oxygen is not due to larger lungs (which therefore have greater air capacity) than those of land animals. In man, for example, the relative lung capacity is the same as in seals and manatees; it is a litle less than that of porpoises but greater than that of whales—in fact, double! Besides, a too great lung development would hinder diving. The oxygen-carrying ability of the blood, finally, in the blue whale and the dolphins is not very different from that in man or the dog.

On the other hand, at each inhalation the diving mammals renew the air contained in their lungs more completely than do land forms: 90 per cent in the large whales, as compared with 15–20 per cent in man. Moreover, the respiratory center of diving mammals is remarkably insensitive to increase in the amount of carbon dioxide in the blood; this has been shown in the American beaver and muskrat as well as in the Florida manatee, the seals, and the porpoises. These first two adaptations thus serve, in one case, to increase the amount of oxygen available at the beginning of the dive and, in the other, to reduce the stimulating effect of carbon dioxide on the respiratory center of the nervous system.

Moreover, other physiological adaptations permit the economical use of the oxygen stored up at the beginning and restrict its employment to the most essential vital activities. As soon as the dive is begun, the heart slows down considerably. In the gray seal the number of beats falls from 100 to 10 per minute, and this low pulse continues during the 15 to 20 minutes of submersion. The occurrence of this phenomenon in the bottlenose dolphin has been beautifully demonstrated by Irving, Scholander, and Grinnell, who succeeded in taking electrocardiograms of animals diving in semiliberty. At each dive there was a corresponding slowdown in the heartbeat, of the order of 50 per cent. Thus the available oxygen is economized during diving. It is the same with the Florida manatee. In the common seal oxygen consumption during the first minutes of the dive falls to one fifth of what it is when the animal is in repose! Moreover, if the blood pressure remains normal in the large arteries (in spite of the slow heartbeat), it falls rapidly in the small arteries to the level of the pressure in the veins, with complete disappearance of the pulse. There is also a considerable vasoconstriction in the mesenteric blood vessels, while the circulation in the brain remains normal. Thus all the oxygen available is at the disposal of the essential vital activities, the rest of the organism being in some way shut off from the circulation.

How do the diving whales avoid divers' paralysis—caisson disease or "the bends"? It is well known that one of the great dangers of diving, for men, is the frequent production, at the time of emergence, of gas bubbles in the blood which may lodge in the heart or brain and cause paralysis or even sudden death. What happens is this: During the descent, the presure increases with depth, and the blood, passing through the lung capillaries, is charged with dissolved nitrogen, which increases in amount as the pressure rises; the blood will later yield this nitrogen to various tissues. If the return to the surface is too quick, the nitrogen can no longer remain dissolved and will separate out in the form of gaseous bubbles which will cause more or less serious disturbances. For a time it was thought that there existed in whale's blood a micro-organism capable of making use of this nitrogen dissolved in the plasma. Nothing of the kind exists in fact, and it would appear that things can be explained more simply. The cetacean does not live, like the human diver, in air constantly renewed. The animal carries in its lungs only a limited amount of nitrogen. Moreover, at the time of diving, the pressure of the water on the sides of the animal compresses the alveoli of the lungs and forces back into the bronchial tubes, the trachea, or the nasal cavities most of the gas not held by the blood corpuscles. In this way the dissolving of the nitrogen in the plasma is correspondingly reduced. Finally, the high rate of heartbeat that accompanies the return to the surface favors the elimination of the dissolved nitrogen. These safety devices, moreover, are by no means absolute, and Scholander has demonstrated the existence, at emergence, of gaseous embolisms in a seal submitted to an experimental dive of 150 fathoms. It is therefore likely that pinnipeds and cetaceans, when they dive to great depths, are also obliged to follow the rule of returning to the surface by slow stages.

### AERIAL LOCOMOTION

WE find two different types of flight in mammals: the flapping flight peculiar to the bats, and the gliding practiced by the flying squirrels, the flying lemurs (Dermoptera), and the marsupials of the genera *Petaurus*, *Acrobates*, and *Schoinobates*. These two types of flight are not of equal importance. For the mammals that practice gliding flight, this is hardly more than a secondary mode of locomotion, and is used principally, though not exclusively, as a means of escape. The bats, on the contrary, have become strictly aerial mammals and are entirely dependent on flying in their search for food and other activities.

GLIDING. The most classic examples of gliding are to be found among the squirrels. Even in the European red squirrel it is easy to observe (in spite of the absence in this animal of wing membranes—the patagium) a clear tendency to practice gliding. When a pursued squirrel reaches the top of a tree, it does not hesitate to launch itself into the void. Its outspread legs and extended tail serve to steady and balance the animal, and it usually arrives safely on the ground or on another tree trunk.

It is not surprising, then, that the North American flying squirrel, well equipped with parachute-like membranes spread between the limbs and the sides, proves to be an intrepid acrobat. Throwing itself from a treetop fifty feet or more above the ground, it glides easily, controlling its direction by varying the tension of its membranes and the slant of its tail. It can even turn at a right angle to avoid a branch. Before making contact with the tree trunk where it will end its course, it flips its tail upward. In response, the body turns up, the speed is checked, and the landing is made

FIG. 17: *Successive stages in gliding flight and landing in the North American flying squirrel.*

facing upward (fig. 17). The trunk may then be quickly climbed, with another gliding descent to follow.

In Asia the flying squirrels of the family Pteromyidæ are represented by many species that frequent the tropical zones as well as the mountain forests. The giants of this group belong to the genus *Petaurista*, some species of which can accomplish glides of 150 to 200 feet.

In Africa flying squirrels of the family Anomaluridæ glide in the same manner. Species belonging to the genus *Idiurus* would seem to be especially skillful gliders. Sanderson has observed in southern Nigeria two species of this genus lodging in groups in hollow trees. If they are disturbed in the daytime a veritable swarm of perhaps a hundred individuals emerges quickly, overruns trunk and branches, and takes "flight" among the trees. The little animals "take to the air in clouds," Sanderson writes, "floating away among the neighbouring trees like bits of soot from a

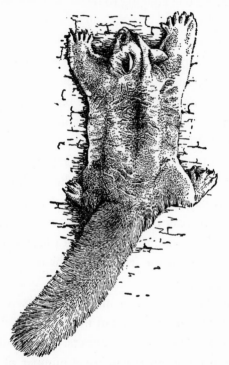

Fig. 18: *A gliding Australian marsupial*, Petaurus sciureus. *From Grassé*, Traité de zoologie, *Vol.* xvii.

chimney, steering themselves over and around obstacles with the facility of birds, and landing silently, hundreds of feet away, without any apparent loss of height."

In Australia the flying phalangers (fig. 18) behave in similar fashion. The sugar glider can glide for 50 yards and the greater glider-opossum for 120. An individual has even been observed to cover 590 yards in six successive "flights"!

The flying lemurs of the Malay Archipelago are almost as skillful. *Cynocephalus volans* easily covers 70 yards or more, and it is noteworthy that a mother in flight is able to carry her young one clinging to her lower surface.

FLAPPING FLIGHT. Among the mammals, this is found only in the Chiroptera, or bats, which have indeed become as aerial as the birds. The largest species, such as the Indo-Malayan *Pteropus vampyrus*, a fruit bat whose wingspread may be more than a yard, are capable of long, sustained flight. The Molossidæ, a family of tropical bats with relatively long and narrow wings, have a rapid flight which recalls that of the swifts. But most of the small bats have an irregular and capricious flight, broken by sudden changes in direction that may be horizontal as well as vertical. The flight of the little common bats called Pipistrelles even has some resemblance to the irregular flight of a large butterfly.

The only attempt so far made to analyze the flight of bats is the work of the German mammalogist Max Eisentraut. Using a motion-picture camera, he has succeeded in recording the wing movements of a number of small species. Without going into technical details, we may sum up his conclusions by saying that mechanically the normal flight of a bat is very much like that of a bird. The wing is lowered forward and downward, then is raised upward and backward (fig. 19). The body is kept almost horizontal and is raised slightly during the downbeat of the wings. The number of flaps per second varies with the species, from 12 in *Myotis* to 16 and 19 in the pipistrelle and the noctule.

Some species, such as the long-eared bat, can hover at a fixed point for some moments. In this case the body is almost vertical, but the wings keep up the same movements and the bat is in a sense flying vertically, the lift being just enough to counteract the force of gravity.

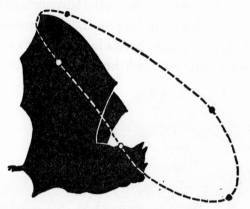

FIG. 19: *Path of wingtip during ordinary flight of a lesser horseshoe bat. After Eisentraut, 1937.*

Gliding flight is used by bats, but they do not seem able to use upward heat currents and to practice soaring, as do many birds.

The tail does not appear to play an important part in steering the flight. In some species the interfemoral membrane is curved forward before landing, probably acting as a brake.

The process of taking flight has been studied in a large mouse-eared bat, hanging from a branch by its hind feet. Instead of letting itself fall before beginning to fly, the animal begins by flapping its wings, with the result that the axis of the body is raised to a horizontal position before taking off.

"ECHO-SOUNDING" FLIGHT NAVIGATION IN BATS. Naturalists have long been deeply interetsed in the ease with which bats can fly in complete darkness and the fact that many of them feed on insects captured in flight at twilight or during the night. Their little eyes alone would seem to be quite unable to guide them in the labyrinths of the caves where many withdraw during the daytime, and still less to permit the bats to locate insects in flight or to avoid collision, in total darkness, with branches or other obstacles.

FIG. 20: *Downstroke of the wing of the little brown bat; the animal was flying on the level at ten miles per hour when the photograph was taken (at* $\frac{1}{100,000}$ *of a second). After a photograph by H. E. Edgerton.*

As far back as the eighteenth century the great Italian naturalist Spallanzani demonstrated that blinded bats remained nevertheless perfectly able to fly about in a room without colliding with walls, furniture, or threads stretched across their way. Shortly after, the Swiss Louis Jurine showed that a bat with reduced hearing is, on the contrary, unable to avoid obstacles in flight. The later experiments of Rollinat and Trouessart in France and of Hahn in the United States confirmed these discoveries.

In 1920 the English physiologist Hartridge suggested that bats flying in darkness were able to sense the presence of obstacles by sending out supersonic vibrations that would be reflected back to their ears. It was only twenty years later, and after the development of radar, that two Americans, Griffin and Galambos, were able to demonstrate how well founded this hypothesis was. With the help of an apparatus that registered these inaudible vibrations, they established a whole series of curious facts.

To begin with, the species they studied—the big brown bat, the little brown bat, Keen's bat, and the eastern pipistrelle—gave out four different classes of sounds: (1) a shrill cry with a frequency of 7 kilocycles, or 7,000 cycles per second, perceptible to the human ear and continuing for about one quarter of a second; (2) a buzz, not audible unless the observer is quite close to the animal; (3) a very rapid and hardly perceptible click; and finally (4) the supersonic "cry," imperceptible to the human ear, of frequencies varying between 30 and 70 kilocycles. Those between 40 and 55 kilocycles are the most common. A bat in repose gives out, on the average, 5 to 10 of these "inaudible cries" each second; but when it takes flight they increase in frequency to 20 or 30 per second and even reach 60 in the vicinity of an obstacle. Buzzing and clicking always accompany the emission of the supersounds (fig. 21).

As yet the production of these four kinds of supersounds is not well understood, but it is certain that the sound apparatus of the bats is very different from that of the other mammals. The larynx, bony and well provided with muscles, is probably the place where these sounds originate.

It would appear to be well established, then, that the bats so far studied surely give out supersounds in flight, and the more so as the obstacle is nearer. These supersounds are reflected by the object to be avoided, and the "echo" is in

FIG. 21: *Upstroke of the wing of the little brown bat. Note the opening of the mouth (to permit the emission of supersounds). After a photograph by H. E. Edgerton.*

turn received by the ears of the animal, which can thus perceive the distance of the obstacle. If, indeed, the ears of the animals are experimentally stopped, their skill in avoiding obstacles is considerably diminished. One may ask, further, how the animal in flight can distinguish the "echo" from the "inaudible cry" that gives rise to it. Now, Griffin and Galambos have shown that during the emission of the supersounds there is a momentary contraction of a minute ear muscle that puts the ear out of action for a moment while the squeak is being made, so that the bat's hearing is not temporarily paralyzed by the loudness of its own squeak, but is keenly awaiting the reflected echo.

What is the range of this supersonic "radar"? It must be restricted, since the supersounds do not carry very far. It has been established, in fact, that the "inaudible cries" given out by bats do not carry more than five yards and that they give a usable echo at about four yards. Two individuals of the same species, therefore, should hardly interfere with each other in flight unless they are very close.[2]

Certain aspects of the problem, however, still remain unclarified. It is unknown how bats in flight succeed in distinguishing the "echoes" reflected by obstacles to be avoided from those reflected by the insects that are being sought. And yet they must make this distinction; the long-eared bat and the whiskered bat, which catch insects on leaves and not solely in the air, must therefore perceive the presence of their prey on the obstacle. If one throws a pebble into the

[2] Horseshoe bats, or Rhinolophidæ, do not emit their supersounds through the mouth, like the Vespertilionidæ, but only through their nostrils, as recently established by F. P. Möhres (*Zeits. f. vergleich. Physiologie*, 34:547–88, 1953). These supersounds—of frequencies varying between 80 and 100 kilocycles—are oriented by the nose-leaf, whose contraction can even increase the range of the echo-sounding mechanism. It is probable that echo-sounding by supersounds does not function when the bat returns to its place of shelter; some species, in fact, will allow themselves to be caught in strings stretched across the entrance to a cave. This fact probably explains also the fatal collisions, observed by Vesey-Fitzgerald, of individuals belonging to different species (noctule and brown bat; pipistrelle and barbastelle). It is likely, also, that a bat that has just captured a large prey is temporarily hindered in the production of supersounds because its mouth is full.

Finally, an odd item of behavior merits investigation from this point of view: Father Licent tells me that in China children catch bats in the following manner. They attract the bats at dusk by whipping long willow rods through the air so that they whistle and ultimately knock down the animals. In Central America, Sanderson successfully used a long pole fixed in the ground by its thick end and given a circular motion so rapid that a high-pitched sound was produced (*Living Treasure*, 1945, pp. 223–4).

air below a bat, it will dive toward the stone and will avoid it by a swerve at the last moment. Clearly the delicacy of the audio-location mechanism is very great.

The study of mammalian locomotion, as we have seen, poses at present a number of curious and unsuspected problems. The study of the diving of marine forms and of the supersonic "radar" of bats has brought us far indeed from the classical analysis of the horse's gaits. But there is nothing to be surprised at in this. Locomotion is in a way the fundamental activity of an animal, that which conditions most of its other activities, and in particular the search for food and for a mate. Parallel with the structural modifications of the skeleton and the muscles, therefore, one must expect to find physiological adaptations of the nervous system, the sense organs, and behavior, as illustrated by the few examples given in this chapter.

### CHAPTER 2

# Food and Feeding Habits

THE classic distinction among herbivorous, carnivorous, and omnivorous forms is so firmly anchored in the minds of all that one might be tempted to suppose that the eating habits of the mammals are completely known to us. In point of fact we are still very far from being acquainted with the mere essentials of what we should know, even in the case of the commonest species. The problem is, indeed, not so simple as it may appear. The diet of a single species may vary greatly in time, as in space. Preferences and nutritional requirements are modified with age, and laboratory animals have already taught us a great deal in this connection. But there is more: unless a species is strictly confined to a specialized diet—and we shall cite some examples of this—the daily menu is strongly influenced by the availability of the various food substances suitable for consumption. It follows that for many animals the diet varies considerably from one season to another, and that in a given season the individuals inhabiting a certain part of the range of a species will not feed on the same things as others that inhabit a different region.

### DIET

TO the difficulties inherent in the variability of most biological phenomena must be added the special technical difficulties met with in the study of the diet of wild species. The simplest approach to the problem, and that which was for long the only one employed, is direct observation of the feeding preferences of individuals living under natural conditions. A good field naturalist, watching the behavior of an elephant, an antelope, or a monkey, can make interesting observations on the fruits, herbaceous plants, or types of foliage sought or avoided by the animal. In similar fashion the bones or skulls brought by a carnivore into the vicinity of its lair often make it possible to identify the captured prey. But this direct method, applicable to species of some size, is of no help to us in ascertaining the diet of a small mammal, which, moreover, is usually nocturnal.

We must then resort to other evidence. The investigation of droppings, for example, enables us to recover numerous fragments of animal or plant origin, some of which are identifiable through careful study under the binocular or ordinary microscope. Hairs, teeth, small bones, seeds, fibers, and plant fragments sometimes permit generic or even specific identification. Dusi's recent work is an example of this. It must be noted, however, that only a part of the ingested material is detected by this examination of droppings; some foods leave no trace of their passage through the alimentary tract.

Investigation of the stomach contents also provides data of interest. If the animal is killed shortly after its last meal, ingested foods will be found in its stomach, and they will be quite easily identifiable. But if this meal has been eaten a longer time before capture, the less digestible foods have a better chance of being identified than the others, and the student will run the risk of gaining a false impression concerning the food preferences of the species. In any case this method, like the preceding, will show us what the animal consumes and not at all what it avoids.

The results of these analyses of the excrement or of the stomach contents will enable us to draw up a list of recognizable foods consumed by a given species, in a given locality, and at a given season. It can be completed by calculating what percentages of the various foods are found in the different samples examined. This prevents giving to such prey as has been identified in only 2 or 3 per cent of the stomachs the same importance as is given to what has been found in 75 or 90 per cent of the same stomachs. Sometimes it can be of a certain interest also to determine the relative volume of the foods ingested and recovered. This may be accomplished very easily by submerging the different foods successively in a graduated test tube previously filled with water to a given level.

VEGETARIAN DIETS. The artiodactyl ruminants—cud-chewing hoofed animals—are the most specialized of all the herbivores. In these mammals the entire digestive tube shows remarkable anatomical and physiological adaptations that help us to understand how their metabolic requirements are met by an exclusively vegetarian diet. Man needs, to be sure, a balanced food ration to keep himself in good health, that is, a ration containing, besides the vitamins and trace mineral elements, a minimum quantity of carbohydrates, fats, and proteins. Now, we know that the Bovidæ, or ox family, the Cervidæ, or deer family, and some other related families are nourished exclusively on herbaceous plants and foliage—foods composed largely of water, cellulose, and carbohydrates indigestible for man. Their organism ought, then, to be capable of finding in this vegetal raw material all the chemical elements needed for the metabolism of a mammal. And this is indeed the case.

It is well known that the stomach of the ruminants is provided with an enormous reservoir, the rumen or first stomach, where the food is stored after brief chewing. This rumen contains an extremely rich flora of anærobic bacteria that is absolutely essential to the good health of the adult animal. It is these bacteria, as Pasteur suspected as early as 1885, that hydrolyze the cellulose and other carbohydrates of plants, for the first stomach secretes no digestive enzyme at all. Further, in the rumen and the second stomach occur important fermentations that, acting on glucose, produce lactic acid, pyruvic acid, and fatty acids. Finally, the rumen bacteria synthesize both protein substances and certain vitamins (of group B).

In the non-ruminant herbivores it is the bacteria of the large intestine (in the horse family and in certain rodents [1]) or those of stomach diverticula (in the hippopotamus and in kangaroos) that have the same function. In both cases the length of the digestive tube, as compared with the total

---

[1] The daily amount of grass ingested by some Microtinæ (field mice and the like) is considerable, equal to or even greater than their own weight. Most of the herbivores must devote a large part of the day to eating, and they cannot fast for long without injurious effects. Schäfer (*Zool. Garten*, 10:29, 1938) points out that the giant panda spends 10 to 12 hours a day in eating. A manatee 15 feet long eats 80 to 100 pounds of plants a day.

*Topography of the home range. A red-deer wallow. Courtesy of Professo*
*Hediger, Basel.*

*Topography of the home range. A termite nest polished by the animals' rub*
*bing in the home range of Burchell's zebra. Note the trampled ground aroun*
*the nest. Buffalos also frequent these landmarks. Photograph by Hediger*
*Courtesy of the Institut des Parcs nationaux du Congo Belge.*

*Topography of the home range. Network of hippopotamus trails. Most of these trails are used for dozens of years in succession. Photograph by Hediger. Courtesy of the* Institut des Parcs nationaux du Congo Belge.

*Topography of the home range. Heap of dung deposited by the West African civet. Photograph by R. Verheyen, taken at Kenonga, Belgian Congo. Courtesy of the* Institut des Parcs nationaux du Congo Belge.

length of the body, is much greater than in carnivores of similar size.[2]

Most of the herbivores so far mentioned eat a great variety of plants.[3] Young shoots, leaves, flowers, tender stems, and even the bark of many plants are commonly eaten by one and the same mammalian species. From one season to another the preferences of a given individual may change, and the relative abundance of certain plants may be a decisive factor in its choice.

There exist, however, a few well established instances in which the vegetarian diet of a species is narrowly specialized. The Australian koala eats only the leaves of the eucalyptus (about two and a half pounds a day, for an adult), to the exclusion of all other plants. And it should be added that the animal is to be found feeding on only a few species: *Eucalyptus punctata, E. microcorys, E. melliodora,* and *E. rostrata.* The three-toed sloth of the neotropical forests consumes only the leaves, buds, and young shoots of *Cecropia palmata* (a tree of the mulberry family) or, lacking that, of *Spondias lutea* (the hog plum tree). A little tree-

---

[2] The habit of "refection," or passing the food twice through the intestine instead of only once, seems to be a common phenomenon in the rabbits and hares. Domestic rabbits usually eat and swallow without chewing their night droppings, which form in the morning as much as half the total contents of the stomach. In the wild rabbit refection takes place twice daily, and the same habit is reported for the European hare (MOROT, C., *Rec. Méd. Vétér.* Paris, 59:635, 1881; MADSEN, H., *Nature,* 143:981, 1939; TAYLOR, E. L., *Nature,* 143:982, 1939). It is believed that this habit provides the animals with large amounts of B vitamins produced by bacteria in the food within the large intestine. The same habit has recently been reported in the common shrew (Crowcroft, P., *Nature,* 170:627, 1952).

[3] Poisonous plants raise some interesting questions. Hediger has observed, at the Berne Zoo, that exotic ruminants often poison themselves by eating *Solanum nigrum,* a poisonous plant that native chamois and ibex "instinctively" avoid. It would be of interest to analyze such behavior and to distinguish its innate and learned elements.

dwelling rodent, the red tree mouse of the humid forests of the northwestern United States, is closely associated with the Douglas fir; the needles and the bark of young shoots of this tree constitute its favorite food, and it cannot do without them, even in captivity. Young leaves are entirely consumed, but the sides and resin ducts of older leaves are discarded. Another curious instance of diet specialization is that of the giant panda, native to the mountainous regions of southeastern Asia. This rare but in some ways familiarly known animal lives almost exclusively on bamboo shoots, and certain bony modifications in the skeleton of its hand may be correlated with this special food habit. The point hardly needs to be emphasized that such narrowly specialized diets are probably a heavy handicap in the evolution of a species, for any change in the flora of its habitat may constitute a risk threatening to cause its extinction. On the other hand, a group of greater ecological plasticity will adapt itself more easily to modifications of the flora.

*Fruits* constitute a food sought by many mammals (fig. 22), especially in tropical regions. Among the bats, the family Pteropidæ of the Old World are almost exclusively frugivorous, and they therefore bear the vernacular name of fruit-eating bats. The preferred kinds of fruit often vary according to the season, but everywhere bananas, guavas, papayas, and other cultivated species are eaten quite as readily as the fruit of wild figs and of numerous native species. In tropical America the fruit bats of the genus *Artibeus* have similar habits; in the West Indies they attack, for instance, the fruits of palm trees of the genus *Acrocomia* and carry them into their sleeping-places, thus aiding in the dispersal of the palms. Many monkeys, such as the red spider monkey, are likewise great fruit lovers. In French Equatorial Africa, according to Malbrant and Maclatchy, the distribution of the mustached white-nosed monkey is "largely conditioned" by the existence of the palm *Elæis*.

*Seeds* constitute a vegetable food notable for its slight water content. This is of no account when the seeds are

FIG. 22: *Fat dormouse eating a grape. Note the attitude of the animal, sitting on its hind paws, and the use of its front members for manipulating the food.*

eaten along with fresh plant material or by species that drink regularly, but it may well be asked how certain desert rodents succeed in nourishing themselves almost exclusively on dry seeds all the year round without ever drinking.

As a matter of fact it has been possible to maintain in good health some rodents of the North African deserts, especially the Egyptian gerbil, and some kangaroo rats and pocket mice of the deserts of the southwestern United States, on a diet of barley and oat seeds in which the water content does not exceed 5 to 10 per cent. These rodents, which were given no drinking water, not only failed to lose

**43**

weight, but fattened normally. Under the same conditions an ordinary white rat rapidly loses 40 to 50 per cent of its weight and cannot long survive. Schmidt-Nielsen's recent studies have shown that the organism of the desert Heteromyidæ presents interesting physiological adaptations. There is no special reserve of water in the tissues, but, on the other hand, the urine is twice as concentrated as in other rodents. There is, therefore, a significant economy of metabolic water which is enough to cover most of the animal's needs. Not all the little desert mammals, moreover, are alike in this matter. The white-throated wood rat is quite unable to live on a diet made up exclusively of dried seeds, and in the deserts were it lives it has to find in succulent cacti the water it needs.

*Bark* is sought by many mammals, especially at certain seasons of the year. In Europe the bark eaters are chiefly represented by the deer, red squirrels, and voles. The damage these animals do to trees is often by no means negligible. The roe deer and the red deer pull off strips of bark from below upward, while the fallow deer gnaws the bark rather like a goat. The red squirrel injures young pine and larch; it denudes surfaces that may be as large as a hand and licks up the sap that exudes from the wound. Sometimes it leaves very characteristic spiral marks. The field vole and water vole gnaw into the wood, the former above, and the latter under, the ground. The hare also sometimes removes strips of bark.

In North America the porcupine feeds in winter almost exclusively on the inner bark of conifers and hardwoods, often denuding the trunks up to a great height. In springtime it attacks the sap-filled cambium of maples, particularly the sugar maple. The Canadian beaver is still more specialized. Its provisions for the winter consist entirely of branches and trunks of poplar, aspen, cottonwood, and willow, from which it gnaws the bark during the cold season. Bark of coniferous trees is not eaten. In spring and summer its menu is varied with aquatic plants and berries. Bradt calculated that in the Michigan colonies he studied each beaver cut down an average of six trees every ten days! The moose is also a great lover of bark, both in winter and in spring.

*Mushrooms and lichens* are not neglected as food by the mammals. In France the red squirrel frequently eats them, including even the poisonous amanitas. Hainard reports having twice seen a squirrel descend to the ground to get a mushroom before climbing up to eat it on a branch. Other observers have noted that this animal sometimes stores them up, impaled on broken branches. The roe deer also eats mushrooms at times, including *Russula emetica*, the subterranean truffle-like *Elaphomyces granulatus*, and *Cordyceps militaris*, which grows on insects. In America squirrels of the genus *Tamiasciurus* seem to eat fungi still more freely than their European cousins; they even dig for subterranean species. In the northern regions of Canada caribou consume a considerable quantity of mushrooms during July and August. Fungi can even constitute an effective emergency ration for species that normally eat few mushrooms. Tevis has recently reported that in 1950, after the failure of the seed crop of conifers and shrubs in the northern Sierra Nevada, chipmunks and ground squirrels turned to the sporophores of hypogeous fungi for food. As these were obtainable in large amounts, the rodent population did not appear to suffer from the failure of the seed crop.

Most unusual is the *nectarivorous diet* of some tropical mammals. Among the bats that feed on pollen and nectar should be mentioned the genera *Glossophaga, Choeronycteris,* and *Lonchophylla* (Glossophaginæ) and *Eonycteris* and *Megaloglossus* (Macroglossinæ). Allen calls attention to the lengthening of the tongue and the modifications in the dentition common to these various genera. It has even been suggested that certain night-blooming tropical plants, like *Crescentia,* are regularly pollinated by the bats, and this may indeed be so.

MEAT DIETS. These are extremely widespread among the mammals and are characteristic of whole orders. Mammals and birds are the favorite prey of typical carnivores such as the Canidæ, the Felidæ, or the Mustelidæ.[4] The large species—lions, tigers, leopards, hyenas, and the like—hunt the ungulates in particular, while the small species are satisfied with more modest prey. It is the diet of these last that so far has been most closely studied. The work of Scott on the food of the northern plains red fox in the Des Moines River valley (Iowa), may serve as a model of such research. It discloses in the first place a marked seasonal variability in the diet: in winter this fox is primarily carnivorous, while in the other seasons insects and plants constitute an important ele-

[4] There exist also some bats that are unquestionably carnivorous: *Phyllostomus hastatus* of tropical America accepts in captivity other bats, small rodents, and birds; *Megaderma lyra,* of the Far East, is normally predaceous on birds, rodents, and batrachians, a fact that has been verified in Ceylon. Among the Australian marsupials the carnivores are represented by the Dasyurinæ and the Tasmanian "wolf" *Thylacinus cynocephalus.* The habits of the little crest-tail marsupial-mouse of the Australian deserts are very curious; as soon as it sees its prey it gazes steadily at it, waves its tail as a lizard does, and pounces on it like a flash (Wood Jones, 1949).

ment in its daily menu. The relative abundance of the various foods naturally affects the precise composition of this menu, but food *preferences* are also definitely in evidence. Thus, the mammals most preferred are prairie meadow mice and, in less degree, lemming mice; the insectivores, to the contrary, seem to be systematically ignored. This is not a unique fact, since Southern and Watson have come to the same conclusion in their study of the European red fox in England. The animal is influenced also by its age in its choice of prey; young foxes seem at first to proceed on the basis of trial and error for the most part, and they tend to nibble at and then swallow whatever they find around the lair.

Some of the large carnivores prey especially on man. It is well known that certain tigers, lions, and panthers become "man-eaters," that is, they acquire a special taste for human flesh. Prater, in agreement with a number of good observers, holds that the success of a chance attack on man is what causes certain individuals to lose the innate fear of our species that is felt by most wild animals. Moreover, a period of famine may embolden a female suckling her young and thus favor the man-eating habit. This perhaps would account for the fact that most man-eaters are females. There are certain observations that favor this view: in India the great famine that occurred in Gujarat, from 1901 to 1903, was accompanied by a rise in man-eating among the tigers and panthers of the region. In Central Africa, on the Rwindi-Rutshuru plain that now forms the southern part of Albert National Park, "epidemics of anthropophagy" in lions broke out around 1860 and between 1904 and 1909, probably coinciding with notable reductions in the numbers of kobs and topis, antelopes native to the plain (Hubert).

*Corpses and carrion* can serve on occasion as food for the carnivores just mentioned, but this is exceptional. Some mammals, on the other hand, commonly seek out this type of food. Thus the spotted hyena is one of the chief scavengers of the African bush-veldt. Although it is quite capable of hunting living prey for itself, it is for the most part content to feed on the lion's leavings. Its stomach, in which digestion would seem to be very rapid, is filled with broken bones, hair, and sometimes feathers; Matthews seldom found undigested meat in it. Prater tells of a large male striped hyena, killed in the Hyderabad jungles, whose stomach was crammed with dried and unbroken bones, probably swallowed in that condition.

*Reptiles:* lizards sometimes constitute a portion of the diet of many small carnivores such as foxes, badgers, and the like. Turtle eggs are sought by others, such as skunks, which can dig up eggs of the snapping turtle from the sand. Some mammals have the more unusual taste for snakes, even including poisonous species. The common European hedgehog is perfectly capable of coping with a viper; Herter has seen one present its quills to the snake and then, at the right moment, seize the exhausted reptile and crush its head or spinal column. The hedgehog's resistance to the viper's poison, while not complete, is quite remarkable; it is perhaps 35 to 40 times greater than that of a guinea pig of the same weight. Curiously enough, it is equally resistant to the poison of bees and to cantharidin, the irritating substance in blister beetles. The mongooses (*Herpestes*), as is well known, are also fierce enemies of snakes. In India they attack highly poisonous species, including cobras. They attack in a variety of ways, but their extreme agility and the bristling of their fur constitute their best means of defense. Although the mongooses, like the hedgehog, are strongly resistant to poisons, a sufficient dose will kill them, for their immunity is not complete.

It is a remarkable fact that the resistance of a mammal to the poison of a snake can be observed in species that never come into contact with poisonous snakes. Vellard has recently shown, for instance, that the Andean skunk (*Conepatus inca*) of the Huaron region of Peru (altitude 13,300–14,000 feet), manifests an undeniable resistance to the poison of the Crotalidæ (rattlesnake family), although there are no snakes to be found at such altitudes. We have to do here with a natural primary resistance different from that of the skunks of lower and warmer regions; these latter commonly attack snakes and manifest a still stronger resistance, a true active immunity.

*Fish* forms the basic diet of some species. The European otter consumes a great variety: eels, trout, minnows, and others; but it does not spurn crayfish, frogs, snails, earthworms, and even rats and aquatic birds. Despite its name, the fishing cat of India is likewise not satisfied with fish and mollusks; it occasionally attacks not only birds but even dogs and cattle. More unexpected is the existence of fishing bats: *Noctilio leporinus* of tropical America (fig. 23), *Pizonyx vivesi* of the Gulf of California, and probably *Megaderma lyra* of India.

*Arthropods* make up the sole diet of the tropical American anteaters (*Myrmecophaga*, *Tamandua*, *Cyclopes*, etc.), of the Old World pangolins and aardvarks and the Australian banded anteaters. These animals present well-known morphological adaptations of claws and tongue which enable them to tear open and explore the galleries of the nests

FIG. 23: *The fish-eating bat with a fish just caught. After Gudger.*

FIG. 24: *The giant anteater, a strictly insectivorous mammal.*

of termites and ants (fig. 24). They consume considerable amounts of the eggs, cocoons, and adults of these insects. In the stomach of a young female of the relatively small three-toed anteater, Enders found more than a pound of ants! The aardvark of Africa, which may reach a total length of six feet, also feeds only on termites and ants that it captures by means of its long, protractile tongue.[5] The pangolins of Africa and Asia do likewise, and the African aardwolf is said to feed mainly on termites.

The small bats of the suborder Microchiroptera are in general insectivorous, and most of them, as already noted, catch the insects in flight, at twilight or during the night. It is likely that bats do not select the prey captured in this manner, but it is always possible for a distasteful insect to be rejected at once after capture. Poulton's careful study of the diet of English bats shows that the identifiable remains of insects, collected from the ground in the retreats where long-eared bats and greater horseshoe bats resort to devour their catch, are composed chiefly of the wings of noctuid (owlet) moths. Among 1,328 identifiable wings only 16 belonged to species without protective coloration, and 10 among these were wings of two species (*Spilosoma lubricipeda* and *S. menthrastri*) that are showy forms with warning coloration, often refused by insectivores in captivity. Is this small percentage due to choice on the part of the bats, or does it indicate only the relative rarity of species with warning coloration in the lepidopterous fauna of the regions under study? Further research is needed before an answer can be reached.

The diet of a majority of the insectivores is in reality much more varied than the name of the order would lead one to suppose. Let us take the European mole as an example. Hauchecorne's research in Germany has shown that of 200 stomachs investigated 178 contained earthworms;

[5] It is possible, however, to keep aardvarks alive in captivity on a different diet. The London Zoological Garden has maintained them for several years by giving them a thick gruel composed of milk, finely ground horsemeat, bran, and raw eggs.

130, the larvæ of beetles; 74, adult beetles; 70, flies; 35, moths or butterflies; 18, Hymenoptera—ants, wasps, and the like; 52, myriapods; 10, mollusks, such as snails; 3, parts of mice; 19, mole hairs; and 71, plant fragments. A single individual mole can eat in the course of a day the equivalent of its own weight in live food; this voracity is one of the reasons why moles are difficult to maintain in captivity. In like manner insects and spiders are consumed on occasion by omnivores such as rodents and even by some carnivores. Prater mentions the example of the Bengal fox, which at the time of termite swarming will come to catch the winged forms above the termite nests. Bears are fond of the brood and the honey of wild bees; in India the sloth bear attacks the nests of bees (*Apis dorsata* and *Apis indica*), and in North America the black bear robs the nests of wasps and bees and even artificial hives. In the mountains of California beehives are often placed high on platforms or surrounded with electrified barriers to protect them from greedy bears. In tropical Africa the ratel or honey-badger commonly robs bee nests. There exists, at least in Africa, a kind of commensalism between this mustelid and birds of the family Indicatoridæ, which indicate to it the presence of the wild bee nests.

Crustaceans constitute the basic food of only a few very specialized forms; namely, the whales of the suborder Mysticeti, in which the teeth are replaced by whalebone (fig. 25). In the South Atlantic, humpbacks, blue whales, and fin whales live almost exclusively on the plankton shrimp *Euphausia superba*. The astronomical quantities of shrimp which must be ingested daily to fill the needs of these marine monsters may well be imagined! The shrimp, however, live in enormous shoals near the surface during the antarctic summer, and it is then that the large whales migrate far south to fatten on this "krill." In winter these whales eat little and their blubber is much reduced in quantity. In the North Atlantic the euphausiid shrimp *Meganyctiphanes norvegica* is similarly consumed in summer.

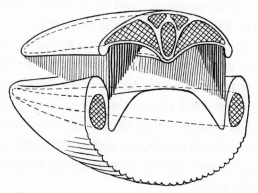

FIG. 25: *Diagram showing the plankton strainer formed by the whalebone of a* Balænoptera. *After Hentschel.*

*Mollusks* serve as the occasional prey of many terrestrial mammals and as the regular food of some marine forms. Thus the sea otter of the California coast appears to live chiefly on the red abalone. After having detached this shellfish from the bottom, the otter rises to the surface, turns on its back, breaks the shell, and eats the soft parts within. The shell is very hard, and so the animal sometimes makes use of one shell to open another, or, better, it places a small stone on its chest and pounds the shellfish on this improvised anvil. This extraordinary behavior—one of the few known instances of the use of a tool by a mammal other than man—was observed by Fisher and has since been seen by Murie, who even succeeded in filming it. Besides the abalones, the sea otter in California also eats sea urchins and crabs. In Alaska its diet is quite different. There the sea urchin *Strongylocentrotus drobachiensis* is its main food, and Murie has found remains of it in 188 droppings out of 198! This instance, among many others, shows how important geographical variations in diet may be.

The arctic walrus is fond of scallops, starfish, and crustaceans. Vibe has shown that in the north of Greenland (Thule district) walruses feed only on bottoms of less than 40 fathoms' depth, where the *Macoma calcaria* community occurs. He counted 1,881 siphons of the bivalve *Saxicava arctica* in the stomach of a single walrus! As this mollusk is not found in greater density than about 40 individuals per square yard at such depths, the walrus must have exploited at least 47 square yards of bottom during a few hours in its search for food!

The southern elephant seals of subantarctic islands eat cephalopods almost exclusively. A great many cuttlebones are found in their stomachs, together with stones and sand. When they are on land, during the reproductive period, they fast, and this period lasts for six weeks to two months each year. The Falkland sea lion also consumes cuttlefish whose "ink" colors the contents of its digestive tract a beautiful yellow, crustaceans (*Mundia* sp.) that color its excrement red, and also fish. It would seem that sperm whales feed almost exclusively on large cephalopods, and there are many stories told by old sailors recounting the titanic combats of these whales at grips with enormous devilfish.

*Terrestrial oligochætes,* such as earthworms, are sought by certain digging mammals. We have already seen that these worms form an important part of the mole's diet. Roonwal has recently noted that the manipur rat of Assam and Burma also seems fond of earthworms; four out of eight stomachs examined contained a large quantity of them; the rest contained insects. This is the only rat known to have such a diet, and it is noteworthy that the incisor teeth of this species are unusually weak. The rare Indo-Chinese civet (*Chrotogale owstoni*) also feeds by preference on earthworms.

To conclude this topic, something should be said about the mammals that feed on *blood*. The most famous of these are the vampires of tropical America. These bats belong to the genera *Desmodus, Diphylla,* and *Diæmus,* of which only the first is at all well known. Its dentition is admirably adapted to this particular diet; the incisors make a shallow wound, but one that bares many capillaries; [6] blood is then taken up by rapid movements of the tongue (Ditmars and Greenhall). Vampire bats normally attack horses, cattle, and barnyard fowls; occasionally man also becomes their victim. They are dangerous chiefly because they may transmit certain diseases, Chagas's disease in particular.

OMNIVOROUS MAMMALS. Examples of this dietary habit are to be found in many mammalian families, the rodents especially. The brown rat, invader of the cities and human establishments of almost the entire world, is able to eat almost anything: birds, other rodents, lizards, insects and spiders, garbage of all kinds, seeds, vegetables, fruits, and so on. There can be no doubt that its lack of dietary selec-

[6] Contrary to what has often been written, there is no anticoagulant in the saliva of the vampires (King and Saphir, *Zoologica,* 22: 281–287, 1937).

tivity has greatly favored its increase in numbers. The grizzly bear is another good example of the omnivores. Murie has carefully studied its diet in Alaska and gives a long list of the foods he has identified in droppings. Here again there are evident fluctuations in diet according to seasons. In spring the bear eats mostly roots, in June and July it feeds on reed grass (*Calamagrostis*) or on horsetail, and in August and September it turns its attention to berries. At any season it does not disdain ground squirrels or gophers (*Citellus*) and in June and July varies its diet with young caribou, baby Dall sheep, and hares. The badger is still another example of the complete omnivore. Neal has shown that in England it eats young mammals (especially rabbits), a great many insects, honey, mollusks, earthworms, grass, bark, tubers and rhizomes, and fruits and berries. To decide whether such an animal is beneficial or injurious would seem, then, to be primarily a matter of point of view.

MINERAL SALTS. It is well known that many herbivorous mammals, especially hoofed animals, have a special taste for salt and other mineral substances. In the eastern and southern African steppes many antelopes gather toward the end of the dry season at the so-called "bracks," where they greedily eat the "salty" soil or lick "salty" stones. African elephants sometimes dig ditches and holes of their own accord in certain places and return regularly to them. The camel is said to need halophytes (plants growing in salty soil) in its diet and to lose weight if they are lacking.

Such needs are usually supposed to indicate dietary deficiencies in sodium chloride, but the problem is probably more complex. One fact is certain: common salt may sometimes be lacking in the natural "salt licks" and "bracks," and in such cases phosphorus and other trace elements may be the chemicals sought. In their recent study of natural game licks in the Canadian Rockies, Cowan and Brink mention the frequent occurrence of manganese and copper in the soils they analyzed. Varlet similarly found that the soils of the elephants' "brush pharmacies" contained plenty of sulfates, magnesium, copper, nickel, some iron, and traces of chlorides.

The behavior involved should be compared with the pronounced taste of certain antelopes, like the bongo, for charred wood, and with that of the stag, when its horns are growing out, for the young grass that grows on areas recently burned over. Furthermore, stag and caribou often eat their own horns after shedding, and it has recently been shown that if calcium and other mineral salts lacking in the soil are then provided for the animals, no cast antlers are eaten.

### THE SEARCH FOR FOOD

ALL the senses of the mammals are used in the search for food. Sight, smell, and touch are most often employed together, but their relative importance varies from group to group.

Pursuit by sight, practiced by most of the large carnivores, implies also an important participation by the sense of smell during that essential preliminary period in which the prey is discovered. Olfaction in wild species still remains to be investigated, but what we know about the sense of smell in dogs enables us to estimate its keenness. The experiments of many workers, especially those of Buytendijk and of Löhner, have shown in undeniable fashion that the dog is not only able to sense odors that escape us but also to analyze mixtures of odors and to pay exclusive attention to one of them. This fact is what explains the behavior of such police dogs as bloodhounds. The ability, developed by training, which they have of recognizing individual odors is truly astonishing. One of Löhner's experiments showed that a second's contact of a piece of wood with the hollow of the hand was enough for the wood to be recognized by the animal in the midst of a whole series of otherwise similar pieces! It is probable, however, that in nature the carnivores need but rarely to make use of such powers of discrimination.

With the scents disentangled and the prey singled out, the techniques of pursuit and capture vary according to the species. African wild dogs and wolves in Asia are noted for hunting in packs and family groups. In the case of the African hunting dog the leader precedes the pack by some hundreds of yards and presses the prey on the course while trying to outflank it so as to head it back toward the rest of the band. This technique is very successful, and this perhaps explains the fear which the wild dogs inspire in herbivores. Percival and many other observers have repeatedly noted that antelopes have little fear of lions and move away from them, when they see them, to a distance of only a hundred yards, whereas they flee for miles if a troop of wild dogs appears on the plain. Coyotes may chase their prey in relays: the pursuing animal is relieved after a time by another member of the pack. Lions and tigers also—and quite frequently— hunt in groups, but at night; probably the growls and other noises they make under these conditions serve to keep the group together and co-ordinated.

Lions have been observed to use the following technique: the male of a pair circles around a troop of antelopes at some distance and gets in front of it, with the wind at the lion's back; it then gives a prolonged roar and thus forces the prey to move toward a place where the female is in ambush. As soon as the victim is within easy reach, the lioness springs and bites the neck of its prey while clawing the skin of its head.

There are many species that in daylight prefer a stealthy approach to pursuit in full view. Foxes and numerous mustelids hunt in this manner. The ermine uses both sight and smell in its search; with wormlike suppleness it slips rapidly along close to the ground, hiding behind the smallest obstacles and rising from time to time on its hind legs. When the prey is overtaken, the ermine bleeds it at the throat immediately.

Other species hunt from cover, along a path or near a water hole. The wolverine hides behind a rock or on a branch of a tree, whence it drops onto its victim's back, often clinging there for a hundred yards or more. Another kind of lying in wait is practiced by certain species, such as the polar bear, which lurks in winter at holes in the ice.

When for various reasons sight cannot play an important part, the sense of smell alone or almost unaided enables the animal to carry on the search for food. The badger, for example, relies chiefly on scent in discovering the young rabbits that this species is clever in removing from the burrows. Probably the same method enables the arctic hare to survive in winter by seeking under several feet of snow the tufts of dwarf willow that form the basis of its diet at that season. Along with olfaction, touch also plays a considerable role. It has been shown, for example, that in the mole the tactile organs of the muzzle, the paws, the trunk, and the tail serve to notify the animal of the proximity of prey, perhaps by vibrations transmitted through the soil; olfaction comes into play only within a radius of less than three inches. Probably the vibrissæ or whiskers of many diving mammals are useful in much the same fashion. Seals often live in places where the water is quite turbid and the light dim. Fraser Darling once watched the activities of a blind seal whose eyes had probably been long since destroyed in fighting but whose condition was nevertheless good, indicating an excellent ability to obtain food without the aid of sight. European water shrews, when hunting under water, bristle their whiskers as they seek contact with prey. We have already discussed the methods by which bats hunt in flight; they show very well how complex some types of elementary behavior may actually be.

Certain methods of gathering food even among the herbivores are unusual and deserve closer study than they have received. We know that the African elephant gathers fruits by means of its trunk, but sometimes the whole tree is uprooted and toppled down; and in still other cases the elephant shakes the tree violently, holding the tree trunk between its tusks. The eland, to cite another instance, has the curious habit of using its horns to break small trees or branches; it wedges the tree trunk between its two horns and, with a twist of its head, breaks it cleanly off (Verheyen).

VENOMOUS MAMMALS. The existence of poisons to aid in the capture of prey was until recent years supposed to be confined to the lower vertebrates. The bite of shrews was reputed to be venomous, but serious students regarded this as mythical. Histologists were recently interested by the structure of certain cells in the salivary glands of the North American short-tailed shrew, and this led Pearson to make a study of the submaxillaries in this species. Having ground the glands with sand in a 0.9 per cent sodium chloride solution, he injected the liquid thus obtained into mice. A rapid effect was observed: less than one minute after the injection the animal trembled, its respiration became slower, and it lay on its side in a state of semi-torpor; with stronger dosage there ensued paralysis of the hind legs, convulsions, and death. Intravenous injection was considerably more effective than either intraperitoneal or subcutaneous injections; a dose as small as the extract of 0.3 milligram to each 20 grams of body weight was found to be lethal for mice in some instances. Pearson showed that the submaxillary glands of a single shrew contain more than 200 times this dose; in contrast, the parotid glands contain no poison at all. Extracts of other organs, prepared in like manner, caused no injury. It would be interesting to know what mammalian families possess or lack this very reptilian characteristic.

### STORAGE OF FOOD

STORAGE of food has been frequently noted in certain mammals. This type of behavior has usually been interpreted as the expression of an adaptation to extreme climatic conditions; in other words, the animal "foresees" a winter or summer scarcity and stores up provisions for subsistence during the unfavorable season. The truth of the matter is probably quite different, and the classical interpretation has the disadvantage of assuming in the non-primate mammals the existence of psychological abilities that they almost certainly lack. It is therefore of the greatest interest, while attacking the problem experimentally, to collect observations made under natural conditions. The explanation of the phenomenon may appear through comparison of the various results obtained.

Among the carnivores temporary storage of food seems to be met with in all latitudes.[7] In the polar regions the prey of bears, foxes, and wolves is often only partially eaten, and the remainder is buried in the snow or left on the frozen ground. But intact prey may also be brought together in a cache. In the United States the northern plains red fox displays this behavior *throughout the year*. During the winter the cache is dug in the snow and in summer it is excavated in sand or a light soil; when it is stocked, the contents are carefully covered up. The fox later finds these "larders" with ease, whereas mock caches constructed by Scott along the animal's favorite trails were never dug into. It must be added that within a given area the number of "reserves" of food would seem to be in proportion to the abundance of game.

The storage of earthworms by the European mole has been the subject of much writing; several authors, indeed, have reported finding masses of earthworms, sometimes a

---

[7] When a leopard cannot consume its victim in a single meal, it drags the remainder up into a tree, thus preserving it from the greed of hyenas. Hoier observed a lump of flesh weighing more than 100 pounds, the remains of a young buffalo, that was hung up by a leopard, more than 12 feet above the ground, in the branches of an acacia.

thousand or more together, during the winter in mole nests or adjacent tunnels. But have we to do here with chance aggregations of the worms or with storage of food by the mole? Degerböl's experiment rather tends to tip the balance in favor of the second hypothesis. Having offered a captive mole more worms than it could consume at once, he repeatedly observed the animal storing them in a corner of its cage. To do this, it dug a hole, placed one to ten worms in it, and covered them with earth. Strange to say, the worms put in reserve were first bitten near the anterior end, which immobilized them without killing them. At one time Degerböl's mole buried 49 earthworms in the walls of its tunnel. "Storage" by the mole, then, would seem to occur when there is a superabundance of prey. The short-tailed shrew, referred to above, similarly forms reserves of mollusks, large scarabæid beetles, and even fragments of small mammals.

Among the rodents the establishment of food reserves is very common. Familiar in Europe are the provision chambers of the hamster, which may contain as much as 200 pounds of cereal seeds, peas, or potatoes. The common vole stores fresh plant material and seeds in summer and in the fall lays up the rhizomes, bulbs, tubers, or roots on which it lives in winter. These stores keep in a remarkably fresh condition, and Heim de Balsac has established the fact that in Lorraine the common vole disbuds the bulbs of *Ranunculus bulbosus* before storing them. The North American squirrels commonly store food. The American red squirrel is a great consumer of the seeds of conifers, as is the Fremont chickaree; both these species gather pine cones while still green and store them in moist, cool places. According to Shaw's observations, each animal may establish several temporary storehouses, each containing three to ten bushels of cones which are thus kept from drying out. These provisions are later distributed among a whole series of smaller caches under stones, leaves, or bark, and even in carefully concealed holes. The American red squirrel is very fond of mushrooms, and gathers them all summer and puts them to dry on branches (Hatt) or under bark. When they are dry it puts them away in its storehouses. Hardy has recently described one of these. It consisted of eight little cavities dug in an old, very dry stump of Douglas fir in a British Columbia forest. Six of the holes were filled with perfectly preserved mushrooms, all fully dried. Fifty-nine specimens belonging to 13 different species were counted, but the single species *Hymenogaster tener* was represented by 30 specimens. Except for a small bit of lichen, the storehouses contained nothing but mushrooms. The interesting point is that these very hygroscopic, or water-absorbent, materials were stored in a dry place, whereas the red squirrel ordinarily makes its stockpiles of green cones in damp earth. The amount of these stored foods actually used, however, is not very great: 10 per cent, according to Cahalane, in the case of the fox squirrel.

In more southern latitudes the same habit is to be met with in other species. The California ground squirrel, which estivates without previous accumulation of reserves, gathers together seeds and nuts in the fall, before its period of winter inactivity. The giant kangaroo rat studied by Shaw in Fresno County, California, on the contrary, collects seeds at the end of winter and the beginning of spring; it distributes them at first (to dry?) in a whole series of small cavities that are a little less than an inch in diameter and depth, carefully covered with soil and quite invisible. Around a burrow inhabited by a single individual, Shaw counted 875 of these caches in an area of about five square yards. From April on, these surface storehouses are emptied and the seeds transferred to subterranean storage places inside the burrow.[8] A related species, the large kangaroo rat of southern Arizona, gathers its reserve stores twice a year, in April and May and from September to November. It would be of great importance to study, in a single species, the variations in this behavior as affected by local meteorological conditions.

And, finally, the American beaver builds up its winter food reserves under water. The branches and tree trunks that will provide enough bark to last through the months of frost and snow are submerged near the animal's lodge, and deeply enough to avoid being "caught" in the ice.

[8] This fact was established as follows: Shaw opened some of the surface caches in March and colored the seeds with mercurochrome, also adding some rice grains. On May 4 the tinted seeds and the rice were found in the underground storage places.

### CHAPTER 3

# Home, Territory, and Home Range

MOST solitary terrestrial mammals resort faithfully to certain sites that serve as their lodging-places or shelters, seasonal or permanent. They return regularly to these homes for sleeping, hiding, or reproducing. In the vicinity of the shelter, the chief occupant of the home often shows itself decidedly intolerant of others of its kind, and forbids them access to it. This aggressiveness is the clearest manifestation of territorial behavior. At the same time, most mammals prove to be more sedentary than is commonly supposed and restrict their movements to a particular area that they regularly frequent. This zone is called the home range, and it differs from the territory in that access to it is not denied others of the same species.

These facts have only recently been established, thanks to the intensive effort of many field workers. But we are still far from being able to decide in what degree they may apply to mammals in general. This chapter is therefore to be regarded as an attempt to classify the facts at present established, and the conclusions reached will serve as working hypotheses to point the way to new observations.

## LODGING-PLACES AND SHELTERS

POSSESSION of lodging-places and shelters, temporary or permanent, though very frequent among the mammals, is by no means universal, and before beginning their study we may briefly survey those species whose constant nomadism prevents any sedentary life at all.

AQUATIC MAMMALS. The pelagic habitat of the cetaceans—whales and their relatives—offers them no possibility of any shelter. They sleep in open water, in a fashion that seems quite peculiar to them. McBride and Hebb have made interesting observations on the sleep of the bottle-nosed dolphin at the Marine Studios in Florida. During the night the sleeping cetacean usually floats near the surface, but with the tail dangling somewhat. If there is no water current in the tank, the animal may remain almost motionless with the head about a foot below the surface. About every half minute a few slow strokes of the tail bring the head of the animal to the surface to breathe. If a current exists, the dolphin will attempt to maintain its position relative to the tank wall by slow beats of the tail either continuously or periodically. The eyes never remain closed for more than 15 to 30 seconds at a time.

The sea otter, although visiting the land at some points in its area of distribution, generally sleeps in open water. Fisher's observations, made off the coast of Monterey, California, are very suggestive in this connection. These animals appear to assume a resting position only when the sea is calm; then they turn on the back, the chin on the chest, the tail occasionally making a few lateral movements. For the night they ordinarily frequent a bed of algæ (*Macrocystis* or *Nereocystis*), always the same one during their stay in a given region, and one in which the herd gathers. They have the curious habit of clinging to the algæ or rolling themselves up in the plants to avoid drifting while asleep (figs. 26 and 27).

FIG. 26: *Sea otter sleeping "moored" to a float of* Nereocystis. *After a sketch by Fisher, 1939.*

FIG. 27: *Sea otter sleeping "wrapped up" in an alga to prevent drifting during the night. After a sketch by Fisher, 1939.*

Among the seals there are species that sleep in the water only at certain times of the year. At the time of reproduction they rest on land, and it is likely that on certain undisturbed coasts species like the monk seal of Mauritania sleep ashore the year round. Weddell's seal, indeed, poses a quite special problem. This Antarctic species does not migrate in winter and remains *under* the ice floe, resorting regularly for air to "breathing holes," which it prevents from freezing over by breaking the ice with its teeth. How, then, does it manage to take any rest? The problem remains unsolved, but possibly at times it takes advantage of air pockets existing under the ice. The walrus sometimes sleeps in a vertical position in the water, with its neck strongly inflated. Vibe considers this position correlated with the dilation of the upper portion of the esophagus.

TEMPORARY SHELTERS. There are many mammals that have no permanent shelter and wander more or less throughout the year on their home range.

Most ungulates, or hoofed animals, belong in this category; but in some cases the females seek isolation and shelter toward the end of gestation. The female chamois, for instance, separates from the herd about a month before giving birth and at that time seeks out an isolated and sheltered place—a thicket, a winding passage in the rocks, a narrow grassy ledge, or the like. Females of the roebuck, of the white-tailed deer, of many antelopes, of the giraffe, and of the African elephant exhibit similar behavior. In all cases the chosen site undergoes no preparation, and the mother returns to it no more, once the offspring is capable of following her about.[1]

Among the smaller mammals many have rudimentary shelters scattered over their home range, where they repair

[1] It may well be that some ungulates of desert regions manifest a great partiality in summer for certain shelters under rocks or even for certain leafy trees. The fact has been pointed out for the Barbary sheep and the addax of the Sahara. In northeastern Mexico bighorn sheep take shelter during the warm hours in summer in small caves where the animals' excrement accumulates, as do the bones of dead individuals. It would seem that in all these cases it is the need for shade that causes the animals' constant resort to these temporary lodging-places.

to sleep, hide, and bring forth their young. The European hare is a good example: nocturnal in its activities, it spends the day in small excavations dug in the ground, under a bush, in high grass, even in the open; in winter it sometimes takes shelter under the snow, which it has allowed to cover it. It often abandons its form, or home, and does not return regularly to the same one, being much more faithful to its trails. Most of the rabbits, hares, and their relatives have similar habits, and many tropical mammals must behave in the same fashion. Thus the little opossum of Central America, the Isthmian marmosa, bears its young in rolled-up and half-dried leaves of the banana tree. It sleeps hidden in dead leaves or abandoned birds'-nests, but it almost never returns two days in succession to the same place. Bats pass the daytime sleeping in various lodging-places; the little insectivorous species retire by day into hollow trees, woodpecker holes, garrets, belfries, abandoned quarries, and the like. It is not rare for certain individuals to keep to the same dormitory during a single summer. Some solitary tropical bats hide during the day in odd places: in India *Hipposideros fulvus* uses porcupine burrows; in South Africa *Kerivoula nidicola* and *K. lanosa* have been found in old nests of Ploceidæ and Nectariniidæ; the Indo-Malayan *Tylonycteris pachypus*, whose paws bear remarkable suckers, sleeps inside bamboo stems; *Pipistrellus nanus* of East Africa hides in dried banana leaves, and *Rhynchiscus naso* of tropical America simply clings with all four feet and in small groups on the underside of a tree trunk overhanging water. All these lodging-places and shelters are clearly temporary, their very nature preventing any prolonged use. It is only certain large fruit-eating bats, which sleep hanging on tree branches, that show a definite attachment to their dormitories, some of which may be used for generations. Thus Eisentraut has observed a roost of *Eidolon helvum* in the Cameroons where about 10,000 individuals gathered.

There are also many primates that have no fixed lodging-place in their home range. The golden potto merely sleeps suspended by its four limbs from a horizontal branch;

FIG. 28: *Sleeping position of a potto.*

another species of potto (fig. 28) sleeps rolled in a ball, with its head between its hind feet. The tropical American howling monkeys wander constantly through their clan territory and spend the night in the trees, wherever they happen to be. The lar gibbons do no more than choose for sleeping particular trees that have heavy leafy tops of sufficient density.

The fact that certain species make some attempt to prepare even a temporary shelter introduces interesting complications. The den of the European wild boar, for example, is generally no more than an elongated hollow in smooth soil, sometimes screened by drooping fir boughs, where the animal retires in the morning to spend the day. The African wart hog may use the burrows of the aardvark for hiding, but more often frequents lairs of its own. Guiraud describes them in Senegal as sites kept meticulously neat, with numerous small, shallow dens dug out, and protected by extensive thickets of bushes that retain their leaves and are not thorny.

Certain tropical American bats prepare the leaves that they use as shelters to hide in. Thus *Artibeus watsoni* uses its teeth to cut two oblique lines converging like a V toward the median vein in the leaves of the palm *Geonoma*. This done, the terminal portion of the leaf falls into a vertical position, so that it forms with the rest of the leaf a kind of verdant tent into which the bat retires (fig. 29). Another species, *Uroderma bilobatum*, makes use of a similar technique that it has adapted to a palm of the genus *Pritchardia* introduced into Panama.

That odd lemuroid, the aye-aye of Madagascar, also builds temporary nests of globular form in leafy boughs, into which it withdraws to sleep in the daytime. The same nest is seldom used for more than one week.

Some anthropoids also crudely furnish the place where they spend the night. The chimpanzee constructs small platforms of branches and abandons them the next day. The gorilla sometimes makes temporary shelters of branches which probably serve also as lodgings for the night.

BURROWS. The burrow is the most widely used type of seasonal or permanent shelter among terrestrial mammals.

*A gorilla "nest" at the foot of a tree. The male usually spends the night in such a shelter, while his female rests in a nest built in the tree. Note the animal's excrement at the entrance of the nest. Photograph by J. P. Harroy, taken in Albert National Park. Courtesy of the* Institut des Parcs nationaux du Congo Belge.

*Nest and eggs of the duckbilled platypus,* Ornithorhyncus anatinus.
*Courtesy of the New York Zoological Society.*

Most of the orders, indeed, include species that construct or make use of burrows. The platypus, numerous insectivores, edentates, marsupials, and rodents dig them. Many carnivores provide themselves with holes during at least a part of the year.

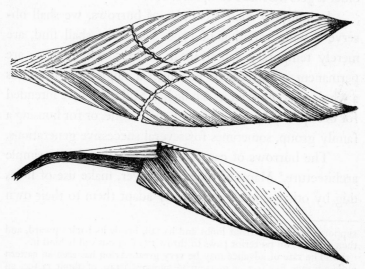

FIG. 29: *Shelter of the bat* Artibeus watsoni, *made in a leaf of the palm* Geonoma decurrens. *Above, the leaf viewed from above, with the two lateral cuts; below, the leaf viewed from the side. After a photograph by F. M. Chapman.*

It would be most desirable to have extensive documentation and many diagrams of typical construction in the matter of animal burrows.[2] But unfortunately these are diffi-

[2] A point on which we are even less informed is the technique used by the animal in digging its burrow. Moles (*Talpa, Scalopus*) use their front paws alternately in loosening the soil; at regular intervals the excavated earth is kicked back with the hindfeet. The Texas armadillo loosens the earth with its nose and front paws, the soil collected under its abdomen being moved back periodically as follows: the animal

cult to obtain. The excavation of a burrow, indeed, is often a long and laborious undertaking. Moreover, no species follows a rigid plan, and all adapt their constructions to local conditions. To make the problem even more difficult, a burrow is constantly worked over by its occupant, and the older it gets the more complex it becomes.

In studying some examples of burrows, we shall observe a wide variation of type. Some, we shall find, are merely temporary subterranean shelters, while others are permanent constructions in which a single animal spends a whole year, or even its whole life. Still others are intended for occupancy by one male or female alone, or for housing a family group, sometimes for several successive generations.

The burrows of carnivores are usually of very simple architecture.[3] Many of them, moreover, make use of holes dug by other animals and merely adapt them to their own

---

supports itself on its front limbs and its tail, bends its back upward, and then uses its two posterior paws to throw the dug out soil behind it.

The rate of advance may be very great. Arlon has seen an eastern mole advance five feet or more in 26 minutes, a rate of about 12 feet an hour. Taber saw an armadillo bury itself completely in two minutes, and this in a soil so hard that one needed a pickaxe to dig a hole. Armadillos, furthermore, have remarkable physiological adaptations for digging galleries, adaptations that recall in some ways those of diving mammals. (See, for example, Scholander, Irving, and Grinnell, *Jour. Cell. Comp. Physiol.*, 21:53–63.)

Another curious problem is presented by the remarkable sense of direction shown by the blind fossorial mammals. Krizat and Godet have clearly shown that the European mole is able to orient itself in the absence of olfactory or tactile landmarks, and to manifest a knowledge of the relations existing between its burrow and its hunting territory. Eloff (*British Jour. Exper. Psychol.*, 42: 134–45, 1951) has likewise emphasized the sense of direction of the blind South African *Cryptomys bigalkei* and the Cape golden mole (*Bathyergus maritimus*).

[3] The polar bear may dig a real burrow in the snow at the time of giving birth to young. An example is provided by Pedersen (fig. 30), who observed one of these dens excavated at the foot of an iceberg. This of course was a temporary habitation, the family deserting it by the month of March.

requirements. Thus the North American coyotes use the burrows of badgers, skunks, or foxes; they limit themselves to enlarging, cleaning, and sometimes furnishing them with an air hole. Even the European red fox may very well take over old burrows of badgers and rabbits, although it is quite capable of digging its own.

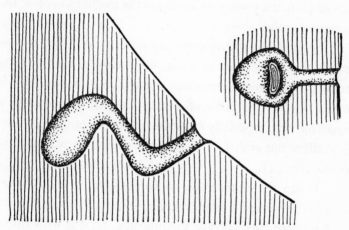

FIG. 30: *Polar bear's den for giving birth to young. Left and below, vertical section; right and above, horizontal section. The whole dug in snow and ice. After Pedersen.*

Its relative, the American red fox, normally constructs burrows of two kinds: a rearing den with a fairly large chamber at the end of a tunnel of varying depth, and temporary burrows that are still more rudimentary. Sheldon's observations, made on marked animals in the region around Lake Cayuga, in New York, indicate that the burrow for reproduction is occupied by the female and her young, which abandon it only when the milk teeth are lost. Kolosov's data tend to show that in Russia the European red fox and the corsak fox have similar habits.

Armadillos also appear to dig only simple burrows. Those of the Texas armadillo vary in depth from two to more than twelve feet and are very seldom branched (Taber). There is a single entrance as a rule, and the nest is located in the enlarged terminal portion of the tunnel. Each individual has and uses four to eight burrows, and each sex has its own, the young remaining in the mother's burrow for several months.

Some of the rodents, the European wild rabbit, for example, also construct very simple burrows. The winding tunnels have several entrances and end in a chamber that is often single. The birth of young most often occurs in a small burrow, especially constructed for the purpose, which is shallow but ends in a chamber provided with a bedding of fur (fig. 31).

When the animals live in family groups and furthermore use the same burrows generation after generation, the ground plan may become complicated. So it is with European badgers. It would seem that a new, or "young" burrow consists only of an entrance and an enlarged terminal chamber, the nest. But since badgers are gregarious and since a single network of burrows is inhabited by successive generations, it is understandable that their dwellings soon become extraordinarily labyrinthine. A burrow ten to twenty years old commonly has three to five entrances; three to six feet within is a rather large chamber, with its dirt floor hardened and tramped down by generations of occupants, that may represent the birth chamber of the original burrow. Other tunnels extend away from this antechamber, terminating in other chambers that serve as dormitories or nests. These last are often located under a large rock or among the roots of a tree and are furnished with bedding that is changed in spring and autumn. There are air holes in some cases, smaller in diameter than the entrance holes. With the passage of time these burrows, as we have noted, become veritable labyrinths, of which certain parts may be

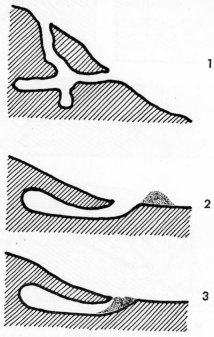

FIG. 31: *The two types of wild rabbit burrows, seen in vertical section: 1, burrow for residence; 2 and 3, burrow for reproduction, open and closed. After Lincke.*

used by other species, such as foxes, rabbits, or rats. Neal refers to an instance in which the tunnels extended over a hundred yards from the entrance. The diagram in figure 32 clearly shows the mode of formation of these labyrinths for the little souslik of the Eurasian steppes.

Many burrowing mammals remain inside during the

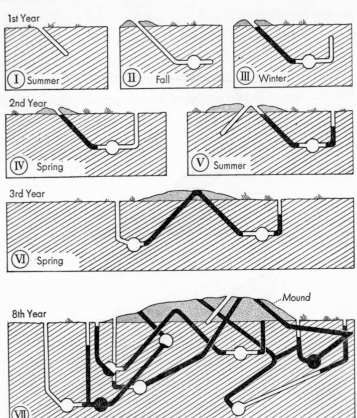

FIG. 32: *Evolution of the burrow of the little souslik,*
Citellus pygmæus. *First year, I–III: I, primitive and tem-*
*porary summer burrow; II, hibernation burrow, autumn;*
*III, the same with the entrance gallery blocked for the*
*winter and with a vertical exit gallery begun. Second*
*year: IV, the same in spring; V–VIII, progressive modi-*
*fication and complication of the system of burrows during*
*succeeding years, with increase in size of the mound. The*
*parts temporarily blocked are indicated in black. After*
Ognev. *From Grassé,* Traité de zoologie, *Vol.* XVII.

unfavorable season of the year or hibernate there. Their
dwellings, of course, permit the storage of supplies that are

often of great importance to the animals. The common vole of Europe digs burrows comprising a nest, so-called resting-chambers, storerooms, escape tunnels leading directly from the nest to the exterior, communicating galleries, and finally exit galleries leading to sources of food and continued in runways outside. In some cases there are also nests above ground in tufts of grass. For hibernating species there is no need at all for stores of food, but in that case the owner of the burrow often is immured in a special chamber.

Some mammals have burrows of two types: one for summer and one for winter. The hamster of Central Europe is an example. Its summer burrow is short and shallow, with a single storage place for food. The winter burrow, on the contrary, is dug to a depth of one or two yards and comprises an entrance gallery, one or two chambers, and several storage places.[4] The northern three-toed jerboa of the Kazakstan deserts also has different domiciles according to the seasons. The permanent summer burrow (one for each sex, the female's being more complicated than the male's) includes the remains of the initial gallery, abandoned and consequently filled up, a permanent exit closed during the daytime with a plug of sand, emergency exits ending four to six inches from the surface of the ground, a chamber furnished with bedding of plant material, and finally a deep, narrow passage to which the animal retires during the warmer hours of the day (fig. 33). Beside this permanent estivating burrow are found also temporary summer burrows in the form of simple unbranched tunnels. The essen-

---

[4] At least this is the arrangement reported by Eisentraut and Krumbiegel; but two nests investigated in Alsace by Didier and Matthias had a different plan: a spacious central chamber with lateral cavities and diverging entrance galleries.

tial characteristic of the winter burrow is that it is deeper and has a chamber always located at the end. While constructing its winter dwelling, the jerboa goes on living in its summer burrow.

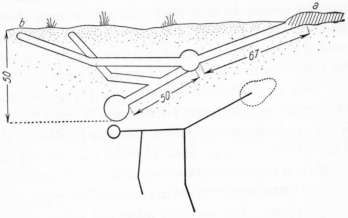

FIG. 33: *Summer burrow of an Asiatic jerboa*, Stylodipus telum, *in sectional diagram:* a, *primary burrow;* b, *blind emergency exit. After Ognev. From Grassé,* Traité de zoologie, *Vol.* XVII.

THE BURROWS OF SUBTERRANEAN MAMMALS. All the burrows thus far described are constructed by mammals that use them for sleeping, hiding, and reproducing. There is another type of burrow, made by subterranean species; that is, species that spend their whole lives under ground and come to the surface only accidentally. Burrowing mammals are to be found in several orders: marsupials (*Notoryctes*), insectivores (*Talpa, Scalopus, Condylura*), and rodents (Geomyidæ, *Spalax, Ellobius,* etc.). All these have certain morphological characteristics in common: fossorial front feet, eyes small or even lacking, loss or reduction of the external ears, and so on. The burrows of only a few of them are satisfactorily known (and there is certainly much to be learned about the biology of such strange forms as *Heterocephalus glaber* [fig. 34] of Africa!), but they all would seem to consist of two parts: the home burrow containing the nest and stores, and the galleries used only for hunting food.

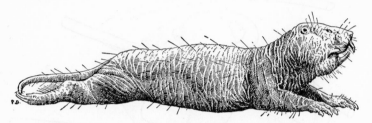

FIG. 34: *A subterranean rodent with almost hairless skin,* Heterocephalus glaber *of Kenya. Drawn from a photograph by Lt. Col. Stockley. From Grassé,* Traité de zoologie, *Vol.* XVII.

The earthworks of the European mole are among the best known. The *nest* is located under a good-sized mound or "fortress," often hidden under a bramble or placed near a tree stump. This large molehill is built over an oval chamber where the animal puts bedding composed of dead leaves surrounded with dry grass. The earthen vault above the nest commonly contains more or less circular galleries (fig. 35). From the central chamber usually extend a variable number of *permanent galleries* used by the animal in going to its hunting-grounds. The walls of these galleries are smooth and well compacted. Commonly enough a permanent gallery extends vertically below the floor of the central chamber itself; this is an escape gallery that also serves to drain the nest. Beyond these permanent galleries is an extensive network of *hunting-galleries*, dug out and altered daily by the animal, which at regular intervals throws the excavated dirt out on the surface of the ground, thus forming the familiar small molehills. The breeding-nest of the female is generally placed in a "fortress" smaller than that containing the winter nest.

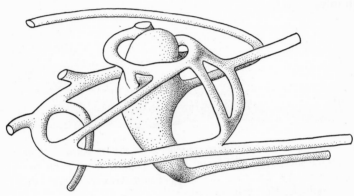

FIG. 35: *Reconstruction in perspective of the nest of a European mole,* Talpa europæa, *surrounded by its concentric galleries. The "dome" of the nest was about 12 inches below the surface in silica-clayey soil; the "well" of the lower part of the nest was at a depth of about 27 inches. After Godet.*

The earthworks of the lesser mole rat are a little more complicated. Dr. Bodnar Béla describes them as comprising a nest, a "pairing-chamber," storage places, sanitary rooms, main galleries and, finally, temporary galleries. The nest is an oval or pear-shaped chamber, furnished with grass, and the smooth, hard walls are thickly plastered with clay. The pairing-chamber is constructed in spring under a molehill sixteen inches high that the animal begins to build the preceding autumn; it is a round chamber eight inches across, the walls covered with clay. After mating has taken place, the owner stops up the room and the gallery leading to it with earth. The storage places are sometimes no more than enlargements of a permanent gallery, but they may also be special chambers; in them may be found potatoes, onions, carrots, and roots. The sanitary rooms open on the main galleries, and when filled with droppings they are walled up by the mole rat. The main galleries, which are the deepest ones, connect the various parts of the dwelling just mentioned; they are lined with a thick layer of clay that makes them very durable and almost waterproof. As for the temporary galleries, they are used only in seeking food; these are winding, near the surface, and of variable diameter. Their walls are not plastered with clay, and, when they are no longer in use by the animal, it often happens that their connections with the main galleries are closed.

The North American Geomyidæ, or pocket gophers, also manifest extraordinary fossorial activity. The burrow of the plains pocket gopher investigated by Smith (fig. 36) belonged to a young female and had been constructed in a year. The total length of the central gallery was about 65 yards; the nest was at a depth of two feet. Of the two storerooms, one was at the end of a lateral gallery, the other in the wall of the central gallery. Secondary galleries on each side of this last probably represented old hunting-galleries; some of these ended in a molehill, while others did not. Most of them had been later filled with dirt, and some served as sanitary rooms. The reserve food was made up entirely of tubers of the Jerusalem artichoke (*Helianthus tuberosus*), from which the roots were removed (perhaps to make them keep?). With the northern pocket gopher, also, the differentiation between main and temporary galleries is quite clear: the nest is always located in the former. The pocket gophers remain active in wintertime and have the odd habit of making tunnels under the snow, at the surface of the ground. In these tunnels they accumulate the debris that

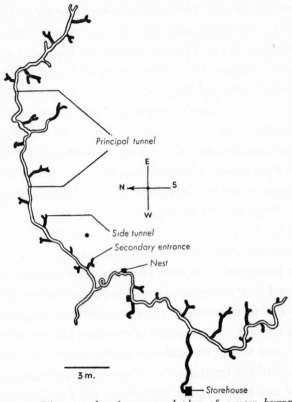

Principal tunnel

E
N ← → S
W

Side tunnel
Secondary entrance
Nest

3 m.

Storehouse

FIG. 36: *Diagram showing ground plan of a new burrow of a plains pocket gopher,* Geomys bursarius. *After Smith, 1948.*

they go on collecting from below, and when the snow thaws long serpentine ridges of earth are left in sight. In Europe the snow vole and the common vole display rather similar behavior. The tuco tucos of South America (fig. 37) would appear to be related in their biology.

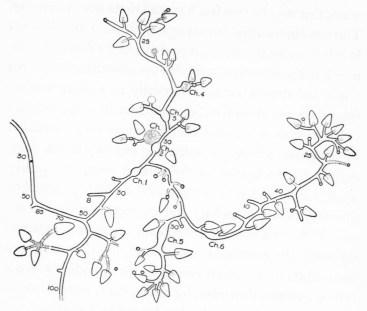

FIG. 37: *Diagram of the burrow of the tuco tuco,* Ctenomys brasiliensis. *The figures indicate depths in centimeters; the small triangles indicate mounds at the surface. After Eisentraut. From Grassé,* Traité de zoologie, *Vol.* XVII.

SOME SECURITY DEVICES OF BURROWS. Certain architectural peculiarities of burrows can be interpreted as security devices against flooding and the intrusion of predators,[5] as well as means for maintaining constant the microclimate inside.

The black-tailed prairie dogs of the western United States build around the entrance of the burrow a kind of

---

[5] It has been maintained that white-throated wood rats "prevent" the access of predators to their nests by means of the spines of the jumping cholla (*Opuntia fulgida*). It is quite true that these rodents can move with ease among the spines of this justly feared cactus, but a recent observation of Reed and Carr shows that as protection the spines have only relative value. A hooded skunk they were pursuing took refuge in one of the wood rat nests, entering through an orifice so well "protected" that a child's hand could not have been thrust into it without danger.

crater that may be two feet high and three feet in diameter. This constitutes a real barrier against floods. Carefully kept in condition by the owner, it prevents heavy rain from running into the entrance tunnel that opens in the center of the crater and descends almost vertically to a depth varying from three to sixteen feet. Some distance from the entrance to this well there is almost always a lateral recess, a kind of listening post, where the prairie dog can stop before going deeper. At the bottom of the vertical tunnel the gallery turns sharply and takes a horizontal or slightly ascending direction before branching and coming to an end at the nest. If the rain is heavy enough for the sheet of water to submerge the entrance crater, the animal takes refuge in the pockets of air which remain in the ascending galleries and thus escapes drowning, for although the rains are sometimes excessive they usually last for only a few hours.

Many mammals temporarily stop up the mouths of their burrows. We have already noted that in summer the northern three-toed jerboa uses sand for this purpose in the daytime, and here we probably have to do with a reaction to the increased heat outside, since in autumn or in early spring the same animal leaves its burrow open during the daytime. In this way the constancy of the microclimate of the nest is favored, a condition necessary to the survival of these small mammals in regions marked by extremes of temperature. Burrowing species as large as the aardvark display comparable behavior.

Other species immure themselves inside their burrows only during estivation or hibernation; such is the case with the Alpine marmot, and in the United States with deer mice, Pacific kangaroo rats, Wyoming pocket mice, and meadow jumping mice. In Madagascar the tenrec walls up with earth the entrance to its hibernation chamber during the dry season. Similar examples could be found in most regions of the world.

In other cases the blocking of the burrow at its mouth is a defense reaction against predators, alpine marmots often reacting in this way when an attempt is made to dig them out.

THE MICROCLIMATE OF BURROWS. One of the most important characteristics of burrows is the constancy of their microclimate. We shall see in a later chapter that most desert mammals cannot survive when removed from their dwellings at full midday, and if some have been successful in colonizing these parts of the world, it is certainly because of their habit of nocturnal activity and the microenvironment of the burrows into which they withdraw in the daytime. Unfortunately we still lack an exhaustive study of this problem, but some observations are very suggestive. Vorhies, for example, states that the desert Heteromyidæ (pocket rats and mice) of the southwestern United States die when the temperature is above 35° Centigrade but that, on the other hand, and even at the hottest periods, the temperature of the air inside the burrows never rises above 33°; in summer it remains at about 28°. Kachkarov and Korovine, in the Kara-Koum desert, showed that in April there could be a difference of 31 degrees between the temperature of the surface of the ground and that of the air in a gerbil burrow four inches from the entrance (59° and 28° respectively); inversely, during the night, the temperature of the ground may be 16 degrees lower than that of the bur-

row (May 7, at 4:30 a.m., 3° and 19° respectively). Heim
de Balsac found that in the Sahara it was enough for an
animal to bury itself four inches deep in order to escape the
extraordinary temperatures of full noon. Moreover, the
constancy of the temperature within the burrows is accompanied by a relative humidity higher than that at the surface
because of the lower rate of evaporation. Thus, the animals
escape underground both from high temperatures and from
dehydration.

"NESTS," HUTS, AND EDIFICES ABOVE GROUND. Some
rodents build "nests" above ground to shelter their young
after birth; others construct more durable huts in which
they live the year around. In both cases they show architectural abilities that are rather rare among vertebrates,
apart from the birds.

The nest of the European harvest mouse (fig. 38) is a
kind of ball made of interlaced gramineous leaves that generally belong to the same plants that support the edifice.
These leaves, often split into strings, thus remain alive as
long as the nest is occupied. There is no regular doorway;
the female pushes her way in and out anywhere near the
top. The nest is often suspended 20 inches above the
ground. Outside the reproductive period the mice live in
holes and they are frequently found in winter in straw
stacks. It is probable that a single female builds several nests
in succession in the course of the summer.

Squirrels in all latitudes also construct globular "nests,"
some of which are used as true nests and others as temporary
lodgings only. Those of the European red squirrel are composed of a layer of twigs, often leafy, with another layer in-

FIG. 38: *Nest of the European harvest mouse.*

side of moss or bark fragments. They are placed in trees, frequently at the base of a large branch. A single individual has several of these nests, and often makes use also of holes in trees or even abandoned crow's nests. In North America the fox squirrel builds summer "nests," light and fragile, and winter "nests" whose more solid construction may last for years. The American red squirrel uses at the same time aerial "nests," old woodpecker-holes, and burrows that connect chambers, six to eight inches in diameter, where the animal stores its reserves of food. The building of ball-shaped aerial nests is not peculiar to the squirrels of cold countries. In tropical Asia the Indian giant squirrel also builds them, a single animal using several located in different trees within its home range.

Very different from these temporary aerial "nests" are the durable structures of other species of rodents. The houses built by the dusky-footed wood rat of the southwestern United States represent the most simple type. Vestal has made an excellent study of these in Contra Costa County, California. They are conical in shape, often built around a tree trunk, and may exceed the average height of a man. Thus the average height of 301 of these nests was four feet, with extremes of 14 inches and 6 feet 9 inches! The average diameter at the base was more than 3 feet. These structures are built wholly of small branches, leaves, and plant debris. They are constantly kept in good condition and shelter only a single individual. Inside are one or more chambers connected by passageways, a nest, and a sanitary chamber. The nest is generally located about half-way up, in the driest part of the structure, and on the north side in those studied by Vestal. The owner of this edifice ranges hardly more than 100 feet from it to collect food. Some wood rats place their houses on branches.

Muskrat and beaver houses have often been described, sometimes in fantastic terms. The muskrat builds houses that are well known not only in North America but also in Europe, where this fur-bearing rodent has been introduced. This hibernation lodge, in which the female also raises her young, is dome-shaped and ordinarily contains only one chamber. The animal enters the lodge through one of several tunnels opening below water level. The house is altered and worked over from year to year by its owner, and in some cases may reach a height of three feet and a diameter of nine at the base. In addition to this lodge, the muskrat builds light feeding-shelters, as well as platforms of plant material, and uncovered "rafts." Interesting regional variations have been noted in this animal's architecture. For example, in some parts of the United States they build no houses and live in burrows, whereas in Maryland they do build houses but always with flat tops. The causes of these geographical variations are not well understood.

The structures made by beavers have been known for several centuries, but the imagination of travelers often ascribes to them a degree of perfection that tends to falsify their descriptions. The American beaver generally builds houses that serve as a permanent habitation for the couple and its two last litters (Bradt, Warren). These houses rest on a foundation of boughs and mud over a peat-moss base, or even on a small natural islet. In all cases they are surrounded with water, and it is not uncommon for a willow bush to serve as the center around which a house is constructed (fig. 39). The walls of the house are composed of piled-up branches, cemented with earth or mud, and the whole may be two feet thick at the base. The dome itself is composed of boughs that always remain permeable to air, providing the chamber below with proper ventilation even

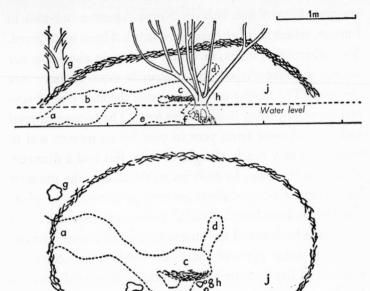

FIG. 39: *Vertical section and ground plan of a lodge of the American beaver, built around a bushy willow (h). The entrance (a) opens into a vestibule (b) communicating with the chamber (c). There are two accessory entrances (e and f). At (d) is a blind corridor. A wood rat has established its own nest at (j). After Grinnell, Dixon, and Linsdale.*

in the depth of winter. The interior of the house consists usually of only a single chamber, the floor of which is always a little above the water level; sometimes lateral alcoves are provided in the walls. The exits always open under water.

Beavers build dams across the watercourse, upstream and downstream from the house. These dams are constructed of tree branches, stones, and earth, and may be straight or crooked. Their length varies from a few to a hundred yards, and in height they range from one to twelve feet, according to circumstances. It would seem that the purpose of these dams is to hold constant the water level of the pool on which the house is built; thus freezing weather never prevents the animals from having free access to their sunken stores of wood and bark. Great admiration has been expressed for the marvelous "instinct" that leads the beavers to choose the best possible location for the dams, and to adjust their height properly. Modern observers have shown, however, that this praise is exaggerated, for in many cases the dams are not in fact built where they would be most efficient. Furthermore, the constant labor of reconstruction of the dams carried on by the members of the colony seems to correspond to a deep physiological need. Tevis has observed in New York a beaver family inhabiting a small lake produced by the construction of an artificial barrier of stones and cementing material. Now, although this barrier was in perfect condition, the beavers worked all summer "repairing" it with mud and branches just as if it were one of their ordinary dams. What is more, it seems that there is an inner need to obstruct all flowing water. Although the level of the artificial pond was to all appearances quite satisfactory, Tevis's beavers set about building a dam across the stream feeding the pond behind the barrier. The only observable result was to flood the surrounding area and to kill a growth of alder—an outcome of no apparent advantage to the colony.

The canals dug by beavers are also of great interest. Their function seems to be to facilitate the transportation by water of the tree trunks and branches cut in the woods worked by the colony. Very infrequently met with in the eastern United States, these canals are more common in the West, and one of them has been described that was 745 feet long.

Even in North America not all beavers live in houses. At least temporarily, many inhabit burrows that they dig in the banks of streams and that open under water. This is especially frequent in localities where the beavers are disturbed by man. The European beaver builds houses like those of its North American relative only in certain remote parts of its range, particularly in Scandinavia and Russia (figs. 40 and 41). The beavers of the Rhone valley appear to have lost this habit since the Middle Ages. It is probable that complete protection would cause it to reappear, since rudimentary houses have been built by some individuals in semicaptivity.

### TERRITORY

IT is well known that during the breeding season most birds show themselves very intolerant of other members of

FIG. 40: *Section of a European beaver pond in the Voro-nezh region of Russia. Note the subterranean canals, with numerous openings, intermediate between the burrows of most European beavers and the canals of American beavers. After Klebovitch, in Ognev.*

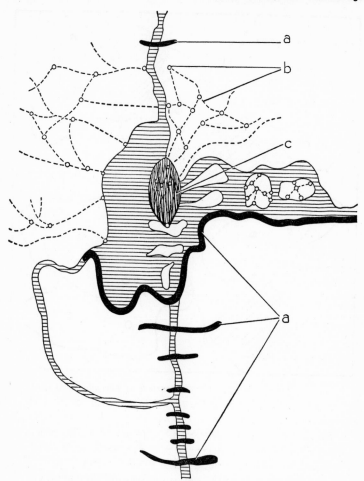

FIG. 41: *Diagram of a European beaver pond in the Voronezh region of Russia:* a, *dams;* b, *subterranean canals with openings;* c, *house. After Ognev.*

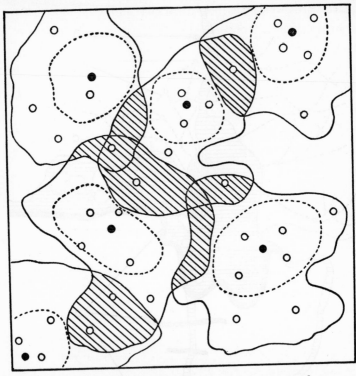

FIG. 42: *Diagrammatic representation of the accepted concepts of territory and home range. Theoretical square with six occupants of the same species and sex. Redrawn from Burt.*

| | |
|---|---|
| ⌇⌇⌇ | Home range boundary |
| - - - - - | Territorial boundary |
| ▨▨▨ | Neutral zone |
| ● | Nesting site (home) |
| ○ | Refuge site |

the same species entering a definite zone around the nest. This zone, called the *territory*, thus becomes the exclusive "property" of the nesting couple for the time required for egg-laying, brooding, and raising the young. The size of the territory varies greatly according to the species. For most European passerine birds it may vary from 1,200 or 2,400 square yards to a little more than two and a half acres; but for many species, such as the English sparrow, the European black swift, and most birds that nest in colonies, it is reduced to the immediate vicinity of the nests. On the other hand the territory may be of considerable extent for certain birds of prey which are strong fliers. The time during which the territory is maintained is also very variable. With many passerines this time is limited to the reproductive period. In some species the reappearance of territorial behavior in autumn may be observed, while others establish a territory in their winter quarters. The same variability is encountered when we attempt to determine the role of the territory. In some cases it serves mating and feeding needs, in others it concerns mating only, in still others (winter territories) it is for feeding only. Thus the one and only characteristic common to all these types of territory is clearly *the intolerance of their "owners" toward other individuals of the same species*, and most ornithologists today agree in defining the territory as *"an area defended by its occupant against competing members of the same species."* [6]

Territories so defined unquestionably exist with numerous species of fish (sticklebacks, Centrarchidæ of North America, some Cyprinidæ and Characidæ), and also with many lizards. Has something of the kind been observed among mammals?

The answer would seem to be yes in certain instances. During the reproductive period the females of the European wild rabbit are extremely intolerant toward other individ-

[6] This definition is adopted by a majority of English authors studying the behavior of wild mammals (see, for example, Burt, 1943). In German-speaking countries the word *Territorium* becomes rather a synonym for *domaine vital*, or home range; according to Hediger's statement of the case (1949), *Heim* is the word corresponding to *territory*.

uals of the species, and each has its "sphere" around its burrow. If another rabbit encroaches on this territory, it is at
once chased away by the proprietor, and there may even be
a brief battle. When the female is engaged in digging a burrow, its aggressiveness is especially noticeable. As for adult
males, each of them also has in like manner its "sphere" in
the warren, but their aggressiveness is much less clearly
marked than that of the females. A similar intolerance on
the part of the females during the reproductive period has
been noted in a number of species: the eastern chipmunk,
deer mouse, white-footed mouse, etc. In other mammals it
is the polygamous male that displays particular intolerance
toward other males threatening its harem. Later on we shall
find good examples of this when we study seal societies and
especially the otaries and southern elephant seals.

In other cases, finally, it is the social group as a whole
that defends its territory against intrusion by other groups.
This is probably true of the familiar beaver and muskrat
colonies, and it is certainly so for the lar gibbon. It has been
observed also in the clans of howler monkeys, and we shall
return to it later.

As with birds, territories purely concerned with food-
getting would seem to exist with certain mammals. Thus,
Burt mentions the red squirrel's defense of its food caches
against others of its kind. Godet also thinks that the European mole has a strictly individual "hunting-terrain," and
that occasional fights between males may signify territorial
defense. Such behavior, however, has not as yet been closely
studied.

There are also certain negative facts to place beside
these positive data. In the case of the California ground

squirrel, Fitch has not succeeded in finding any trace of a territory whatever; at the height of the breeding-season five or six adult males may live together in a single burrow. Heim de Balsac, moreover, has frequently observed fully adult male long-tailed field mice living during the spring, five or six together, in a single nest-box, and this at a time when the females isolate themselves with their young. We may remark in passing that these observations simply demonstrate the lack of aggressiveness of rodent males that are polygamous or promiscuous; there is no indication that the females are not more intolerant, as Southern has shown in the case of the wild rabbit.

Some good observations on the carnivores also exist, which show that several families live together peacefully in the same burrow, *during* the rearing of their young. In the Mount McKinley National Park in Alaska, Murie saw two she-wolves raising their litters at the same time in the same den. Sheldon reports that this is frequent with the American red fox, and Hainard has observed two females of the European red fox combining their litters and taking turns in nursing the whole group of young. In his study of the prairie spotted skunk in Iowa, Crabbe has shown that the several dens are not "owned" by single individuals or by single families, but are used in common by the whole local population, like the network of paths connecting them. Scott, finally, has been unable to discern that any true territory is maintained by the northern plains red fox; and, in his opinion, the "scent signals" that the male places by urinating on stones and other objects have rather a sexual significance, indicative of the rutting period.[7]

[7] While we await a clear demonstration of the significance (terri-

In general, and in so far as the paucity of observations permits judgment, it would seem that territorial behavior is far from being as important in mammals as in birds, and very often it is limited to the temporary defense of the nest or of certain parts of the home range. It is most clearly manifested in monogamous and polygamous species.

### THE HOME RANGE

AS already stated, the home range [8] is the area over which the individual or the family group normally travels in search of food. A fundamental negative characteristic differentiating it from the territory is that the home range is not the exclusive "property" of the individual that frequents it. Thus, it is not defended by its occupant against other members of the same species, and several home ranges may overlap without giving rise to conflict.

We are better informed on the extent and variations of the home range of the mammals than on their territorial behavior; indeed, thanks to the technique of setting traps in grids, it is possible to gain an approximate idea of the area regularly frequented by a previously marked individual. It surely would not be wise to rely too confidently on the figures thus obtained, and Hayne has given us a timely reminder of the limitations of the method. Comparisons can still be made, however, and numerous authors, especially in

---

torial, sexual, or both) of the various "scent signals" encountered on the mammalian home range, it seems preferable to study them separately; this is what we shall do in the chapter on social co-ordination (page 225). I think that the odoriferous secretions of mammals serve at once in sexual attraction and in the delimitation of the home range, just as do the acoustic and visual "signals" among birds.

[8] *Domaine vital* of French authors and *Territorium* of Hediger.

North America, have persistently studied the characteristics of the home ranges of the small mammals.

The brown rat, for instance, is much more sedentary than is generally supposed. Davis, Emlen, and Stokes have applied themselves to the study of its movements from place to place in the city of Baltimore and in the country. In doing this they first caught a number of individuals which they marked and released. Later a large proportion of these marked individuals were recaptured, and thus it was easy to ascertain the size of their home range. Of 362 rats marked and released, 119 were recaptured in the city after a week or more. Among the recaptured, 71 per cent of the adult males and 77 per cent of the adult females were taken within forty feet of the place where they had been captured the first time. On a Maryland farm the same experiment was carried on for a year with analogous results: 75.3 per cent of the adult males and 84 per cent of the adult females were recaptured within less than forty feet from where they were first caught; only 10 per cent of the females went from one to another of the farm buildings.

Extensive information on the home ranges of North American small mammals is to be found in the numerous papers of Blair, Burt, and Mohr. On the whole, the published figures indicate great variation among the species and, in the same species, between the sexes for different habitats and in different years. Generally the area of the home range varies from a fraction of an acre to a few acres; that of the males is often, but not always, greater than that of the females.[9] With desert mammals the area is as a rule larger than

[9] Sheldon has shown that in the American red fox only the female

with species of similar size living in temperate regions. The greater or lesser possibilities for food and cover furnished by the habitat would seem, then, in some way to determine the average extent of the home range. The density of the population, on the other hand, has some influence, and any overpopulation tends to reduce the home range of the individuals composing the population. But this "compressibility" is not unlimited; if we artificially overpopulate a habitat, the population of which is already in equilibrium and near the "carrying capacity," we can show that only a small proportion of the enforced immigrants are able to gain a foothold; most of them are obliged to emigrate. Blair's experiments with deer mice in George Reserve, Michigan, give ample proof of this, as do those of Calhoun on the brown rats of Baltimore. This mechanism is certainly what compels many young to emigrate away from their birthplace. Only a part remain to fill the places made vacant by the death of adults; the rest disperse to seek a less populated region at a distance. We shall return to these matters in the chapter devoted to the physiology of wild populations.[1]

The home range is not a prerogative of species inhabiting temperate or subtropical regions; even in the equatorial forest the small mammals are remarkably sedentary. Davis provides us with some Brazilian examples. Most of the

---

has a rather fixed home range, the male being much more given to wandering. One of these males traveled 23 miles in 11 days, and another, marked in late September, was retaken in early December at a distance of 40 miles!

[1] D. H. Salman has recently published a very pertinent study of the various factors, ecological and ethological, which govern the territorial behavior of the eastern cottontail rabbit; the conclusions reached in this work are certainly of very general application.

species he studied by marking failed to go more than three hundred feet or so from the place where they were first trapped. The same is true of arboreal forms; the woolly opossum remains in a single tree for several months!

Just as the home range of small species appears restricted, so that of the large mammals is sometimes extended. The brown bear in Russia frequents a zone of about 10 to 13 square miles. As for the Alaskan grizzly bear, Murie's observations indicate that the diameter of its home range does not exceed 9 miles. The family home range of wolves, studied by the same naturalist in the Mount McKinley National Park, may have as great a diameter as 50 miles! We shall return later to the home ranges of ungulate herds (ch. viii), and for the present shall only state, with Fraser Darling, that the area of a deer range varies with the abundance of food.

TOPOGRAPHY OF THE HOME RANGE. The mammals, particularly the large species, often lay out very exact landmarks within the home range. Apart from the main domicile, several secondary quarters exist, and even temporary refuges, as a rule. A single European hare always has several forms, just as a single Texas armadillo uses from 4 to 8 burrows concurrently. In addition to living-quarters, the home range may include wallowing-places for mud baths (deer), playgrounds and sunning-grounds (badger), and dung pits (badger). With the large mammals certain trees, rocks, or termite nests serve as landmarks or as "rubbing-posts" for the animals which visit them regularly (fig. 43). There is almost always a network of paths or trails connecting these different points, more or less noticeable to the casual ob-

server but well known to beasts of prey and to poachers.[2]
With the large ungulates, in regions where man does not
disturb them too much, these paths are often used generation after generation, and they may become real trails. This

FIG. 43: *A male European bison "marking" a tree by barking a portion of the trunk with its horns. After this preliminary action, the animal will urinate on the ground near
by, and then will roll in its urine. Having done this, it
will return to the tree and rub its back, impregnated with
urine, against the barked tree trunk. After a sketch by
Hediger, 1949.*

is the case with the migration "routes" of caribou in the
great Canadian North, as well with the elephant "roads"
that were formerly common in eastern Africa; Percival
describes these "roads" as perfectly smooth and free from
vegetation, as much as 3 or 4 yards in width, and following
the line of easiest slope in mountainous country. Our rav-
aging "civilization" hardly allows such manifestations of the

[2] Even the arboreal primates exhibit behavior of this type. Malbrant and Maclatchy refer, for example, to "trails laid out in the foliage,
veritable aerial routes" existing in the "food-gathering territory" of bands
of tree-dwelling guenons (*Cercopithecus cephus*).

*Beaver dam in Oregon. It is about two feet high. Note use of rock as base. Photograph by V. Scheffer. U.S. Fish and Wildlife Service.*

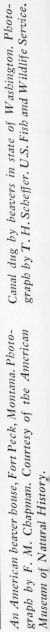

Canal dug by beavers in state of Washington. Photograph by T. H. Scheffer. U.S. Fish and Wildlife Service.

An American beaver house, Fort Peck, Montana. Photograph by F. M. Chapman. Courtesy of the American Museum of Natural History.

might of great animals to exist any longer in the modern world. It is along these paths or trails that one generally finds "signposts"—secretions of the skin glands, urine, heaps of dung, barked trees, and the like (ch. viii). They undoubtedly play an important part in the daily life of the mammals (fig. 44).

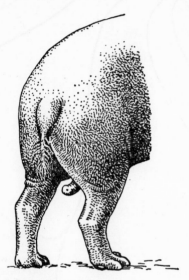

FIG. 44: *The hindquarters of a male pygmy hippopotamus, showing the recurved penis and the peculiar appearance of the tail. This anatomical arrangement facilitates simultaneous "marking," by urine and feces, of the animal's territory. After Hediger.*

One of the main advantages of the home range is probably that it assures to the individual frequenting it not only its daily food but also increased protection against predators. Davis very justly remarks that an animal taken by surprise on its home range finds with minimum delay a hiding-place in which to take refuge or a pathway along which to make

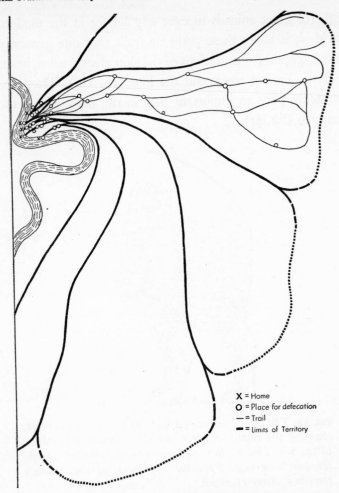

X = Home
O = Place for defecation
— = Trail
■ = Limits of Territory

FIG. 45: *Diagram of several hippopotamus territories (Belgian Congo). Note the aquatic home of this species, which mates, gives birth, nurses its young, and in case of danger takes refuge, in the water. The pear-shaped territories are furrowed with trails, the latter landmarked with places for defecation. Used by courtesy of the* Institut des Parcs Nationaux du Congo Belge *and Prof. H. Hediger.*

its escape under the best possible conditions (fig. 45). On the other hand, a small rodent set at liberty outside its familiar range always takes much longer in finding shelter. This intimate knowledge of the surroundings made possible by an established home range probably explains also the ease with which many mammals accomplish their return to nest or lair—their homing; the keenness of their sense of smell provides them with guideposts unknown to human perceptions.

The sedentary nature of many small mammals, further, has consequences that would have hardly been suspected before the intensive studies of the last few years. Howard, having marked 675 young deer mice before they left the nest, found that 70 per cent of the young males and 85 per cent of the young females settled down no more than 500 feet from their birthplace. A high degree of inbreeding results from this; 4 to 10 per cent of the 186 litters observed were produced either by parent-offspring matings or by matings between sibs.

CHAPTER 4

# Defense and Protection

IT is always a difficult matter, even for an objective observer, to estimate the value of the methods of defense and protection used by animals under natural conditions. Such and such behavior, attitude, or morphological character may seem to us to have a certain protective value even though it may actually be of no great use against the natural predator of the animal under observation. The scientific study of the behavior of wild mammals is only in its early stages, and it is likely that with further study the problem of their means of defense and protection will reveal itself to be much more complex than it now appears.

### DEFENSIVE ATTITUDES

FLIGHT is the habitual reaction of the great majority of mammals before what they take to be an enemy. There is no need to mention examples of this behavior, common to both large and small species in all environments. It is not to be supposed, however, that flight in the presence of danger is resorted to invariably. Instead of fleeing, the animal often assumes an absolute immobility that enables it to escape detection. Some species frequently behave in this manner and others very rarely. As to the reasons why flight is pre-ferred to complete immobility—or vice versa—we can only suggest hypotheses.

With most mammals flight before an enemy takes place only when the predator (or man) comes within a "critical distance" of the animal. Once this distance is at-tained, the animal makes off. If the animal is pursued and the distance between it and its enemy is dangerously di-minished, the pursued may suddenly change its behavior and, abandoning flight, puts itself on the defensive (figs. 46, 47). If it is hard pressed, the defense reaction is released—a highly variable response according to the species concerned and employing all the weapons available to the animal (horns, hooves, tusks, teeth, etc.[1]). The "critical distances," of course, vary with the species and, in the same species, with sex, age, and local conditions. It is a curious fact that the critical distance is less for some animals when ap-proached by, say, an automobile than when approached afoot.

Among the social species the group often displays re-markable organization for the detection of approaching danger. Although it would seem that the Alpine marmots have no true "lookouts," each animal is very much on the watch; when it perceives danger, it whistles, and this whistle puts the rest of the colony on the alert. A similar warning-system exists in some rodents other than the marmots, such as the mountain viscacha of Peru. Darling reports that, in the Scottish Highlands, when a herd of red deer is resting, one or more individuals keep watch in every direction. If,

---

[1] The Panama howling monkeys may break off branches to throw at intruders; red spider monkeys do the same (Carpenter), but the use of pebbles as projectiles by baboons has never been verified.

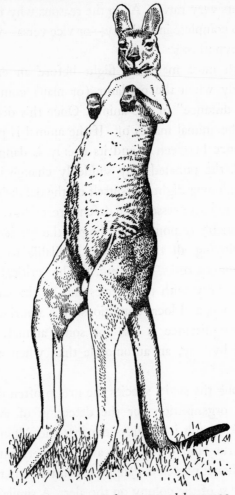

FIG. 46. *Defense posture of the great red kangaroo. Drawn from a photograph furnished by the New York Zoological Society.*

on the other hand, one deer is reposing by itself, it lies with its back toward the wind, keeping watch by sight over the zone in front and by scent over that to the rear. Musk oxen tend to arrange themselves in a circle when threatened; the

FIG. 47: *Three-toed anteater in a "tripod" attitude, head down, on the vertical trunk of a tree. After a sketch made by the author on Barro Colorado Island, Canal Zone, September 1951.*

young are grouped in the middle and the adults surround them, their powerful heads facing outward in all directions. Such behavior was perhaps very efficient against beasts of prey, but it has rather favored the destruction of the species by Eskimos and Indians, once these were armed with guns.

All the mammals that are covered over with a more or less tough armor (armadillos, pangolins), and those with hairs modified into sharp quills (hedgehogs, porcupines, etc.), assume special attitudes of defense appropriate to these structural characteristics. In the armadillos there even seems to exist a close relation between the structure of the scapular shield and the usual posture of defense. Thus armadillos of the genus *Tolypeutes*,[2] which have the scapular shield shaped in sections like a horseshoe, roll themselves into a ball when threatened, their head and tail ends fitting together in a remarkable manner (fig. 48). The species of *Euphractus*, on the other hand, which have the shield much more flattened on a low arc, cannot do the same but press themselves against the ground if they are taken by surprise and caught running about. The very curious animal *Chlamyphorus* (fig. 49) uses its posterior shield to close the burrow in which it takes refuge. As for the Old World pangolins, whose armor is made up of broad, horny scales regularly arranged to overlap like shingles on a roof, they are all able to roll themselves into a ball, like *Tolypeutes* (fig. 50). The female of the Indian pangolin even protects its young in case of danger by placing it on her belly and then curling her long protective tail around herself.

It is a common sight to see the European hedgehog roll itself into a ball and erect its quills. Although there is no

[2] This genus does not even dig burrows.

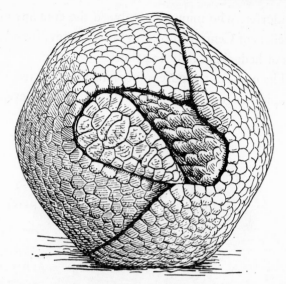

FIG. 48: *Posture of defense of the armadillo,* Tolypeutes conurus. *After a photograph by Eisentraut.*

FIG. 49: *The armadillo* Chlamyphorus truncatus.

doubt that this attitude is protective, it is questionable whether it affords perfect defense against all predators, for the hedgehog does form part of the menu of several carnivores, various Mustelidæ, the vultures, and the great horned owl, for example. Still, the German naturalist

Uttendorfer, who minutely analyzed the contents of 102,-
000 pellets of Central European birds of prey, found the remains of hedgehogs only 134 times!

The quills of the porcupines inhabiting the tropical and
subtropical regions of the Old World form an even more

FIG. 50: *A pangolin,* Manis tricuspis, *rolled into a ball.
Drawn from a photograph by H. Lang.*

efficient means of defense. When an Indian crested porcupine is irritated, it erects its quills (fig. 51), grunts and puffs
loudly, and produces a curious rustling sound by clashing its
quills together. But this is not the limit of its defense. If the
aggressor approaches, the porcupine, moving backwards,
throws itself quickly upon it, and the contact of the sharp
quills may inflict serious wounds on the enemy. Prater cites

two especially convincing observations: in one case a panther was mortally wounded, and in another case an almost adult tiger, its liver and lungs perforated in many places, was found dead a few yards from its victim. The American procupine is less dangerous but is no more limited to a pas-

FIG. 51: *Attitude of defense, with quills erected, of the African porcupine,* Hystrix africæ-australis.

sive defense. If a dog approaches one too closely, it erects its quills, elevates its back, raises its tail slightly, and bends its nose down under its body. Keeping its back always toward its assailant, it strikes out repeatedly with its tail, always leaving some quills in the flesh of the aggressor. The structure of the tips of the quills enables them, moreover, to advance by themselves in the body of the victim, because of the contractions of the muscles in contact with the barbs of the imbedded quills (fig. 52). Shadle and Po-Chedley cite an instance in which a fragment three quarters of an inch long progressed almost two inches in thirty hours, and another only a quarter of an inch long advanced almost an inch and three quarters in less than two days.

Another very special type of defensive attitude, as we have mentioned, is complete immobilization, or "freezing behavior," in common parlance often called "playing pos-

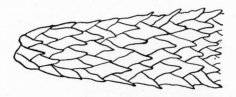

FIG. 52: *Appearance of the tip of a quill, magnified about 45 times, of the American porcupine. After Shadle and Po-Chedley.*

sum." Fawns of the deer family provide us with a good example. For the first few days after birth the mother leaves them alone where they were born, and, at the slightest alarm, they "freeze" on the spot in perfect immobility. In many cases their spotted fur helps to make them hardly visible in the midst of the dappling of light and shade on the ground beneath the underbrush. This behavior has often been compared to that of the Virginia opossum. It is well known that in case of danger this marsupial can "play dead"; it lies on its side (fig. 53), limp, its tongue sometimes hanging out of its half-opened mouth, its eyes closed, and its heartbeat slow. This state may last for several minutes, during which the animal passively lets itself be handled; when the danger passes, the opossum resumes its normal behavior. It must always be noted that we have to do here with a relatively rare reaction, and it is possible that the performance is to be compared rather with the analogous states to be observed sometimes in certain birds, the protective function of which is not always clear.[3]

A last very special type of defensive attitude is the discharge of fetid secretions. Examples are found in several

FIG. 53: *Virginia opossum "playing dead." After a photograph by Viola McColm.*

families: among the civets (Viverridæ), the species of the genera *Viverra* and *Viverricula* use the perineal gland for this purpose; in the Herpestidæ the large species, like the striped-necked mongoose and the crab-eating mongoose, empty their stink glands when danger threatens. It is among the skunks (Mustelidæ), however, that this mode of defense reaches its greatest development; their anal glands are very large indeed, and the substance they secrete can be shot out with astonishing precision to a distance of up to about

[3] Very similar behavior has been reported for the jackal, the honey badger, and the striped hyena (Prater).

twelve feet (fig. 54). Before discharging this malodorous secretion, skunks first assume "threatening attitudes" that vary widely according to the species. Some stamp on the ground with their hind feet while others, such as the spotted

FIG. 54: *Position of the striped skunk,* Mephitis mephitis, *before the ejection of the secretion of its anal glands.*

skunk, walk for perhaps five seconds at a time on their front feet with the hindquarters elevated. It is a curious fact that the skunks, like the civets and the mongooses that use stink glands, have a special pattern of coat coloration. Its black

FIG. 55: *A skunk,* Spilogale gracilis, *"standing on its hands." In part after a drawing by M. M. Colbert.*

and white contrast sharply, and the association of this conspicuous coat with the use of malodorous secretions has been often emphasized (fig. 55).

Musk glands discharged in fright are found in a wide variety of species. The peccary, for instance, has one on its back, eight inches in front of the tail. When the animal is excited, the hairs of the back and neck bristle and the dorsal gland emits a musky secretion whose odor can be perceived by man at a distance of several hundred feet. Here it is not easy to see the defensive utility of this behavior, and it would seem rather that many intermediary stages exist between the emotional secretion of certain cutaneous glands induced by a state of fear and their intentional utilization for defense against an aggressor.

### AUTOTOMY OF THE TAIL IN MAMMALS

THE extreme fragility of the tail in lizards is well known. Many species when seized by the caudal appendage free themselves by leaving it in the hunter's grasp. This experiment can be readily carried out with the European green lizard, and its tail may even break off during fights between males. Later a usually incomplete but quite clear regeneration occurs.

Caudal autotomy, or self-amputation of the tail, for escape also exists among mammals, but the manner in which it is accomplished has been studied only rather superficially. Cuénot was one of the first to call attention to this curious phenomenon, but he has been followed, since 1907, by only a very few naturalists.[4]

If we seize a long-tailed field mouse by the tail, we al-

[4] Mohr (1941) reports tail autotomy in 20 species of the genera *Perognathus, Glis, Dryomys, Eliomys, Muscardinus, Apodemus, Mus, Epimys, Graphiurus,* and *Claviglis.* This autotomy is often followed by a beginning of regeneration. Von Haffner (*Zool. Anzeiger,* 135:66, 1941) has studied this phenomenon in the forest, garden, and common dormice. His histological researches have shown that when part of a vertebra remains it will regenerate a vertebra similar to the original one but having also some resemblance to the last tail vertebra. When the tail is broken off at the level of an intervertebral disk, the latter regenerates a cartilaginous structure.

most always see that the cutaneous sheath of the tail separates at some point and remains in the hand, while the animal escapes. The wound scarcely bleeds at all, and the denuded portion of the tail dries up and falls off in two or three days. In this type of autotomy there is no voluntary or reflex action on the part of the animal. The caudal sheath breaks at the edge of one of the corneous rings with which the tail is provided, and does not adhere to the vertebræ with their accompanying muscles and blood vessels. It is possible, moreover, to observe autotomy quite as well in a field mouse recently dead as in a living individual. Gögl has made a careful histological study of this phenomenon and concludes that the autotomy always occurs at the level of a zone of least resistance. In the garden dormouse and the common dormouse there are only four to six possible points of breakage.

Has this peculiarity some protective value for the species that manifest it? Does this security device often act as such under natural conditions? These are questions which are very difficult to answer objectively in view of the meager information now at our disposal. One thing only is certain: in wild populations of species in which escape autotomy has been reported, a considerable proportion of individuals with amputated tails has been observed. Cuénot reports that he has seen more field mice with incomplete than with intact tails, and Hainard confirms the frequent occurrence of this mutilation. It would be of interest to have exact percentages for different localities. Enders notes that 20 to 25 per cent of the spiny rats taken by him on Barro Colorado Island, in the Panama Canal Zone, had incomplete tails.

### THE PROBLEM OF CONCEALING COLORATION

THE temporary or permanent resemblance of the coat in certain mammals to the dominant ground color of their favored habitat long ago captured the attention of naturalists. According as rodents or carnivores were concerned, it has been interpreted as a means of protection against predators or as a form of camouflage facilitating the approach to prey. In both cases natural selection would favor species with "protective" coloration and would therefore account for the origin of this adaptation.

In reality the problem is not so simple as it would at first appear to be, and it seems appropriate to take up in succession the seasonal color change of arctic and alpine mammals and the permanent concealing coloration of desert species.

SEASONAL COLOR CHANGE OF ARCTIC MAMMALS. It is undeniable that among the species inhabiting the polar regions of the northern hemisphere many assume in summer a dark coat and in winter a white one. Further, it would seem that the duration of the winter coat is in direct relation to that of the period of snow. The different forms of the arctic hare of the great American North offer a good example. For example, the subspecies *grœnlandicus* of Ellesmere Island, at 80° north latitude, remains white the year round, while the subspecies *canus* of Hudson Bay assumes a dark coat from late June to late August. The molting date of the snowshoe hare is also influenced not only by latitude but also by altitude. Thus Smith has noted, in the Green Mountain massif (Vermont), that at mid-June the hares were in summer pelage at 2,800 feet, in lighter pelage already at 3,200 feet, and in pelage still spotted with white at 4,000 feet, at which altitude the snow lasts into May. The European varying hare gives evidence of a similar adaptation to local conditions. In the north of Scandinavia it becomes white in winter, as also in the Scottish Highlands (subspecies *scoticus*). On the other hand, in southern Sweden, in Ireland (subspecies *hibernicus*), and in the Faroe Islands (subspecies *seclusus*) it retains a dark livery the year round. The arctic fox, in its typical form, becomes white in winter, but in Iceland, where the climate is less severe, it generally retains its dark coat throughout the year. Among the Mustelidæ, also, we find good examples of seasonal color change. The ermine assumes for the winter a pelage that is all white except for the black tail-tip; the change in coloration appears to take place earlier in the autumn on mountains than in flat country. Thus Hainard observed a perfectly white ermine in October at Anzeindaz in Switzerland (2,500 feet), and one that was entirely brown at Bernex (500 feet). In mountains the summer pelage seems likewise to appear later than in flat country. In mild climates, as in Ireland or central and southern England, it is not uncommon for ermines to remain brown all winter, while in Scotland they are white during the cold season. The weasel also turns white in Scandinavia during the winter, at least in places where the snow lasts more than a hundred days. In England it generally remains brown in winter, whereas it turns white in the Alps, but not invariably (Hainard mentions several observations of brown weasels in December and January, at 2,000 feet in the Alpes Vaudoires).

There are exceptions, however, to this seasonal adaptation of coat color to that of the surroundings. In the first place there are species which remain brown while living most of the year amid the snows; this is true of the musk ox, reindeer, caribou,[5] and wolverine. Among the lemmings, the Hudson Bay and Greenland collared lemmings turn white in winter, while the brown lemming and Norway lemming remain in somber livery all year. Still, it is not rare to meet with collared and brown lemmings in the same habitat. Hamilton says that he has even caught them in the same burrows, under the snow. Other mammals, on the contrary, remain white even in summer. This is true of the polar bear and of Peary's caribou. In regard to these animals it may be said, however, that they are precisely species that live on backgrounds of snow or ice almost all the time, summer included.

More perplexing is the problem of the blue fox. It is well known that the arctic fox has two distinct forms: the "normal" form, brown in summer and white in winter, and the "blue" form, which retains all year a dark bluish-gray coat color. These two phases are genetically distinct, the "blue" apparently dominant and the "normal" recessive. What is more remarkable is the different frequency of these two phases in different parts of the distributional area of the species. Through the work of Braestrup and of Elton we are in fact certain that the "blue" foxes (at a disadvantage in winter because of natural selection) make up no more than 1 to 5 per cent of the total population of arctic foxes in Baffin Land and the Canadian arctic, whereas they represent 50 per cent of the population in western Greenland. The

[5] With the exception always of the Ellesmere Islands form (*Rangifer pearyi*)—smaller than typical *arcticus*—which retains an almost wholly white coat throughout the year.

difference in coat color, further, would seem to be associated with other characters; the fecundity of the two phases appears to be different (higher in the "normals"), and above all their diet is not the same, "normal" foxes living on lemmings for the most part and the "blues" on birds, fish, and arctic hares. Let us keep in mind for the time being this first *correlation between a pigmentary character and other characteristics of physiological and psychological nature;* we shall come upon others later on, and they are probably of very great theoretical importance.

What do we know, at the present time, regarding the cause of this seasonal color change? Is this characteristic genetically determined, or are we concerned with a simple phenotypic variation, sensitive to the least changes in environmental conditions? Raising the species just mentioned outside their natural habitats should solve this problem. No systematic experimentation on a large scale seems to have been carried out, but what we learn from the few planned experiments or chance observations that have been made tends rather to suggest that the two mechanisms may work together to produce the same result.

Degerböl and Möhl-Hansen, having received in the autumn of 1936 seven living specimens of the Greenland collared lemming caught in northeastern Greenland, undertook to breed them in the neighborhood of Copenhagen. These animals acquired their winter pelage only in January–February of 1937, whereas in their native region they become white late in September or early in October. Later on, from 1937 to 1942 and in spite of the fact that the winters were very hard (the temperature having gone down to −30° C), their offspring retained their summer coat in the wintertime. Only a few of them temporarily displayed blue-gray or light-gray fur.[6] In this case the disappearance of the winter coat was probably determined by the modification of an environmental factor, since it happened at the start and in all individuals. The responsible factor may be the daily period of light. We shall see in a later chapter that Bissonette and Bailey have been able, in the laboratory, to induce out of season the appearance of the white winter coat in two species of weasels, by progressively reducing the daily period of light to which the animals were exposed. In addition, two Russian zoologists, Novikov and Blagodat-skaia, have arrived at similar results, working on the varying hare of Siberia. On November 25 they took 10 white hares that had finished their fall molting. Four of these served as controls and four were submitted to artificial lighting that was progressively lengthened by a quarter of an hour each day to reach 15 hours on February 1; two males, finally, were kept in darkness from November 25 to June 1; in all three cases the diet and temperature were identical. When the spring molt of the controls began in late March to early April, it did not occur in the two males that remained in total darkness, and they were still white on June 1. In the second series, on the contrary, the progressive increase in daily period of light stimulated the appearance of rut at the beginning of December and of the spring molt in January. All these observations and experiments tend, then, to show that a disturbance of the annual rhythm of variation in the length of the days can affect the succession of molts. But

---

[6] In this species the first litter of the year, born in March and therefore under the snow, has the winter coat from the first (with the claws enlarged on the third and fourth fingers), whereas the young of later litters are born with the summer coat.

this is not enough to solve the whole problem of winter color change in arctic mammals.

The fact is that other species transplanted from their country of origin continue to whiten in winter, and this in spite of the fact that the annual rhythm of photoperiods is changed. Cott reports, for example, that the arctic foxes living in the London Zoo continue to become white in winter, despite the very mild climate of southern England. In this case, therefore, the characteristic is genetically determined and unaffected by environmental variations, contrary to the case of the Greenland collared lemming.

As reconstructed by Degerböl, the history of the subspecies of the varying hare that now inhabits the Faroe Islands is also very suggestive. The fauna of these islands included no land mammals before the eighth or ninth centuries. At about that epoch domestic mice were introduced by the first inhabitants, and today four distinct subspecies exist there. Toward 1768 it was the brown rat's turn. Finally, from Norway in 1854–5 a pair of varying hares was imported, whose descendants have multiplied ever since and given origin to the new subspecies *seclusus*, which has thus become differentiated in less than a century. Now, in the years immediately following their introduction all the hares of the Faroes turned white in winter, like their Norwegian ancestors. Twenty years later half of the total only became white in winter, and thirty years later at most one quarter! Toward 1890 only a very small percentage of the population whitened in the cold season, and today all the hares keep their dark coats throughout the year. During this same time the size has become smaller, the length of the molars is less than in the ancestral form, and some other characters bring this new subspecies *seclusus* closer to the subspecies *scoticus* of Scotland.[7] In such a case the disappearance of the white winter coat cannot be attributed to a mere phenotypic change due to one or several environmental factors. Here *the modification has been progressive and has required almost forty years to become universal*. This suggests a hereditary change or mutation spreading little by little throughout the population.

Let us suppose, for example, a mutation "winter fur dark" recessive to the form "winter fur white" and occurring from time to time among the typical varying hares of Norway. On the one hand this mutation would have little chance of appearing in the homozygous form because of the large number of individuals composing the total population and crossing freely among themselves. On the other hand the rare homozygotes that did appear (much more visible in winter than normal individuals with white fur) would be more seriously threatened than these by predators. This same mutation, quite to the contrary, if it occurred in the Faroes among a smaller population (in which recessive mutations have therefore a better chance of appearing in homozygous form), will have the advantage in winter over the individuals that whiten, because of the rarity of snow. Natural selection will therefore act in its favor, and the number of homozygotes will tend to become greater and greater. This may possibly be the explanation of the phenomena observed in the Faroe Islands; but it remains necessary to make crosses between *seclusus* and the Scandinavian *timidus* before asserting its truth.

[7] Which, to be sure, whitens in winter.

THE PERMANENT CONCEALING COLORATION OF DESERT MAMMALS. Most of the mammals permanently inhabiting the desert regions of both the Old and the New Worlds wear a very typical coat. The prevailing colors are the pale buff and tawny hues of the soil, and the general coloration of the animal thus corresponds very faithfully to that of the background, especially in a sandy desert. This appearance is due chemically to a partial depigmentation and to a predominance of the phæomelanins.

We have to do here with a fact of very wide application. In the Sahara, for example, Heim de Balsac's studies have shown that of 50 species, 39, or more than three quarters, are of a "desert" shade. Among the exceptions are two hedgehogs, a wild boar, the dama gazelle, the jackal, the hunting dog, the Lybian striped weasel, the honey badger, the Barbary ground squirrel, and the garden dormouse. Still it should be noted that the wild boar has a rufous band running from neck to tail that is lacking in other races, and that the dormouse is clearly depigmented in comparison with the races of Barbary and Europe. Moreover, all these "exceptions" inhabit the northern or southern borders of the Sahara rather than the desert proper. In central Asia and Asia Minor the same fur coloration is to be seen in desert rodents (*Dipus, Eremodipus, Ctenodactylus, Pygerethmus*, etc.), the corsak fox, and the Pallas cat. It is to be observed also in the desert rodents in the southwestern United States (kangaroo rats, some deer mice, antelope jackrabbits, etc.) and in the Australian desert marsupials (*Dasycercus cristicauda, Dasyuroides byrnei*).

It is a very significant fact that typical desert coloration is not confined to terrestrial mammals. It is to be found again among the bats that, however, fly only at night and spend the daytime in rocky clefts or in caves where vertebrate predators are hardly a menace. In the Sahara, for instance, the eight species of Chiroptera all have a paler tint than have related forms living in nondesert country; *Otonycteris hemprichii*, belonging to the Afro-Asiatic desert zone, has a pale yellowish fur, quite the color of sand (on which this species probably never settles down!). *Eptesicus isabellinus* has fur that is much lighter than that of the European *Eptesicus serotinus*. The case of *Pipistrellus kuhlii* is most curious from our present point of view: The distribution of this species includes, in fact, the Mediterranean and desert regions; in southern Europe its coat is dark brown, almost black; in the Algerian Tell (a hilly, maritime region) it becomes verdigris green with the membranes much diluted in color; in the northern Sahara, finally, this bat is yellowish or whitish gray with the membranes cream-colored or grayish. Nor do the subterranean rodents escape the general rule, although they pass almost the whole of their lives away from the light. Kachkarov and Korovine mention an *Ellobius* of central Asia that has fur of the same general tint as that of the other rodents.[8]

The "desert" coloration of the fur is certainly genetically determined and is quite different from a mere phenotypic variation. It does in fact persist, even if the animal's environment is changed. Sumner was able to show its continuance, in captivity, through four to twelve generations

[8] These same authors point out, however, that the underground rodents are much sought after by predators on the Asiatic steppes; thus *Myospalax* make up more than 75 per cent of the hoarded food of *Buteo hemilasius* in eastern Transbaikalia.

of deer mice, and the same can be said of the North African jirds and gerbils reproducing in captivity in Paris.

The widespread concealing coloration of the fur in desert mammals that scarcely emerge from their burrows except at night, and its presence in species for which it almost certainly has no protective value (bats), would lead us to believe that *this pigmentary character is perhaps merely the correlative* of other morphological or physiological peculiarities having still greater utility in the desert environment and also giving scope to natural selection. It is known, for example, that the light-colored Jersey cattle become more readily adapted to tropical regions than do dark-colored breeds. Now, the skin of these animals would seem to contain more sweat glands, which would improve their resistance to heat. It is also known that certain pigmentary characters of the brown rat are correlated with modifications of behavior as well as with variations in the weight of certain endocrine glands and in basal metabolism.[9] The problem of desert coloration should be re-examined from this angle, for the more our knowledge of mammalian genetics advances, the more evident it becomes that the effects of certain genes on pigmentation are only secondary to physiological modifications of much greater importance.

SOME OTHER CASES OF ADAPTIVE COLORATION. The dark-colored lava flows found at several places in the deserts of the southwestern United States support a fauna of small mammals among which are some whose color is remarkably close to the general shade of the rock. Benson has published

[9] See, for example, Keeler, *Jour. Heredity*, 33:371, 1942, and Schopbach, Keeler, and Breenberg, *Growth*, 7:83, 1943.

a beautiful study of the rodents of the Tularosa Basin in New Mexico. This is an extensive valley bordered on the west, north, and east by mountains and on the south by a sandy desert. In this basin one finds both dunes of white gypsum and quartz sand and black lava flows. The latter are practically *isolated* in the middle of the valley and have an area of a little more than 145 square miles. Now, if we compare the small mammals *confined* to these two habitats (excluding, of course, forms common to both), we note very considerable differences. In the genus *Perognathus* the subspecies *P. apache gypsi*, living among the dunes of gypsum sand, is almost white, whereas *P. intermedius ater*, of the lava flows, is quite black.

It is not to be supposed that in all cases the coat color of small mammals living on recent lava flows will match so closely the color of the rock. Hooper, for example, studying the rodents of the lava fields in Valencia County, New Mexico, did not find such close adaptation in coat color. Of the eight forms belonging to this biotope and hardly ever leaving it, only three (*Peromyscus nasutus*, *Neotoma albigula*, and *Neotoma mexicana*) showed some tendency toward darkening, certain individuals of these three species being more pigmented than the average of those living elsewhere than on the lava. The most probable explanation of this difference lies in all likelihood in the different degree of isolation of the lava flows in the Tularosa Basin and in Valencia County. In the first case the flows are isolated along 29/30 of their circumference; in the second, on the contrary, one tenth to three fifths, approximately, of the periphery of the flows is contiguous to other rock formations, which favors mixing of the rodent populations. At

Tularosa selection can work upon a practically isolated population, whereas at Valencia its effects are in part counterbalanced by a constant movement of emigration and immigration.

Like phenomena are to be found in certain mice (*Peromyscus*) of sandy regions: *P. polionotus leucocephalus*, which lives on geographically isolated sandy islands, is much paler than *P. polionotus albifrons*, which inhabits beaches not sufficiently isolated to prevent the immigration of some *P. polionotus polionotus*, a subspecies that ordinarily lives on the darker terrains of the interior.

DOES CONCEALING COLORATION REALLY PLAY A PROTECTIVE ROLE?   In the course of this chapter we have repeatedly mentioned the action of natural selection as a factor in the origin of adaptive colorations. We have also noted that pigmentary characters are very often correlated with other important characters of a physiological and morphological nature that can themselves afford scope for such selection. What, then, is the real utility of concealing coloration? Are we to think that it has only a distinctly secondary protective value against vertebrate predators, and that this advantage in itself is too slight to be of any use to the species in the course of its evolution? Experimentation should enable us to solve this problem.

The main argument so far advanced against the value of concealing coloration in mammals rests in fact upon the nocturnal habits of most of the species concerned. "It is clear," says Heim de Balsac, "that a protection of this kind can be effective only with regard to predators that hunt by sight and in the daytime. It seems to us impossible to admit that concealing coloration, however perfect it may be in daylight, can work to any effect in the darkness of night."

The recent experiments of Dice reveal that the truth is in all probability nothing of the kind. This author has carried out fully convincing experiments showing that concealing coloration can work perfectly with respect to nocturnal birds of prey and can have a truly protective effect.

Let us examine this remarkable work in some detail. The predators employed were the barn owl and the long-eared owl. The prey consisted of different varieties of deer mice: the recessive form "ivory" and the form "discard-gray." Only adults of similar size and activity were used.

Since previous experiments had shown that on the floor of a room free from obstructions owls are able to catch their prey in total darkness, presumably by means of the sense of hearing, Dice made use of the following apparatus: the floor of an experimental room was divided into two equal parts, each of which was about 9 by 10 feet in size. The floor of the two halves of the room was covered with an artificial soil whose color either matched closely or contrasted with the pelage colors of the mice used in the tests. Wooden sticks, painted to match the color of the soil, were planted in a checkerboard in the artificial soil and these vertical posts were connected by horizontal pieces of rough, split lath. The space above the floor of the experimental room was thus broken up by this "artificial jungle" into little cells, so that the mice had partial cover. The experimental room was lighted by lamps whose intensity could be varied at will, and it was ascertained, as a preliminary, that the nocturnal birds of prey employed could still use their sight at extraordinarily weak lightings (from a distance of 6 feet or more, under an illumination as low as 0.00000073 of a foot candle!)

Each form of the deer mouse was put in the presence of the owl for 15 minutes, first on a ground of the same color, then on one of a different color from that of its pelage. Further, in each half of the experimental room there were always, at the same time, four concealingly colored and four conspicuous mice.

Thus was realized experimentally a population composed of the *same* number of concealingly colored individuals (A) and conspicuous individuals (B) hunted by the same predator. If concealing coloration plays no role, the number of concealingly colored mice taken (a) and that of conspicuous mice taken (b) should be the same. But if one form is captured in preference to the other, it must be admitted that selection intervenes. In this case the relative selection in favor of or against type A will be measured by the difference between the observed value of (a) and its theoretical value, that is to say one half of $(a + b)$, this difference being itself divided by one half of $(a + b)$. Thus:

$$\text{Index of selection} = \frac{a - \frac{1}{2}(a + b)}{\frac{1}{2}(a + b)} = \frac{a - b}{a + b}$$

Dice's index of selection will evidently vary between 1.0 and −1.0, zero corresponding to complete absence of selective effect.

A large number of trials were of course necessary to get statistically significant results (as shown by the chi-square test), and Table 3 gives an idea of the extent of these experiments. The conclusion derived from them is quite clear, and, under Dice's conditions, concealing coloration

**Table 3.** *Experiment showing the protective role of the concealing coloration of the forms "ivory" and "discard-gray" of Peromyscus maniculatus against the barn owl (Dice)*

| ILLUMINATION (IN FOOT-CANDLES) | MICE TAKEN | | | | CONSPICUOUS MICE TAKEN | CONCEALINGLY COLORED MICE TAKEN |
| --- | --- | --- | --- | --- | --- | --- |
| | ON SILICA SAND | | ON GULLY SOIL | | | |
| | "IVORY" | "DISCARD-GRAY" | "IVORY" | "DISCARD-GRAY" | | |
| 0.24 | 1 | 4 | 3 | 1 | 7 | 2 |
| 0.017 | 4 | 2 | 3 | 1 | 5 | 5 |
| 0.004,8 | 1 | 4 | 4 | 1 | 8 | 2 |
| 0.001,4 | 2 | 11 | 9 | 7 | 20 | 9 |
| 0.000,10 | 7 | 7 | 11 | 3 | 18 | 10 |
| 0.000,026 | 4 | 6 | 6 | 4 | 12 | 8 |
| 0.000,013 | 3 | 7 | 7 | 6 | 14 | 9 |
| 0.000,003,5 | 0 | 4 | 7 | 1 | 11 | 1 |
| 0.000,002,0 | 2 | 5 | 4 | 5 | 9 | 7 |
| 0.000,000,53 | 1 | 1 | 2 | 1 | 3 | 2 |
| 0.000,000,31 | 4 | 4 | 2 | 2 | 6 | 6 |
| 0.000,000,08 | 3 | 3 | 8 | 4 | 11 | 7 |
| Darkness | 1 | 0 | 1 | 2 | 1 | 3 |
| Totals | 33 | 58 | 67 | 38 | 125 | 71 |
| Totals excepting animals captured in darkness | 32 | 58 | 66 | 36 | 124 | 68 |

*The index of selection here is 0.292 and the chi-square of the deviation from a 1 : 1 ratio is 16.333, a highly significant amount.*

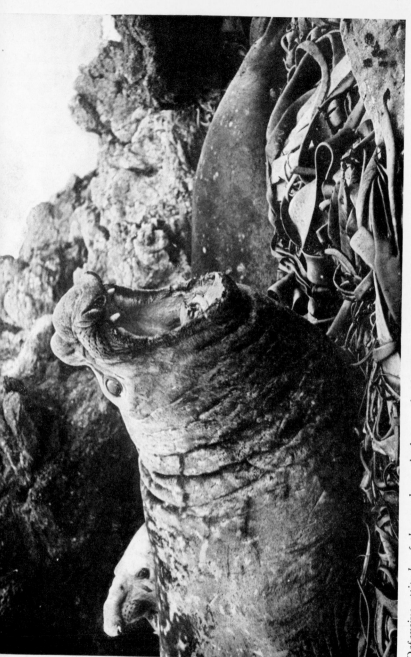

*Defensive attitude of the southern elephant seal, Macquarie Island. Photograph by Dr. Sapin-Jaloustre. Expeditions polaires françaises.*

*Vicuna giving birth. Note position of mother and newborn. Photograph by Hediger. Zoological Garden, Basel.*

*American bison giving birth. The mother is eating the afterbirth. Photograph by Hediger, Zoological Garden, Basel.*

has consequently some protective value, even at degrees of illumination quite unusable by the human eye.

It would, further, be wholly unsound to hold that for a pigmentary character to have a selective value it must assure absolute protection. The absolute does not exist in biology, and one of the great merits of population genetics is to have demonstrated that "surprisingly slight selective advantages may control the direction of evolution and may have strong effects in accelerating its rate." [1]

It would certainly seem, then, that concealing coloration has some value in itself, even if this character is merely correlated with other characters that can otherwise give opportunity for the working of natural selection.

[1] Simpson, G. G. (1944). *Tempo and Mode in Evolution*, pp. 81–3, and see Allee, Emerson, Park, Park, and Schmidt. *Principles of Animal Ecology*, 1949, pp. 648–56.

### CHAPTER 5

# Sexual Life and Reproduction

THE sexual life of the mammals is infinitely more reserved and circumspect, in general, than that of other vertebrates. Among them we scarcely find any equivalent of those courtship activities in which birds display the most brilliantly colored portions of their plumage. The sounds they emit during the rutting period are for the most part far from seductive to the human ear, and the mediocre keenness of our sense of smell prevents us from entering the strange world of odors that appears to play a great part in the sexual and social life of the mammals. If it be added to all this that most wild species are nocturnal, or extremely shy in their relations with man, the reason for the poverty of our knowledge will be easily understood. It would be most important, however—if only to comprehend better the biology of our own species—to know the sexual behavior of a great many species belonging to a large variety of orders. Our present information, in fact, is unfortunately limited to very few forms, and it is probable that future observations will rather considerably modify the provisional conclusions we arrive at today.

## THE OVIPAROUS MAMMALS

THE monotremes, those strange primitive mammals [1] of Australia, have kept among other reptilian characters a mode of reproduction unique among mammals. The platypus and the echidna in fact lay true eggs provided with a thin and leathery shell, from which hatch young that are nourished on the mother's milk.

The reproductive habits of the platypus have been known in some detail only in recent years, thanks to the observations of Burrell and of Fleay. The sexes come together after a short period of hibernation, from mid-September to mid-October in Victoria. This meeting takes place in the water, and there is a slight nuptial performance, during which the male holds the female's tail in his beak and the two animals swim in circles. Coition also occurs in the water, after which the female retires into a breeding-burrow separate from the one ordinarily lived in. There she places bedding composed of water-soaked leaves, the humidity of which seems to be required by the egg. In some cases the burrow is closed with one or several earthen plugs. Incubation of the two eggs is short, eight to ten days in the instance observed by Fleay. The young are blind for the first eleven weeks and are weaned at the age of five months.

The echidnas of the genus *Tachyglossus* do not dig burrows, and it would seem that the egg is laid directly [2] in

[1] Apart from some Pleistocene remains found in Australia, we unfortunately know nothing of the fossil history of this group that shows, we should note, a curious mixture of primitive and highly specialized characters.

[2] As a matter of fact this direct transfer of the egg from the cloaca to the pouch has never yet been actually observed. What makes this seem quite likely is the presence of excrement in the pouch along with the egg.

a pouch that develops during the breeding period. From this egg hatches an offspring that remains constantly in the pouch until its spiny covering develops. Later the mother places her young in some dry and well-shaded nook to which she returns to nurse it until it can feed for itself.

## REPRODUCTION IN THE MARSUPIALS

ALTHOUGH the existence of marsupials in Australia and in America has been known for several centuries, and though some of these creatures are among the favorite guests in zoological gardens, we have but little knowledge of their sexual and reproductive habits. What has been observed, however, is very strange and should stimulate new observations.

It is well known that in the placental mammals, that is, all the mammals now living except the monotremes and marsupials, the embryo gets all the nutritive materials necessary for its growth by way of the placenta, which assures a constant diffusion through its body of materials from the maternal blood. This device permits a long gestation period. Nothing of the kind exists in the marsupials (except for the Paramelidæ), where the placenta is lacking or rudimentary. The embryo thus has no more to depend on than its store of yolk material, which is soon exhausted. Thereupon it is born, and it will continue its development in the marsupial pouch where, clinging to the mother's nipples, it will have the benefit of an abundant nourishment with protection against variations in the outer temperature.

Most of the marsupials so far studied have a well-marked reproductive season. In the Virginia opossum the female is seasonally polyœstrous, which means that throughout a part of the year (January to October in Texas) it exhibits a succession of œstrus cycles, each lasting 28 days, during which, however, the female seems receptive to the male for only 24 to 48 hours. Coitus is dorsal, the male mounting his partner and holding her with teeth and paws; when in copulation the male and female lie on their sides.

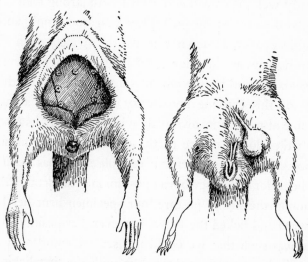

FIG. 56: *The genital region of the South American marsupial,* Lutreolina crassicaudata, *at the right in the male (note the position of the scrotum), and at the left in the female (note the marsupial pouch). Redrawn after Krieg.*

Other species such as the Tasmanian rat kangaroo, are also polyœstrous. The following forms have only one œstrus period per year: the marsupial cat, the koala, and many Macropodidæ, such as the great gray kangaroo, the red kangaroo, and the dama pademelon (fig. 56).

Gestation in all these animals is very short: twelve days and a half in the Virginia opossum, 8 to 12 days in the marsupial cat, 16 days in the silver-gray opossum, and 38 to

40 days for even such a giant species as the great gray kangaroo.

At the end of gestation the offspring is still in a very immature state and small in size. That of the Virginia opossum weighs only two grams and is no larger than a bee; its hind limbs are only mere buds whereas its front legs are already well developed and armed with strong claws. The newborn young of the great gray kangaroo is only an inch long, its eyes are closed but its mouth is widely open. Only its front paws are functional; the hind ones remain bent and crossed, covered by the tail. It is a remarkable fact that in spite of this extreme immaturity the newborn animal is capable of making its own way, without help by its mother, from the cloacal orifice to the entrance of the marsupial pouch. Hartman, to mention one observer, has described the behavior of the newborn opossum in great detail: "After assuming the sitting posture, our specimen bent her body forward and licked the vulva; however, her position at this time was such that we could not see the embryos, which very likely passed into the pouch with the first licking of the genital opening. Hence we went to the outside where we could plainly hear her lap up the chorionic fluid; then suddenly a tiny bit of flesh appeared at the vulva and scampered up over the entanglement of hair into the pouch to join the other fetuses, which now could be seen to have made the trip without our having observed them. Unerringly the embryo traveled by its own efforts. Without any assistance on the mother's part, other than to free it of liquid on its first emergence into the world, this ten-day-old embryo, in appearance more like a worm than a mammal, is able, immediately upon release from its liquid medium, to crawl a full three inches over a difficult terrain. Indeed, it can do more: after it has arrived at the pouch it is able to find the nipple amid a forest of hair." Hartman then anesthetized the mother with ether and took some embryos out of the pouch; one of them, placed near the vulva, returned at once into the pouch; two or three others did the same but took a little longer; a fourth got lost at first and needed twenty minutes before it succeeded in finding a nipple. Only twelve days after conception these embryos not only have a digestive tube and a respiratory apparatus enabling them to feed and breathe normally, but they also possess a neuromuscular development advanced enough to enable them to move by themselves from the vulva to the pouch.

Somewhat similar behavior has been observed in the red kangaroo, the great gray kangaroo, and the short-tailed wallaby. Figure 57, borrowed from Matthews's work, shows well the position of the mother, whose intervention would seem to be limited to licking the fur between the vulva and the entrance to the pouch. The average duration of the embryo's journey is 15 minutes for the great gray kangaroo and from 5 to 30 minutes for the red kangaroo. If the offspring accidentally falls to the ground or fails to find the opening of the pouch, the mother makes no attempt whatever to help it. But Hediger has seen a great gray kangaroo mother at the Basel Zoo aid her offspring with her lips, and Schneider, at Leipzig, has seen another do the same with her paws.

The sojourn of the young in the marsupial pouch (fig. 58) is prolonged: 7 to 8 weeks for the marsupial cat, 90 to 100 days for the Virginia opossum, and 4 months in the case of Lesueur's rat kangaroo! During all this time the mother's role is not merely passive, and it seems to be established that the control of the sphincter that closes the entrance to the pouch is voluntary on her part. There is another curious phenomenon in the koala which has been described ap-

FIG. 57: *Female gray kangaroo assisting the passage of the embryo from the cloaca to the marsupial pouch. After Matthews.*

parently for the first time by Minchin. Toward the age of six months the young begins to be weaned from mother's milk and becomes gradually adapted to the vegetal diet of the species consisting exclusively, as we have already noted, of eucalyptus leaves. Now, at the time of the weaning, it would seem that the mother is able to provide her offspring with a kind of pap made of eucalyptus leaves which the young eats directly from the mother's anus. This vegetable "soup" contains no excrement and is produced during only one month, every two or three days, between three and four o'clock in the afternoon. At this period the growth of the young is greatly accelerated.

Not all females among the marsupials have a pouch. It

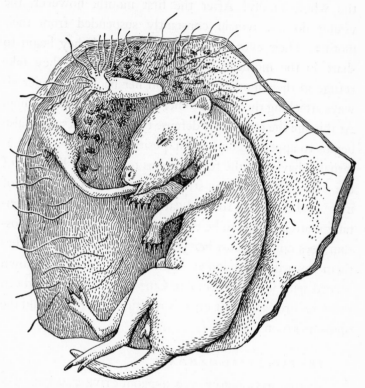

FIG. 58: *Young brush wallaby in the mother's pouch. Natural size. After J. Vosseler, 1930.*

is lacking, for example, in the crested-tailed pouch-mouse, the murine opossum, and the marsupial banded anteater. Here the young merely cling, though firmly, to the mother's nipples. Beach has studied in some detail the behavior of a female murine opossum weighing 51 grams that was carry-

145

ing five young. When walking she had to keep her hindquarters elevated to prevent the young from being rubbed
on the ground; the latter clung so firmly to the nipples that
by laying hold of one with forceps it was possible to lift
the whole family! After the first month, however, the
young do not remain constantly suspended from their
mother. Their eyes open at this point and they begin to
share in the mother's food. When frightened they take
refuge in their mother's fur or on her back, no longer always attaching themselves to her nipples, as before weaning.
At this age the attitude of defense typical of this species also
begins to appear: mouth open, position sitting up. The maternal behavior of the female seems to be much like that of
the white rat: gathering strips of paper to build a kind of
nest [3] and searching for and carrying back young accidentally scattered. It is to be emphasized that the murine opossum does not transport her young in her mouth but pushes
them toward her abdomen so that they will of their own
accord seize upon her nipples. Curiously enough, newborn
rats could release or set off this reaction as well as could the
opossum's own young.

### THE PLACENTAL MAMMALS

SEXUAL PERIODICITY AND REPRODUCTIVE SEASONS.  Female mammals (the higher primates excepted) are not sexually receptive at all times. Copulation takes place, on the
contrary, only at a specific period in the sexual cycle, that
of *œstrus* or "heat." Ovulation occurs at the same time,

[3] Such materials are carried either in the mouth or by means of
the tail. Use of the tail for the transportation of nesting materials is
known also in the Virginia opossum (Pray, *Jour. Mammal.*, 2:109, 1921),
in the South American opossum (Hediger, *Zool. Garten*, 7:28, 1934), and
in the dark rat kangaroo of Australia.

whether spontaneously or as a result of coitus as in many lagomorphs, certain Sciuridæ, Felidæ, and Mustelidæ, and in some Soricidæ. Œstrus is accompanied by a whole series of psycho-physiological phenomena to which we shall return later in this chapter; it is preceded by a phase marked by growth of the Graafian follicles, known as *proœstrus*, and followed by *metœstrus*, which itself precedes a period of sexual quiescence, called *diœstrus*. These stages together make up the œstrus cycle, the duration of which is variable: five days in the white rat, 19 to 22 days in the horse, 28 days in the rhesus monkey, 34 to 35 days in the chimpanzee, and so on.

The number of ovarian cycles per year varies widely according to the species. In this connection it is convenient to distinguish two main categories: the *monœstrous species* having only one œstrus per year, and the *polyœstrous species* in which several œstrus cycles occur successively in the course of a single year. The polyœstrous group can itself be subdivided into *permanent* polyœstrous species in which the cycles are repeated with a regular periodicity, and *seasonal* polyœstrous species in which there exists a prolonged phase of sexual inactivity (anœstrus) that may last for several months.

It is as yet impossible to formulate a truly precise statement on sexual periodicity in the various groups of mammals. It would seem, however, according to the recent review of the subject by Asdell, that the females of the Ursidæ, of most of the Canidæ, of the pinnipeds, and of some Cervinæ have only one œstrus per year, while many bats, most of the primates, the tropical Felidæ, some cetaceans, most of the Sciuridæ, Heteromyidæ, Cricetidæ, and

Muridæ, the elephants, the tropical Cervinæ, and the Bovinæ are permanently polyœstrous. Among the seasonal polyœstrous forms are to be found certain lower primates (Senegal bush baby), the Felidæ of temperate regions, many Sciuridæ, some Geomyidæ, the Caprinæ, and the Equidæ. In general it would seem that species inhabiting the temperate regions tend particularly to reproduce at a certain period of the year, but our knowledge of the biology of tropical forms is far too imperfect to permit us to be very positive in the matter. It would be a mistake, further, to believe that all mammals with seasonal reproduction carry on the reproductive process at the same season in a given country. The differences between various groups are very striking. Thus, in our latitudes, many rodents reproduce in early spring, whereas the Equidæ favor the end of spring and the beginning of summer, the Caprinæ the end of summer and early autumn, and the Cervidæ the beginning of winter. Abundance of food can also have an influence: some Muridæ that are permanently polyœstrous in the laboratory have in nature a more or less prolonged anœstrous phase in summer and in winter.

It is not rare, also, to encounter variations of sexual periodicity within a single species due to climatic or other ecological differences. The European field vole, for example, reproduces in England only from February to October (Baker and Ranson), whereas it does so the year round in the south of France (*Département du Tarn*, Raynaud).

During the period of sexual inactivity it is common to find important morphological changes in the genital tract. Matthews and Godet have shown that in the European mole an involution of the gonads and accessory glands takes place between June and November; in the female the vagina becomes closed and one finds in that region only a scar with pigmented borders; at that time it is even difficult to recognize the sexes, the clitoris having the same size as the penis.

The male gonads are often more active during a certain portion of the year than during others. This annual cycle in testicular activity has been thoroughly studied in some species. In the thirteen-lined ground squirrel, for example, spermatogenesis is most active just before the end of hibernation, in March; in April and May mating occurs, and in June the testicles decrease in size, leaving the scrotum and returning into the peritoneal cavity. In consequence the males of many wild mammals have a period of rut, corresponding to the female period of heat. Most of the males of domesticated species, however, as well as those of many tropical forms, seem capable of reproducing throughout the year.[4]

SEXUAL PROMISCUITY, POLYGAMY, MONOGAMY. Much has been written on the structure of the family group in wild mammals. Yet this subject remains one of the least known, and it is unwise to make any attempt at generalization. Most of the reports of older authors rest on impressions rather than observations, and only by the marking of wild individuals followed through several seasons will it be possible to get any idea of what happens in reality.

Many small mammals (rodents, insectivores, bats) seem

[4] But Groome (*Proc. Zool. Soc. London*, (A) 110:37, 1940) has shown that a true annual cycle of testicular activity exists in certain tropical bats of the family Pteropidæ.

to practice complete sexual promiscuity. The receptive female is mounted by the first male at hand, and, after the sexual act, no relation whatever exists any longer between the two partners. The young are raised by the mother, and at each period of heat it is a different male that couples with the same female as a result of chance encounters. The males may occasionally fight among themselves during the breeding season, and in the absence of females; but this would seem to be rather a manifestation of the aggressiveness of rutting animals than a real struggle to "take possession" of a partner.

Quite different is the behavior of the polygamous species, to be discussed at greater length in the chapter devoted to the social life of mammals. In these species the males, at the breeding season, gain possession of a true harem that in some cases they may jealously defend against the enterprises of other males. In this connection we shall describe the behavior of deer, sea lions, and sea elephants. It would be a mistake, however, to suppose that such spectacular performances are universal. In an excellent study of the wild rabbit, Southern gives proof that during the breeding season the adult males each take over a "sphere of influence" in the colony, with each female also clearly manifesting very definite territorial behavior. A single male is thus concerned with several females (one to seven), but marking experiments pursued from 1940 to 1942 do not seem to indicate the least constancy in conjugal bonds from one year to another. Furthermore, the "jealousy" of the males does not appear to be very great, since Southern noted on only two or three occasions any show of chasing away a strange male.

The monogamous family, in contrast, is very rare

among mammals. Yet it would seem to exist among certain Canidæ, in the American beaver, and in the lar gibbon. Murie has published an account of his precise observation of wolves in Mount McKinley National Park, Alaska. In one den an easily recognizable pair raised five young during the summer of 1940, living the while with two adult males and an adult female; toward the end of the summer two more males came to join the group. Throughout the autumn and winter of 1940–1 the seven adults and five young wolves hunted together. In the following spring the structure of the group underwent modification; the young individuals disappeared; the original pair returned to the den of the preceding year, where it raised four new offspring; the adult female, not mated in 1940, mated with one of the extra males and raised six young in a near-by den before returning in July with her family to live in the den of the other pair. Here we thus have proof of a conjugal bond between two individuals lasting through two years in succession. In most foxes the monogamous couple seems not to last beyond the reproductive season. In the lar gibbon, on the contrary, Carpenter has reported that the family group consists permanently of the two parents and a number of young. It would seem that the same is true of the American beaver, where the typical colony is made up of the two parents and the two last litters.

PRELIMINARIES TO MATING. Observers are for the most part very sparing of details on this phase of the reproductive cycle. There are many reasons for this: spectacular attitudinizing is rare and almost never takes on the appearance of true courtship, as with many birds. Furthermore, the meeting of the sexes very often takes place at twilight, or even at night, and much care and luck are needed in order to be a witness of the event without disturbing the animals. In many cases, therefore, our knowledge is based essentially on captive individuals.

The species are many in which the preliminaries to mating are quite simple and consist merely in the pursuit of females in heat by males. This is true of many rodents and in particular of the white rat, an albino mutation of the brown rat and a favored laboratory animal. The female white rat gets in heat late in the day, and œstrus lasts only thirteen hours on the average. It is indicated by a revival of activity, suddenness in movement, and a quivering of the ears or of the entire body. The male, which hitherto has paid no attention to her, now approaches the female and nuzzles or licks her. The female runs away, with her partner in pursuit, but the chase is usually a short one, and the male overtakes her and mounts her from the rear. The female then elevates her pelvis and hollows her back,[5] while the front paws of her mate hold her firmly. Copulation then takes place. A very similar type of behavior has been described for a great many Muridæ.[6] Sometimes the pursuit is more prolonged and is accompanied by various sounds. The male hedgehog circles for hours around his female, puffing and extending his snout toward her. Sometimes the two animals bite or scratch each other or seem to be fighting. With

---

[5] This receptive posture is typical of the rat in œstrus and can be evoked, in the absence of the male, by mere digital stimulation of the hindmost part of the back and around the base of the tail of the female.

[6] Among others, the deer mouse, white-footed mouse, rice rat, dusky-footed wood rat, golden hamster, boreal redback vole, and house mouse. (See Reed, 1946, for more details.) I have myself observed something very similar in the North African zebra mouse.

the North American short-tailed shrew the pursuit of the female by the male is accompanied by a series of unmusical clicks; if the female is not receptive, she repulses the male with loud squeaks and sometimes a long, shrill chatter. The initiative in the preliminaries to mating is not always the prerogative of the male. The female of the Ord kangaroo rat, for example, pursues the male and noses at his genitals. In the European red squirrel, carefully studied in semi-captivity by Raspopov and Issakov at the Moscow Zoo, the odor of female urine is decidedly exciting to the males, and if a male does not pursue a female, she will roll on the ground before him, rubbing her genitals on the snow. Analogous behavior is frequent in the carnivores. The cat in heat rolls herself on the ground and rubs herself against objects everywhere, while giving a characteristic low vocalization. The crouch is a most specific posture; the animal rests on chest and forearms, with pelvis and tail elevated, and tends to execute treading movements of the hind legs. The female sable in heat urinates frequently and touches her enlarged genitals to stones or other projecting objects, which are thus covered with an oily and odorous secretion.

It is not rare for the male to discharge urine upon the female during the preliminaries to mating. The rutting male of the European wild rabbit chases the females, elevates his haunches so that he walks "stiff-legged," lays his tail flat along his back,[7] displaying its white underside (fig. 59), and

[7] This exhibition surely plays an important part in bringing the sexes together. Southern has several times seen males walk stiffly away from a female for half a dozen yards, giving her a full view of the elevated tail, then approach her again, and repeat this kind of display three or four times in succession. The male sometimes circles around the female while pointing the white spot of his tail sideways toward her, or

sends toward his desired partner a jet of urine that seldom misses its mark. A male has even been seen to leap on a female and urinate on her in passing. The male American porcupine, closely studied by Shadle and his associates, first

FIG. 59: *Diagram showing the posture of the male wild rabbit while "tail flagging." After Southern.*

explores by smelling any trace of urine and all foreign objects near by, then the body and the genitals of the female. If he is sufficiently stimulated sexually, he sniffs at her, rubs noses with her, and then rears up on his hind legs and tail and walks upright toward the female, usually with the penis fully erect. When the two are face to face, the male emits some jets of urine on his partner. In the case of the moose the male paws the ground and urinates repeatedly on a small area where he awaits his female.

A great variety of prenuptial play has been described in widely differing groups. It would seem that most forms of this play can be reduced to prolonged pursuits interrupted by battles between males, attempts at copulation, and manifestations of aggressiveness. Lataste more than a half century ago described the "waltzing" of Wagner's gerbil, in which the two sexes may circle together on one spot. The "fights" (fig. 60) of Alpine marmots are especially fre-

he may go back and forth in front of her with his tail twisted in the appropriate direction at each passage.

FIG. 60: *Prenuptial play of the Alpine marmot: spring "fights."*

quent during the reproductive period. The roebuck in heat tirelessly pursues his doe day and night, emitting a characteristic panting sound (fig. 61). This may continue for a long time, and the course followed, while often sinuous, may be circular.

FIG. 61: *Prenuptial pursuit in roe deer.*

Roan antelopes, according to Verheyen, perform a special ceremony before copulation. The male, with hesitating

**155**

steps, walks slowly around the motionless female, which follows him with her eyes. When he nears the hindquarters of his partner, he begins by gently rubbing one of the female's hind feet with his corresponding front foot and by sniffing at her sexual parts. This behavior is usually repeated several times, for the female moves away more than once and sniffs in turn at the male's genitals before accepting him.

FIG. 62: *A male reindeer sniffing at his female, as shown in a "biological sketch" by a Paleolithic mammalogist. Copied from an engraving from Laugerie-Basse. Muséum national d'Histoire Naturelle, Paris.*

Consent is itself indicated by a special attitude on the part of the female: the tail is slightly raised and turned to one side, the hind feet are separated somewhat, and the neck is depressed. The sable antelope shows similar behavior (fig. 62). The male Cape eland also circles around the desired female, sniffing at her sexual parts, soliciting her by lowering his neck to the horizontal while extending his head as much as possible, and trying to rest his neck on his partner's back. Hediger reports somewhat similar behavior also for the impalas of the Belgian Congo. Here it is not a matter of two isolated individuals pursuing each other but of a group of twenty or so males circling around a troop of about seventy females and young. From time to time the males may fight amongst themselves (fig. 63) before begin-

FIG. 63: *Male impalas fighting. After a photograph by Wolff.*

ning to circle again for about five minutes at a time. The Indian elephants caress each other with their trunks (fig. 64) while sounding a whole series of cries, grunts, and

FIG. 64: *Prenuptial play of Indian elephants. Right, male. After a photograph by K. M. Schneider, 1930.*

trumpetings. The two sexes of the Falkland sea lion often sit facing one another and, with snakelike movements, twist their necks from side to side, thus caressing each other on the front and sides of the neck and occasionally rubbing their mouths together. Sometimes the female gently nibbles at the male's neck. With the vast humpbacked whales the excitement of the rutting season may be so great that, not content with swimming side by side and giving each other resounding blows with their flippers, they may also throw themselves completely out of the water and fall back with a mighty splash that is beyond description.

COPULATION. Following such preliminaries, the male mounts the female. In almost all cases, among small mammals as among the largest, copulation is dorso-ventral, the male astride his partner.

The act may be very brief, but repeated. This is true of the rodents, where in a short time 65 to 75 repetitions (exceptionally as many as 175) have been observed in the golden hamster, and 224 within two hours in Shaw's jird! Frequently both animals lick their genitals thoroughly after each copulation. In the American porcupine, where the male does not hold the female with his front legs, the number of copulations is not so great but each one lasts longer, from one to five minutes. The male short-tailed shrew, the only insectivore studied in some detail from this point of view, mounts the female from behind and holds her not only by clasping her lumbar region with his front legs but also by grasping with his mouth the fur on the back of her neck or shoulders. Copulation in this species is of variable duration, from a few seconds to 25 minutes; it may be repeated six times in an hour and more than 20 times in a day.

Copulation in the carnivores is generally accompanied

by characteristic calls and vocalizations. The male seizes his female with his teeth, at the base of the neck, while being astride her. The copulation of the Mustelidæ is prolonged— a half hour in the sable, an hour in the ferret, from 5 to 20 minutes in the striped skunk, and is repeated up to a dozen times.

Copulation in bats has been studied in but a few species, and this only in recent years. The little brown bat and the small-footed myotis copulate in the fall, and occasionally in winter, on the vertical walls of caves, the animals hanging head down. The male takes the initiative; he mounts the female from behind and with his teeth grasps her hair at the base of the skull. He then pushes his hindquarters backward and downward, bringing his erect penis beneath her interfemoral membrane and, with a forward movement, close to the vaginal orifice (Wimsatt).

Yet some cases of ventral copulation are known, in which the two sexes unite belly to belly. This would seem to be true of the hamster, according to Petzsch, and also of the two-toed sloth (Britton and Enders). Contrary to what was formerly thought, beavers practice dorso-ventral copulation, like most other mammals.

Some mammals copulate in the water. Beside the cetaceans, this is true of the muskrat, the European otter, the sea otter, the pigmy hippopotamus, certain tapirs, the harp seal, and the gray seal.[8]

MONKEYS AND APES. Because the sexual behavior of only a few species is well known, it is impossible at the

---

[8] At least in some colonies, like that of Ramsey Island. In others (Rona) coupling takes place on land (Davies).

moment to generalize. We must, therefore, limit ourselves to giving a few examples taken from the most thorough studies (Carpenter, Yerkes).

The female Panama howling monkey when in heat makes herself conspicuous by her provocative posturing and, above all, by rhythmical movements of the tongue, which is protruded and moved rapidly in and out and up and down. The male replies with the same lingual movements. Copulation is dorso-ventral and quick. The initiative may be taken by either sex, and, within a clan, a single female may be covered by several males successively.

In the rhesus monkey the female in heat is easily recognized by her sexual swelling and coloration, her hyperactivity, her enticing approaches and gestures, and an increase in grooming behavior. To copulate, the male places his hands on the hips or midspinal region of the female while supporting most of his weight on her hind legs, which he grasps with his feet in the popliteal region. Copulation consists in a series of quick insertions of the penis ending in ejaculation. After dismounting, the male characteristically eats the ejaculate that adheres to his penis. The female meanwhile usually grooms the male. During her œstrus period of nine days, one female has relations with an average of three males.

The sole peculiarity of the female lar gibbon while in œstrus is a slight eversion of the vaginal orifice with changes in the turgidity and color of the labia. When the two sexes meet, they engage in a momentary embrace. The male then explores the vaginal opening of the female, and she presents to him with her body bent forward the ischial callosities held high over sharply flexed legs. Intromission of the penis is accomplished from behind and below. The sexual act usually takes place on tree branches.

As with the several species just mentioned, coupling in chimpanzees occurs preferably while the female is in œstrus. In the lesser chimpanzee it takes place for the most part during the middle third of the cycle. Either sex may take the initiative in the sexual approach. Quite often copulation is preceded by a kind of play in which the male follows the female around, both slapping the ground with hands or feet. As this movement gains speed, the animals become excited. When the female is receptive, she crouches before the male and he mounts her from behind, resting with all his weight upon her or remaining half upright. It is a curious fact that the morphological or psychological traits of certain males make them clearly preferred by certain females.

ANOMALIES OF SEXUAL BEHAVIOR. The existence of autoerotic manifestations and homosexual behavior among mammals has been pointed out repeatedly. The anomalies were supposed to be caused by the abnormalities of life in captivity, until they were observed in wild species under natural conditions.

Autoeroticism would seem to be frequent in males. Pearson has noted it in a short-tailed shrew that was sleeping. The stag in rut gently rubs the tips of its antlers to and fro through the herbage and this stimulation promptly induces erection and ejaculation (Darling). Male bottlenosed dolphins masturbate by rubbing the penis on the bottom or against other males, even on other aquatic animals, such as turtles or sharks (McBride and Hebb) and the Indian elephant does it by means of his trunk (Schneider). In the

rhesus monkey manual and buccal masturbation is extremely common among adult and immature males (Carpenter).

The manifestations of autoeroticism in the female sex
are more difficult to demonstrate; but Carpenter has repeatedly observed manual or buccal stimulation of the nipples in the case of a rhesus female.

Homosexuality exists without question in the two sexes.
Males attempting to mount other males have been observed
in the house mouse, several of the small bats, adult and
adolescent rhesus monkeys, and even the bottlenosed dolphin. In the last-mentioned species the "active" male swims
on his back and goes under the "passive" male. Attempts
made by females in heat to mount other females are still
more common, and have been observed in the brown rat,
the guinea pig (90 per cent of the females in certain breeds
regularly show this behavior), the short-tailed shrew (Pearson), the rhesus monkey (Carpenter), and the chimpanzee
(Young). The nymphomania of cows that even try to get
astride of other individuals is also well known.[9]

GESTATION. Table 4 shows the length of the gestation
period and the number of young per litter for a number
of species representative of the various orders of mammals.
It will be noted that the duration of gestation is roughly
proportional to the size of the animal—from around three
weeks for the small rodents to almost two years for the
rhinoceros and elephant.

A closer look at the data, however, reveals some ex-

[9] For a physiological study of this deviation in behavior see
Garm, O. (1949), *Acta Endocrinologica*, Suppl. 3, pp. 1–144, Copenhagen.

ceptions that merit our attention for a moment. Certain Mustelidæ (the badger, the martens, the long-tailed weasel), the bears, and the armadillos have gestation periods abnormally prolonged when compared with related forms of similar size. The reason for this lies in a *delayed implantation* of the fertilized egg, the development of which is thus interrupted during a more or less lengthy period. Thus, in the badger, copulation takes place in July or August in southern England, but implantation of the blastocyst is accomplished only in December or early January, after five months of quiescence. Growth of the embryo then becomes rapid, and the young are born eight weeks later, toward the end of February. In the Texas armadillo the process is similar. Here fertilization takes place in July or August and is followed by a period of about fourteen weeks during which implantation is delayed; this occurs in December and the embryo develops rapidly until the time of birth in February or March. In Argentina the embryo of another armadillo (*Dasypus hybridus*) also remains free for two months before becoming implanted in the uterine wall. A like phenomenon has been reported for the roe deer (copulation in July–August, implantation in late December or early January, birth in April–May), for the Alaska fur seal, and for certain bears.

In the bats of various countries rut and copulation often occur in the fall; [1] this is true of the pipistrelle, the serotine, the large mouse-eared bat, and the long-eared bat in Europe, of *Pipistrellus abramus* in Japan, and of the little brown bat, the gray myotis, the Indiana myotis, and the Keen bat in the

---

[1] The occurrence of a second copulation, in spring, after the awakening from hibernation, is not excluded in some cases.

**Table 4.** *Length of gestation and number of young per litter in some mammals. (After Asdell, Baumann, Mohr, etc.)*

SPECIES/LENGTH OF GESTATION (IN DAYS)/NUMBER OF YOUNG PER LITTER

INSECTIVORES

*Erinaceus europæus* 34–49
4–6

*Talpa europæa* about 28–42
1–7

*Scalopus aquaticus* about 42
2–5

*Blarina brevicauda* 17–20
3–8

*Sorex araneus* 21–28 5–10

BATS

*Myotis myotis* 50–70 1

*Nyctalus noctula* 70–73 1–2

*Tadarida cynocephala* 77–84
1

PRIMATES

*Urogale everetti* less than 54
1

*Galago senegalensis* about 120
1–2

*Nycticebus tardigradus* 174–
180 1

*Lemur macao* about 146 1–2

*Indri indri* about 60 1

*Hapale jacchus* 140–150 1–3

*Ateles ater* about 140 1

*Alouatta seniculus* about 140
1

*Macaca mulatta* 146–180
1–2

*Papio hamadryas* about 183
1–2

*Hylobates lar* 200–212 1

*Pan satyrus* 216–261 1–2

EDENTATES

*Bradypus griseus* 120–180 1

*Myrmecophaga tridactyla*
about 190 1

*Dasypus novemcinctus*
about 260 4–5

RODENTS AND LAGOMORPHS

*Lepus europæus* about 42
1–4

*Lepus americanus* about 38
1–7

*Citellus columbianus* 23–24
2–7

*Citellus tridecemlineatus* about
28 5–13

*Cynomys leucurus* 28–32
2–10

*Marmota marmota* 35–42
2–5

*Tamias striatus* about 31
2–8

*Sciurus vulgaris* 32–40 3–5

*Sciurus carolinensis* about 44
3–5

*Glaucomys volans* about 40
2–6

*Muscardinus avellanarius*
about 21–28 2–7

*Castor canadensis* about 128
1–6

*Cricetus cricetus* about 20
4–18

*Peromyscus maniculatus* 22–27
4–6

*Sigmodon hispidus* about 27
2–10

*Clethrionomys gapperi* 17–19
3–8

*Microtus pennsylvanicus*
about 21 1–9

*Ondatra zibethica* 22–30
1–11

SPECIES/LENGTH OF GESTATION (IN DAYS)/NUMBER OF YOUNG PER LITTER

*Gerbillus (Dipodillus) dasyurus
simoni*  20–21  1–7

*Pachyuromys duprasi*  19–22
3–6

*Mus musculus*  18–20  4–7

*Apodemus sylvaticus*  23–26
2–9

*Micromys minutus*  about 21
5–9

*Erethizon dorsatum*  about 112
1–2

*Hystrix africæ-australis*
about 112  1–4

*Myocastor coypus*  135–150
about 9

*Hydrochærus isthmius*
104–111  1

CETACEANS

*Tursiops truncatus*  about 330
1

*Phocæna phocæna*  about 183
1

*Physeter catodon*  about 365
1

*Balænoptera physalus*  305–365
1

CARNIVORES

*Ursus americanus*  200–210
1–3

*Ursus arctos*  210–250  1–3

*Procyon lotor*  about 63  1–7

*Nasua nasua*  about 77  4–5

*Lutra lutra*  61–63  2–4

*Martes americana*  220–265
1–5

*Martes martes*  270–285  1–4

*Martes pennanti*  338–358
1–5

*Mephitis mephitis*  about 62
4–7

*Mustela frenata*  229–236
5–8

*Mustela vison*  39–76  3–10

*Mustela furo*  about 42  5–13

*Aonyx capensis*  about 63
2–5

*Canis latrans*  60–65  5–10

*Canis lupus*  about 63  3–12

*Vulpes vulpes*  about 56  3–7

*Vulpes fulva*  49–55  1–8

*Lycaon pictus*  63–80  2–6

*Thos adustus*  57–60  3–7

*Crocuta crocuta*  about 110
1–2

*Felis leo*  105–113  2–6

*Felis tigris*  105–109  1–6

*Felis pardus*  92–95  1–4

*Felis onca*  93–110  2–4

*Felis concolor*  90–93  1–4

*Felis sylvestris*  about 68  3–6

*Felis lybica*  about 56  2–5

*Lynx canadensis*  about 60
1–4

*Acinonyx jubatus*  about 95
2–4

PINNIPEDS

*Arctocephalus australis*  about
330  1

*Arctocephalus pusillus*  330–
365  1–2

*Otaria flavescens*  about 330  1

*Leptonychotes weddelli*  about
310  1–2

*Phoca vitulina*  about 280
1–2

PROBOSCIDIANS

*Elephas maximus*  607–641
1–2

SIRENIANS

*Trichechus manatus*  about
152  1

PERISSODACTYLS

*Rhinoceros bicornis*  530–550
1

SPECIES/LENGTH OF GESTATION (IN DAYS)/NUMBER OF YOUNG PER LITTER

*Equus zebra*   about 365   1
*Tapirus indicus*   390–395   1
ARTIODACTYLS
*Hippopotamus amphibius*
   about 237   1
*Chœropsis liberiensis*   201–210
   1
*Sus scrofa*   112–115   3–12
*Phacochœrus æthiopicus*
   170–175   3–4
*Camelus bactrianus*   370–440
   1
*Capreolus capreolus*   about 280
   2
*Alces alces*   240–250   2

*Cervus canadensis*   210–230
   1–3
*Cervus elaphus*   about 234
   1–2
*Odocoileus virginianus*
   about 210   1–2
*Giraffa camelopardalis*
   420–450   1–2
*Bos gaurus*   about 270   1–2
*Ovis canadensis*   about 180   1
*Oryx beisa*   260–300   1
*Taurotragus oryx*   255–270   1
*Antilope cervicapra*   about 180
   1–2
*Rupicapra rupicapra*   153–210
   1–2

United States. Sperm is then stored in the uterus of the female, where it remains alive all winter; in the spring ovulation occurs, and the egg is fertilized in the oviduct. An experiment by Herlant proves that it is really the stored sperm that fertilizes the eggs, for this physiologist, having stimulated premature ovulation in mid-December in the serotine and in the greater horseshoe bat by injecting pituitary and placental extracts, observed the fertilization of the egg and the beginning of embryonic development occurring two months in advance of the normal rhythm. Retarded fertilization does not exist, however, in all the European species. Courrier has shown that in the south European *Miniopterus schreibersi* ovulation and copulation both take place in the autumn; but during the hibernation of the mother the development of the fetus is slowed down and birth occurs only in the following spring. This slowing down of embryonic development in winter is probably correlated with the climatic conditions peculiar to the habitat of this species, since the other species of *Miniopterus*, all inhabitants of warm regions, appear to have a much shorter period of gestation (110 days, for example, in *Miniopterus australis* of the New Hebrides).

A few cases of *superfetation*—that is, the occurrence of a second fertilization before parturition, and the overlapping of two gestations—have been established with certainty. Hediger has shown, for example, that the female European hare is usually covered a second time one to five days before the birth of her young.

PARTURITION. The actual birth of young has been observed in very few species—most often in captivity—and the mother's behavior on this occasion is but poorly known to us. The most common position would seem to be lying down, but some species give birth while standing. The agouti gives birth while in a squatting position. In the bats the female ready to bring forth young suspends herself sometimes by all four feet, back downward, in such a way that the newborn is received in the "apron" formed by the interfemoral membrane (fig. 65). In other cases parturition takes place in the normal resting-position, with head down. In *Erophylla planifrons* the mother is supported by only one of her two hind feet, the other assisting in the emergence of the newborn and in the rupture of the embryonic membranes.

In the ungulates Hediger distinguishes two different types of behavior. The females of the Equidæ and the ruminants, having given birth while lying down, arise at once, break the membranes that enclose the newborn, eat the afterbirth, bite off the umbilical cord if necessary, and carefully lick the young, including its anal and genital regions. The second category includes species like the wild boar or the hippopotamus, and here the females do not busy themselves with their young immediately after birth by eating the afterbirth and licking the newborn.

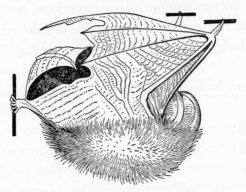

FIG. 65: *Position of the female long-eared bat just after the birth of her young. After Eisentraut, 1936.*

The primates give birth quite often in an upright position. A female lar gibbon has been seen to bring forth while hanging from a branch, and Yerkes describes and figures parturition in the chimpanzee: the mother stands up or crouches on all fours, and she eats the afterbirth.

In cetaceans and the hippopotamus, parturition takes place in the water. It has been possible to observe the process precisely in the bottlenosed dolphin (and even to film it), at the Marine Studios in Florida. Labor appears to be short (21 to 23 minutes in the two cases studied); the mother turns about immediately to bite through the umbilical cord, and the young goes to the surface to breathe within ten seconds of its birth. An hour and a quarter after it is born

*Birth of young in the bottlenosed dolphin or porpoise,* Tursiops truncatus: ABOVE, *early stage;* BELOW, *late stage. Photographs by Marine Studios, Marineland, Florida.*

*Mother bottlenosed dolphin and newborn young asleep, another female apparently standing guard. Photograph by Marine Studios, Marineland, Florida.*

the offspring begins nursing. In the Florida manatee, finally, the mother carries the newborn on her back, completely out of the water, for 45 minutes; then she gradually immerses it during the following two hours.

Head presentation seems to be most frequent in a majority of the orders where the young are ordinarily born single. It has been observed in the elephant, the moose, the bison, the giraffe, the chamois, and in many primates (macaques, baboons, gibbons, gorillas, chimpanzees). In many ungulates the head appears resting on the front feet. Among the cetaceans head presentation would seem to be more frequent in the whalebone whales, and breech presentation in the toothed whales. In bats the legs and the tail often appear first. For rodents or carnivores with large litters and young of smaller size, head presentation is less frequent.

In the Muridæ and the Cricetidæ it is common for a period of heat to follow immediately after the female has given birth.

### CHAPTER 6

# Development and Longevity

IN this chapter we shall consider some aspects of the different phases in the life cycle of the individual, from birth to death. These successive stages—growth, maturity, and old age—certainly pose a whole series of most interesting problems.

### DEVELOPMENT

THE NEWBORN. There is an evident correlation between the length of gestation and the condition of the newborn young: the longer the fetus remains in the maternal uterus, the more advanced will be its development at the time of birth. A few examples will illustrate this general law. The newborn white rat, after 21 days of gestation, is a little naked creature, blind and totally dependent upon its mother for what it needs to live. The guinea pig, on the contrary, after 67 to 68 days of development within the uterus, is born with its eyes open, covered with fur that protects it pretty well against cold, and capable very soon of feeding itself. The hare (fig. 66) and the rabbit (fig. 67), though closely related species, present the same contrast in the appearance of their newborn.

It is thus possible to distinguish two main categories of young: those which depend entirely on their mother during a more or less prolonged period of time, and those with development sufficiently advanced at birth to enable them to

FIG. 66: *Newborn European hare.*

FIG. 67: *Newborn wild rabbit.*

find their own food very soon. Most of the rodents belong to the first category; their imperfect thermo-regulation makes them true poikilotherms (cold-blooded animals), which gives them some advantages. Adolph and Fairfield have recently shown that newborn rats are endowed with remarkable resistance to cold and to lack of oxygen. At 3°

the respiratory exchange may fall to zero in the young (age 0 to 10 days) without fatal results, and these little rats can even survive for two hours, at 10°, in an atmosphere of nitrogen! Bears similarly have young that are but little developed at birth. Those of the brown bear are the size of a large rat, though the mother weighs more than 200 pounds, and those of the black bear have a weight of less than a pound. They are nourished for the first two months exclusively on the mother's milk, and, as they are born in the depth of winter, they are protected from the cold as much by her thick fur as by the hibernation shelter.

The young of many ungulates are very different. In the roe deer the first hour of life is spent in being licked and cleaned up, while the young individual is already attempting to get to its feet; after the second hour the fawn can leave its birthplace under its own power. The newborn chamois can get to its feet and even walk slowly a few moments after it comes into the world, when its hair is still wet with amniotic fluid. It does not follow its mother, however, until it is a week old, and it begins to eat grass at ten days, although nursing lasts for about two months. The young Mongolian wild ass can run at the end of an hour, but quickly grows tired. The behavior of a newborn giraffe has been witnessed by Davis at the Zoological Park in Washington; the young maintained its equilibrium on its feet only five minutes after being born and began to nurse three quarters of an hour later, even before the placenta was expelled. The agouti begins to nibble at plants within an hour of its birth, and the mountain vizcacha does likewise. The young American porcupine also comes into the world remarkably well developed. It weighs over one pound, whereas its mother hardly exceeds thirteen, and it is able to climb trees and eat leaves and tender shoots on its own account when two days old. It is curious to note that it displays from the start the defense reaction described in a preceding chapter. The young hare, on the other hand, has a special defensive attitude that it loses later on (Hediger). It leaps toad-fashion at the disturbing object, growling and trying to bite. Somewhat similar behavior has been described in the antelope jackrabbit and the blacktail jackrabbit, which when frightened rear up on their hind legs and endeavor to strike with their front ones.

LACTATION. We are especially ill informed concerning the length of the lactation period in wild mammals. This is difficult to determine precisely, moreover, because the young continue to suck for a long time after having begun to feed for themselves. The condition of the teeth is not, in itself, a sure means of gauging the ability of a young animal to obtain its food independently (fig. 68). In many Phocidæ the definitive dentition is present from birth, and yet Weddell's seal, for example, is not weaned before reaching the age of 45 to 50 days. Most small rodents nurse no more than 10 to 20 days, but the walrus continues to do so for almost two years.

Another point on which we have little documentation is the composition of the milk in the various groups. But there would seem to be very sharp differences according to the species, as Table 5 shows.

Thus, if we compare cow's milk with that of the harp seal, we see that the latter contains 12 times more fat and 3 to 4 times more proteins than the former. On the other hand, it shows no sugars, even though Sivertsen's analyses were made on fresh milk.[1] What can be the reason for such a peculiarity? It is unknown at present. At most we can refer to the similarity of reindeer milk to that of seals and

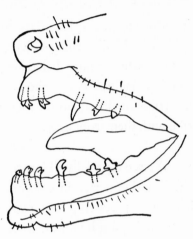

FIG. 68: *Milk teeth of a young mouse-eared bat eight days old. After Eisentraut.*

whales. May we not have to do here with a character favoring the growth of the young in regions of cold climate, rather than with a special peculiarity of the pinnipeds and cetaceans? Future research will clear up this point, but at the moment it would seem that some relation exists between the protein content of a particular milk and the rapidity of growth. Table 6, borrowed from Sivertsen, gives some examples of that correlation. Here again we need studies on more species before drawing conclusions with certainty. Richness in calcium and phosphorus also appears to be related to peculiarities of growth. In the seals, where the

[1] Sugar has recently been found in whale's milk by J. C. D. White (*Nature*, 171:612, 1953), but in lesser quantity than in cow's milk.

**Table 5.** Composition of milk produced by some mammals (in grams per 1,000 grams of milk).

| | HORSE | COW | SOW | GOAT | BITCH | REINDEER | HARP SEAL[1] | HOODED SEAL[1] | BLUE WHALE[2] | FIN WHALE[2] |
|---|---|---|---|---|---|---|---|---|---|---|
| Water | 900 | 880 | 840 | 862 | 770 | 677 | 437.9 | 498.5 | 471.7 | 541.0 |
| Fats | 22 | 34 | 50 | 48 | 93 | 171 | 428.2 | 404.3 | 381.3 | 306.0 |
| Proteins | 20 | 33 | 37 | 48 | 97 | 109 | 119.8 | 66.5 | 127.9 | 131.4 |
| Sugars | 60 | 44 | 50 | 46 | 31 | 28 | 0.0 | 0.0 | ? | ? |
| Ash | 3.6 | 7 | 6.3 | 8.5 | 9.1 | 15 | 9.14 | 8.64 | 14.3 | 14.8 |
| $K_2O$ | 1.05 | 1.74 | 0.99 | 1.3 | 1.41 | 2.11 | 1.61 | 1.25 | ? | ? |
| $Na_2O$ | 0.14 | 0.80 | 0.74 | 0.6 | 0.81 | 2.33 | 1.16 | 1.41 | ? | ? |
| $CaO$ | 1.24 | 1.65 | 2.40 | 2.0 | 4.53 | 5.08 | 0.94 | 0.92 | 4.26 | 5.27 |
| $MgO$ | 0.13 | 0.21 | 0.14 | 0.16 | 0.20 | 0.39 | 0.30 | 0.33 | ? | ? |
| $P_2O_5$ | 1.31 | 1.45 | 3.00 | 2.91 | 4.93 | 4.38 | 3.35 | 2.80 | 6.23 | 7.75 |
| $Cl$ | 0.31 | 1.10 | 0.67 | 1.00 | 1.63 | 0.70 | 0.44 | 0.95 | 0.20 | 0.39 |

[1] Analyses by Sivertsen.
[2] Analyses by Heyerdahl. The rest of the figures are taken from *Handwörterbuch der Naturwissenschaften*, 1932, p. 987.

weight of the young increases much more rapidly than the size during lactation, the milk is very rich in fats and relatively poor in calcium. In the whales, on the contrary, where the young suckle for six to seven months, the considerable increase in size is accompanied by a high milk content in mineral elements essential for skeletal growth.[3]

**Table 6.** *Correlation between protein content of milk and rapidity of growth of young (After Sivertsen)*

| | MAN | HORSE | COW | PIG | SHEEP | DOG | CAT | RABBIT | HARP | SEAL |
|---|---|---|---|---|---|---|---|---|---|---|
| Number of days needed for doubling birth weight of young on the average | 180 | 60 | 47 | 18 | 10 | 8 | 9 | 6 | 5 | |
| Protein content of milk, in grams per 1,000 | | 19 | 20 | 33 | 37 | 70 | 97 | 95 | 104 | 119 |

The positions assumed by the mother during lactation vary with the species. Most of the ruminants give suck while standing, but there are exceptions like the roe deer. The rodents feed their young while lying down, save for some large species like the capybara. Pigs and hippopotami also give suck while lying down. The doe hare sits on its hindquarters while nursing its young, and the wild rabbit may lie on its back. The Florida manatee nurses its young under water, the mother browsing on aquatic plants while the baby takes its nourishment. The suckling of the bottlenosed dolphin is very brief, taking only a few seconds; the mother swims slowly and turns on her side, and the milk is squeezed out by a contraction of the muscles surrounding the mammary gland as soon as the young animal touches the nipple. This occurs generally among the cetaceans.

Regurgitation of food by parent animals, after wean-

---

[3] In the blue whale the length of the young increases by about 30 feet in seven months.

ing, has been observed in several wild Canidæ, particularly the wolf and the European red fox.

CARE OF THE YOUNG. Generally the mother alone attends to the rearing of the young, and the latter remain with her for a time varying from a few weeks in many small mammals to several months in the larger species.

The male parent, however, may sometimes share actively in raising the offspring. Murie has shown that the male wolf provides a large part of the family food, and Hainard saw a male fox repeatedly bringing food to the burrow. Burt has noted similar behavior on the part of the male long-tailed weasel. In other cases the male parent confines himself to defending the offspring from intruders; this has been reported in some ungulates (banteng, yak, European bison, roebuck) as well as in the African porcupine. Even among the rodents, finally, where the male usually has no concern with the female after mating, some interest in the young has been noted on the part of the males (in captivity, to be sure). Horner, for example, reports that several males of deer mice assisted in the maintenance of the nest or in the transportation of the offspring.

It may be true that in certain gregarious mammals all the young of the herd, above a certain age, are brought together and "looked after" by a few adults. This is probably the case with giraffes, according to Percival. When they are several weeks old, the little giraffes leave their mothers and collect in homogeneous groups "looked after" by one or two guardians. If in play they separate too far from the rest of the herd, one of the "nurses" rounds them up again.

The cleaning of the burrows enables the young to enjoy meticulously neat surroundings, in some species at least. In this respect the coyotes, marmots, badgers, and lesser mole rats are in high repute. Eating their own excrement is normal behavior for many rodents and is not necessarily injurious. Geyer and his collaborators, for example, have

FIG. 69: *Transportation of the young in the European red squirrel.*

shown experimentally that coprophagy is essential for normal growth in the white rat.

TRANSPORTATION OF THE YOUNG. This is accomplished in very different ways according to the species concerned. When danger threatens, many rodents, Canidæ, and Felidæ carry their young away one by one, taking hold of them with the teeth by the skin of the back, the neck, or the abdomen (fig. 69). She-bears do likewise, taking the whole

FIG. 70: *Female bear carrying her young. After a Globe photograph.*

FIG. 71: *Transportation of its young by a female Sumatra pangolin,* Manis javanica. *After Haenel, 1931.*

head of the cub in the mouth (fig. 70). The giant anteater carries her single offspring astride on her back, and the pangolins carry theirs astride the base of the tail (fig. 71). Many young marsupials ride on their mother's back, after leaving the pouch. Finally certain rodents, such as the common redbacked vole and the common vole, merely cling desperately to their mother's nipples when in danger.

Among the tree-dwelling mammals also we find several different methods of transportation. The sloths (fig. 72) set their young on the abdomen, howling monkeys and guenons carry theirs on the belly, many platyrrhine mon-

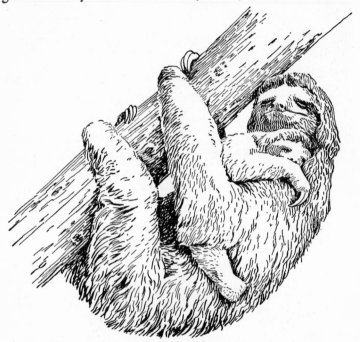

FIG. 72: *Female three-toed sloth transporting its young. Barro Colorado. After a photograph by Gross.*

keys and several types of macaques and langurs carry their infants both dorsally and ventrally; the gibbons hold theirs low down over the pelvis, almost over one leg. Panama howling monkeys are also very careful of their young when the latter begin to move about by themselves in the trees. On several occasions Carpenter saw mothers helping young to make a difficult crossing by bending branches near together and by making a bridge of their own bodies.

Very young bats are carried by their mothers in flight, clinging to nipples or fur by means of their milk teeth (fig. 68). This feat becomes quite remarkable in the red bat, for a single female may have and carry as many as four offspring! It is a curious fact that the "flying lemurs" or Dermoptera carry their young in the same way during their volplaning from tree to tree.

The sea otter commonly carries its young on the abdomen when it is swimming on its back (fig. 73), and it

FIG. 73: *Sea otter swimming on its back and carrying its young on the abdomen. After a sketch by Fisher, 1940.*

suckles and sleeps in the same position; but after it is two days old, the female lets her offspring float amongst the seaweed that forms its "nursery" when she must dive in search of food. The young walrus continues for some time to ride astride the neck of its mother, and the little hippopotamus does not scorn the support of its mother's broad back.

The young of many ungulates seem at a certain stage of development to have an innate tendency to follow their mothers or, in their absence, other individuals of different species. Couturier emphasizes, for example, the propensity of chamois less than three months old to rush to meet any moving body, even a man. Heck also relates that after he had passed in a carriage near a young wild zebra, the animal began to follow the vehicle.

Should we connect with this type of behavior the formation of "caravans" of offspring reported in certain shrews, the hedgehog, and the weasel? Wahlström has closely studied the phenomenon in the bicolor white-

FIG. 74: *A female common shrew and its "caravan" of young. After Schröder and Schoenichen, 1938.*

toothed shrew: the mother is followed by her offspring, the first of which takes hold of the mother's skin with its teeth, near the base of the tail; the rest follow in line, each holding similarly to the one in front of it (fig. 74). The result is a file or "caravan" whose members are so firmly joined that one can sometimes raise the whole group by lifting the mother. The young display this type of behavior only during the first three weeks after birth, and the caravan breaks up when its members regain their nest.

PLAY. The most superficial observer cannot fail to notice the existence among young mammals of certain activities without evident object that seem to afford pleasure to those taking part in them. Such behavior we call play, by analogy with what we are familiar with in the human species. We are completely ignorant about the cause of these activities and their significance in animals, although there is no lack of speculation on the subject, as a glance through Beach's recent general review will indicate.

Most of the playing is collective. Young fawns of the red deer, for example, very often play at racing. Darling tells us how they sometimes leave a given place more or less together and dash forward, but without there being any real finish line. Sometimes a member of the group chases the others until it has touched one of them and then the pursuer in turn becomes the pursued. At other times the race takes place around a hillock, which may become the goal that the winner is to attain, as in "king-o'-the-castle." Walking or running in single file, like "follow-the-leader," is also engaged in by many young ungulates and by numerous monkeys. The young of carnivores often chase inanimate objects, such as a rolling pebble or bone. These make-believe victims are often set in motion again by a stroke of the paw, when they are recaptured. A coyote has been seen playing with a crow that it allowed to escape before catching it again, and it is common for small rodents to serve in the same way for the amusement of the young before being eaten. McBride and Hebb saw young dolphins juggling objects floating on the surface or chasing small fish before letting them go and catching them again. Mock fights with wrestling and biting are common—among fox cubs, for instance (fig. 75). The game of leapfrog is played by several

R.H.
Bernex
22 mai 35

FIG. 75: *Young foxes engaging in a mock fight. Sketch furnished by Robert Hainard.*

species, such as the European badger, as is proved by the fine photograph in Neal's book (fig. 76). Sliding is a favorite game of the otters, in Europe as in North America, and many observers have described how they let themselves go on their bellies down a wet river bank or on a snowy slope (fig. 77). Minks do the same.

Among solitary types of play there has been included a whole series of behavior patterns, certain of which have

FIG. 76: *European badgers playing leapfrog. Drawn from a photograph by E. Neal.*

probably a different significance. It would seem that the simplest of them are only manifestations of superfluous energy. Such are apparently aimless running and jumping, even that odd "exercise dance" of the North American porcupine, described by Schadle, during which the animal, raised on its hindquarters and tail, rocks rhythmically from side to side alternately raising and stamping the hind feet. The young individual in many carnivores (wolves, foxes, otters) sometimes chases its tail and thus gets into a frantic roundelay on one spot. The tendency of young mammals to bite and scratch apparently at random also belongs in this category, in all probability.

FIG. 77: *Otters sliding. Redrawn from Liers.*

Young chimpanzees have a curious propensity for decorating themselves with leafy branches, flowers, and pieces of cloth or paper. Yerkes tells us also that they may smear flat surfaces with their excreta, and Kohler has seen them wet white clay with saliva and use it in the same way. Meng, the young gorilla a year and a half old observed by Julian Huxley at the London Zoo, on three occasions traced the outline of his shadow with his forefinger upon the wall of his cage.

INNATE BEHAVIOR AND LEARNING PROCESSES IN YOUNG MAMMALS. Modifications in the behavior of the young animal during its period of growth make a most interesting study; they can indeed give us some insight into the relative importance of innate and learned factors in juvenile behavior, and it is to be regretted that up to now so few observations have been made on this engrossing problem.

What is known would seem to indicate in the first place that there is a definite sequence in the appearance of the various behavior patterns which is characteristic of each species. In the European red squirrel, for instance, Eibl-Eibesfeldt has recorded the following evolution in behavior: for five days after birth the young individual, hairless and blind, does no more than suckle, being quite unable to move its limbs in co-ordinated fashion. On the sixth day it utters its first cry of distress, and at this time some pigment appears in its skin. On the eighth day the fur begins to grow out, on the twenty-third the lower incisor teeth break through the gums, and on the thirty-second the eyes open. On the thirty-sixth day cleaning movements are seen, on the forty-second the young first leave the nest of their own accord, and on the forty-fifth they are able to eat ant pupæ for themselves. On the sixtieth day the first nut is opened, on the sixty-eighth the first rough nest is built, and on the seventy-fourth the mother leaves her young. The first attempt at copulation was observed at the age of 130 days, in a young male.

Chronological sequences of this kind certainly are not absolutely fixed, and retardation of the growth processes— through inadequate nutrition, for example—very probably cause delay in the maturation of behavior. But such schedules none the less enable us to make comparative studies of the relative times at which the various behavior patterns appear.

Rearing young animals in captivity can also give us information regarding the respective roles of heredity and learning in the modification of juvenile behavior. If we can separate young mammals from the mother at a very early age and raise them in isolation, any modifications observed are very likely to be due to maturation of the innate behavior patterns and to trial-and-error learning. Students of Konrad Lorenz have recently made such studies on some European species, and without surveying their conclusions in detail we may recall a few of their interesting results.

The first rough attempts at shelter construction characteristic of the species occur early in life and even in individuals isolated from their kind. Eibl-Eibesfeldt's badger, for example, made its first attempt to dig a burrow at 101 days and undertook its first olfactory marking of its territory on the 118th day, when its first wrestling play was observed. The common dormouse, raised in isolation by Zippelius and Goethe, built its first sketchy globular nest at the age of 55 days and quite without parental contact. These examples therefore tend to prove that the methods of shelter construction in mammals are in large part innate.

Quite to the contrary, it would seem that the defense reactions of young animals against normal enemies of their species are principally learned. Young African giant rats, born in captivity in Paris, were totally indifferent in the presence of a good-sized python and even approached calmly to sniff at its snout. Conversely the same snake was violently attacked by the parent rats, which had probably become acquainted with it in their native Africa. Yerkes's young chimpanzees also showed themselves relatively indifferent to a snake, although adult animals had shown fear of it. In this connection Yerkes even refers to the influence of "social tradition."

In any case the part played by the parents in the "education" of their young has long since been emphasized by many observers. Thus, Liers informs us that young otters do not enter the water of their own accord but are dragged in by their mother, who pulls them by the skin of the neck and catches small prey (crayfish, frogs, and little fish) to lure them on. Moreover their first attempts at swimming are awkward, the young learning little by little to swim properly. In the gray seal also the mother plays an active part in her offspring's first efforts to swim. Goddard [4] describes one of these "swimming lessons" as follows: "One of the young seals went into the sea and joined its mother. . . . At first the youngster appeared to be floating with its head under water, and every now and then it churned up the water with its hind limbs and made a big splash. The cow then swam underneath it and pushed it above the surface with her back. For a minute or two she carried it on her back, but the calf did not seem able to maintain that position for very long. As soon as the cow's back broke the surface, or even came near it, the calf slipped off, as it naturally had no means of holding on. Every now and then, when the calf appeared to be in distress, the cow put her head under its forequarters and pushed its head above water. After a time the calf was able to swim quite well with its head above the surface."

It goes without saying that such behavior should be re-

[4] In G. Watt, *The Farne Islands*, London, pp. 186-7.

corded in moving pictures whenever possible, the camera lens being more impartial than the eye of the overenthusiastic observer.

SEXUAL MATURITY. Maturity of the gonads and the resulting ability to reproduce signalize an important stage in individual development. Although this does not mean that growth ceases, it none the less signifies psychologically the end of the period of juvenility and the beginning of maturity.

Not much is precisely known about the age at which various species of wild mammals reach maturity. In Asdell's work, cited in the preceding chapter, are to be found a number of facts that give us some idea of the great differences in this respect existing among the main orders.

Some of the small rodents become sexually mature at a very early age. The female meadow vole can reproduce at the age of 25 days and the male at 45. Sexual maturity in the hispid cotton rat is reached at about 40 to 50 days, that of the brush mouse at 50 days, that of the nutria at 8 months, that of the fox squirrel and of the woodchuck at 1 year, and that of the American beaver at 2 years. Many of the small European bats reproduce at 12 to 15 months, but the female of the Florida free-tailed bat can do so at 7. In the carnivores the age of sexual maturity varies widely: 10 months for the European red fox, a year for the American otter, the fisher, and the stoat, 2 years for the sable and the coyote, and 6 years for the brown bear. Maturity in the pinnipeds and cetaceans comes relatively early: 2 years in the common seal, the finback whale, and the fin whale; 3 years in the white whale, 4 years in the bottlenosed dolphin, 4 to 5 years in female walruses, and 5 to 6 in their males. Ungulate sexual development is also rapid, considering size: the roe deer is mature at 14 months and the red deer at 18, the bighorn sheep at 2 years and a half, and the chamois at 3 years. The rhinoceros can reproduce after age 4 to 5 and the Indian elephant after 15. Among the primates puberty is attained at 14 months in the female common marmoset, toward 3 years in the female toque monkey, around 8 to 10 years in the lar gibbon, and at 8 years and 11 months, on the average, in the female chimpanzee.

DURATION OF THE GROWTH PERIOD. We know still less about this subject than about the preceding, and the few observations that have been made concern only increase in weight, which, beyond a certain age, is not necessarily parallel with growth.[5]

We have no intention of undertaking here an analysis of the mechanisms responsible for growth. Such problems are of particular interest to biometricians and physiologists, and they have been fully discussed in some recent works.[6] We wish only to dwell on some special points that have important ecological bearings.

The accompanying graph (fig. 78) is typical for curves of weight increase in all mammals studied hitherto. It reflects observations of two rodents from Palestine kept by Bodenheimer under conditions as similar as possible to those in which they live in the wild state. We see that the period of rapid growth in the male Shaw's jird ends at the age of

[5] In old animals weight often tends to go on increasing slowly, due to the accumulation of fat, when the growth of the skeleton has long since come to an end.

[6] See especially J. Huxley, *Problems of Relative Growth*, London, 1932, and G. Teissier, *Les lois quantitatives de la croissance*, Paris, 1934.

about 150 days and that maximum weight is reached during the second year, after which the animal slowly loses weight. In the case of the Cairo spiny mouse the growth of the male is similarly almost complete at the end of about 150 days, but afterwards the weight tends to increase slightly up to

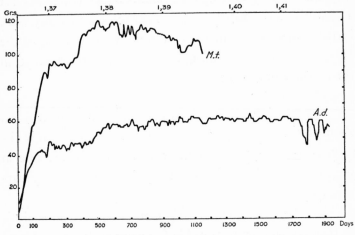

FIG. 78: *Growth curves of a male Cairo spiny mouse (A. d.) and of a male Shaw's jird (M. t.) from birth to death. After Bodenheimer.*

the third year. Shortly before death there is a slight emaciation with large fluctuations in weight. Female growth curves, less regular because of successive pregnancies, would show a slight retardation when compared with those of males. Growth curves of white rats and white mice of pure stock, raised in the laboratory under constant conditions of temperature and diet, show the same characteristics. In the case of the white rat, for example, we can distinguish, with reference to the total weight and that of the main organs, three successive stages in the life cycle: the growth period, extending from birth to the age of about 400 days; the period of maturity, from 400 to 600 days, and lastly the period of senility or loss in weight, beyond 600 days.

Unfortunately there is no comparable documentation for the large mammals. Regarding the higher primates, the studies of Grether and Yerkes have shown that young chimpanzees of both sexes increase in weight progressively and regularly from birth to their seventh year. At that time puberty intervenes, and beyond this stage the males become larger than the females. At the age of twelve both adult weight and psychological maturity are reached. Some authors believe that the slow growth of the primates [7] is correlated with the fact that their mental powers are more highly developed than are those of rodents or ungulates. It would seem wise to wait until the growth of more species has been studied before accepting this hypothesis as proved (fig. 79).

The statements just given on the growth rate of some mammals are valid, furthermore, only under well-defined conditions. It is common knowledge that the number of young in a litter, like the quality of nourishment, can affect the growth rate of offspring. The studies of McCay and his co-workers [8] on the white rat afford striking proof. They showed that it was possible to check the animals' growth rate markedly by reducing the amount of available food. Moreover, in slowing up the growth rate they clearly increased the longevity of the "retarded" rats as compared with controls of the same stock. And this increase in length

[7] Schultz estimates that generally speaking the growth period lasts 3 years in the prosimians, 7 years in the Old World monkeys, 9 years in the gibbons, and 11 years in the anthropoid apes (and 20 years in man).

[8] See especially *Journal of Nutrition*, Vol. 10, 1935, p. 63 and Vol. 18, 1939, p. 14. These results have since been confirmed by several authors.

FIG. 79: *An example of modifications due to growth of a morphological character. Skulls of the chacma baboon, Papio porcarius, at different ages. From above downward: 1, newborn; 2, skull with milk teeth; 3, adult female; 4, adult male. Behavior changes due to growth are even more impressive.*

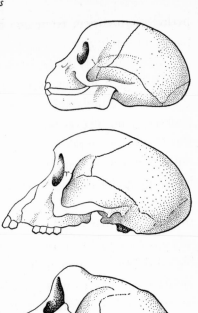

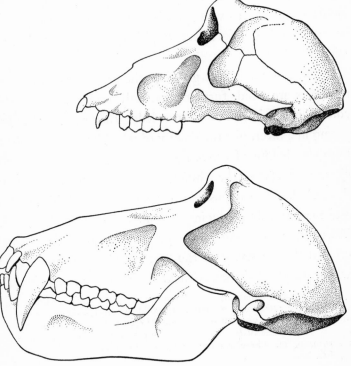

194

of life was not inconsiderable, since in one case it approached 100 per cent!

## HIBERNATION

WHEN conditions become unfavorable, some species of mammals are able to pass into a lethargic state that may last for weeks or even for months. This phenomenon being especially noticeable in some of the familiar rodents and bats of our latitudes, it has been called "winter sleep" or hibernation. As a matter of fact, however, something quite analogous occurs in certain species in warm countries during the hot and dry summer season, and such *estivation* seems hardly to differ in attributes or mechanism from hibernation.

First of all, what groups are known to exhibit this phenomenon? The female platypus hibernates from mid-September to mid-October in Victoria, Australia, and the Australian spiny anteater does likewise when the temperature drops sufficiently.[9] In the United States the Virginia opossum, which has recently extended its area of distribution considerably toward the north, spends several months in a state of torpidity [1] during the winter cold; in Australia the pigmy opossum behaves in similar fashion in the state of Victoria. Among the insectivores the European hedgehog begins its sleep when the outside temperature goes below 15 °C.; its body temperature drops and in midwinter is about

---

[9] The ability to endure fasting shown by this species has been mentioned by several authors; in captivity it may go more than a month without eating.

[1] Without much reduction in its body temperature, it would seem; Davis points out, however, that in Brazil (near Teresopolis) the woolly opossum becomes lethargic when it is cold at night, and its body temperature goes down (this author found a rectal temperature of 16.5° C. when the temperature outside was 10° C.).

6° C. In Madagascar the tenrec hibernates during the dry season of the austral winter, that is, from May to October. Rand describes its winter burrow as consisting of a first part running parallel to the surface, followed by a second descending part stopped with earth, and ending in the hibernation chamber. This chamber is very clean, containing neither hairs nor excrement, and here the animal sleeps, in a rolled-up position. Among the bats of temperate regions the Vespertilionidæ retire for the winter into caves, attics, and hollow trees or other natural cavities. Some species of Rhinolophidæ and Molossidæ do likewise. All are true hibernators with very low body temperature and with slow and irregular breathing. Sound as their sleep may be, many observers have recorded temporary awakenings, with certain individuals changing places inside the same grotto. The rodents also present numerous examples typical of hibernating mammals. In Europe the best known are the fat dormouse, the common dormouse (fig. 80), the garden dormouse, the hamster, and the Alpine marmot. In North America the ground squirrels, the marmots, and the jumping mice hibernate, and in the Old World deserts the jerboas regularly estivate. Even such primitive primates as the mouse lemurs (*Chirogaleus* and *Microcebus*) of Madagascar hibernate, and I have recently demonstrated that their body temperature can then drop below 20° C. There is much more to be learned from a detailed study of the duration and other features of hibernation in a given species at different points of its range. In regard to the ground squirrels, for instance, not only does the duration of hibernation in the different species appear to be directly proportional to the severity of the climate, but Fitch's researches on the Cali-

fornia ground squirrel of the San Joaquin region in California have revealed that not all individuals in the *same* population behave in the same manner. A large proportion of
adult females hibernate from the beginning of summer to

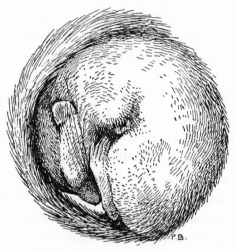

FIG. 80: *Dormouse in hibernation. Note the position of the
animal. Drawn at the end of March when animal was in
a very emaciated condition.*

December or January,[2] whereas hibernation is much less frequent and shorter in the adult males and in the young of
both sexes; moreover there are great variations within the
same population from year to year. The carnivores also afford some instances of hibernation, but here the sleep is
always less profound than in the preceding examples, and
in particular the body temperature remains at a degree close
to the normal for waking individuals. Bears may sleep in this

[2] Not far from the place where Fitch made his observations the
dates of hibernation are quite different; about 20 miles away, but at a
higher altitude (4,500 feet instead of 1,100), the California ground squirrels hibernate from November 1 to April 1!

way for several months in the winter, and without eating anything at all. The European badger hibernates in northern Russia and northern Scandinavia but remains active all winter in England and in France, as well as in the Caucasus.

The general term "hibernation" thus includes a whole series of states ranging from mere transitory torpor, without clear reduction in temperature, to the true winter sleep accompanied by a large and lasting drop in body temperature.

What do we know about the physiological mechanisms of true hibernation? Much has been written on the subject, and in Kayser's recent review of the facts we have a good resumé of the literature. Without going too much into detail, we may say that in true hibernators there appears in autumn a reduction in the heat production needed for keeping the temperature up, the lethargic state being preceded by a disturbance of the thermo-regulation, involving both the mechanisms of heat production and of heat loss. The imperfectly homoiothermous or warm-blooded animal then becomes poikilothermous or cold-blooded, and the body temperature falls to a point close to that of the environment (in bats rectal temperatures below zero Centigrade have been recorded!). At the same time there occurs a distinct involution of many endocrine glands: anterior pituitary, adrenal cortex, thyroid, parathyroids, and gonads. Even the islets of Langerhans become modified; in winter only insulin cells are to be found, although in summer there are two different kinds of cells. The great reduction in metabolic rate in the sleeping animal is accompanied by a slowing down of the heartbeat, respiratory movements are few and irregular (Cheyne-Stokes breathing), and the increased concentration of carbon dioxide no longer brings on increased ventilation. Yet regulation is not entirely absent during the winter sleep, and if the outer temperature drops too much the heartbeat becomes more rapid. While the period of lethargy lasts, stored fat is burned to supply the energy needed by the fasting animal.

Recent experimentation has thrown some light also on the question of what factors induce hibernation. Reduced temperature seems to play a necessary part for species in our latitudes, and Kayser reports that he has never observed torpidity in an individual of a hibernating species that is kept at a temperature above 13° C. In addition to temperature the second factor necessary to winter sleep is fasting.[3] By combining cold and fasting, it has been possible to hold fat dormice in winter sleep for a year. Further, the sleep can be brought on in the hamster or fat dormouse if removal of the pituitary and cold are combined with fasting, with the injection of insulin or of a hypothermia-producing drug, or with the removal of the adrenal medulla. But in all these cases the animals never survive for more than a few days, and the sleep thus induced is only an approximation to real winter torpor.

Whatever its precise physiological mechanism, hibernation does afford a definite advantage to the species that practice it. The large proportion of hibernators in the small mammal fauna of subarctic and desert regions goes to show that it has probably played a determining role in the populating of zones marked by climatic extremes that but for this physiological adaptation would be uninhabitable.

[3] This may be the main factor in species that inhabit warm and dry regions and estivate in summer.

### LONGEVITY

THERE are many ways to approach the problem of life duration in wild species. In a later chapter we shall deal, for example, with the study of population structure according to age and with the life expectancy at the time of birth. In all these cases we shall see that a majority of individuals live much shorter lives than the possible maximum, because of the various mortality factors incident to natural conditions. Thus many small rodents that could live perfectly well for several years in the laboratory, where they are protected from predators and disease, do not live for more than several months in nature.

Since this chapter is devoted to the successive stages of the life cycle, we shall consider here only the data on the *potential length of life* of wild mammals; that is, the maximum ages that the various species can attain. It is of course true that potential longevity can be measured almost exclusively in captivity, for under natural conditions only an extremely small percentage of individuals become very old, and it is exceptional to encounter one that shows clear signs of senility. This is probably the reason why some authors have thought that growth could continue throughout life in several small mammals, the Microtinæ in particular. Recent research has shown that nothing of the kind occurs (fig. 78), and so far as we know at present, continuing growth is an attribute of reptiles and fishes only. Information provided by zoological gardens, however, is helpful only in connection with certain groups that are easy to feed and that reproduce readily in captivity. For many species that are difficult to feed properly the zoos furnish data of questionable interest.

We are indebted to Major S. S. Flower for an excellent compilation of observations made by the great zoological gardens on the longevity of many species. We have drawn upon this work for some data that have been gathered in Table 7, which contains in addition a number of records published since 1931. Examination of these figures will show

**Table 7.** *Approximate potential longevity observed in some mammals (in years)*

INSECTIVORES
    *Blarina brevicauda* 2½
BATS
    *Pteropus giganteus* 17
    *Desmodus rotundus* 12
PRIMATES
    *Pan satyrus* 40
    *Pongo pygmeus* 26½
    *Hylobates lar* 23½
    *Cercopithecus æthiops* 24
    *Erythrocebus pyrrhonotus* 20
    *Macaca mulatta* 29
    *Papio cynocephalus* 25
    *Papio porcarius* 45
    *Cebus fatuellus* 25
    *Hapale jacchus* 16
    *Lemur fulvus* 25½
    *Nycticebus coucang* 10
    *Galago garnetti* 9½
    *Daubentonia madagascarensis* 7½
RODENTS
    *Petaurista alborufus* 13½
    *Petaurista inornatus* 11
    *Sciurus carolinensis* 14½
    *Ratufa indica* 16
    *Marmota marmota* 13½
    *Castor canadensis* 19
    *Eliomys quercinus* 5½
    *Peromyscus maniculatus* 5½
    *Micromys minutus* 2½

    *Cricetomys gambianus* 4½
    *Gerbillus gerbillus* 5
    *Meriones calurus* 5½
    *Jaculus jaculus* 6½
    *Pedetes caffer* 7½
    *Hystrix cristata* 20
    *Dasyprocta mexicana* 13
    *Chinchilla laniger* 6½
    *Hydrochœrus capybara* 8½
CARNIVORES
    *Felis leo* 30
    *Felis tigris* 19
    *Felis pardus* 21
    *Felis onca* 22½
    *Felis concolor* 16
    *Cryptoprocta ferox* 17
    *Viverra zibetha* 15½
    *Viverra civetta* 13½
    *Genetta pardina* 12½
    *Herpestes vitticollis* 12½
    *Hyæna hyæna* 24
    *Crocuta crocuta* 25
    *Canis lupus* 16½
    *Canis latrans* 14½
    *Vulpes fulva* 12
    *Alopex lagopus* 14
    *Lycaon pictus* 10
    *Lutra lutra* 11
    *Martes martes* 15
    *Mellivora ratel* 23½
    *Potos flavus* 19

Ursus arctos   34
Thalarctos maritimus   33½

PINNIPEDS

Zalophus californianus   23
Otaria byronia   17½
Arctocephalus pusillus   20
Halichærus grypus   18
Phoca vitulina   19

PROBOSCIDIANS

Elephas maximus   69

PERISSODACTYLS

Equus caballus przewalskii
   27½
Equus burchelli   28
Rhinoceros unicornis   47
Tapirus americanus   30½

ARTIODACTYLS

Pæphagus grunniens   22
Bison bonasus   18½
Bison bison   22½
Syncerus caffer   15½
Ovis musimon   19

Ammotragus lervia   15½
Hemitragus jemlahicus   16½
Rupicapra rupicapra   22
Bubalis buselaphus   18½
Connochætes gnou   16
Cephalophus maxwelli   9
Kobus defassa   16½
Antilope cervicapra   15½
Gazella dorcas   11½
Oryx algazel   18
Giraffa camelopardalis   28
Dama dama   15½
Rusa unicolor   17½
Cervus elaphus   19
Cervus canadensis   22
Camelus bactrianus   25½
Lama glama   20
Sus scrofa   19½
Hippopotamus amphibius
   41½
Chæropsis liberiensis   17½

that man has the greatest potential longevity of all the mammals, inasmuch as he can—barely—exceed one hundred years. Next to man, the groups that have very long lives are the elephants, hippopotami, horses, rhinoceroses, monkeys, and certain carnivores. The figures given for bats indicate that they also have a remarkably high maximum longevity. The groups that have a notably brief potential lifetime are mainly the small insectivores and the small rodents. It should not be forgotten also that we know almost nothing about the matter in a number of most interesting groups, such as the cetaceans, the edentates, the marsupials, and the monotremes.[4]

[4] Some species that live well in captivity are very long-lived: a two-toed sloth lived 11 years; a giant anteater, 14 years; a *Euphractus villosus*, 15½ years; a common wombat, 26 years; and an Australian spiny anteater, 27 years! Some species considered delicate will live a long time under suitable rearing-conditions.

### CHAPTER 7

# *Migrations*

TRUE migrations may be defined as seasonal and regular passages between an area where reproduction takes place and a zone in which the winter is spent; as everyone knows, many birds make such double journeys between the temperate or subpolar regions and the tropics of the Old World or the New. But the word *migration* is often used to designate other and very different phenomena that are quite unrelated to the true migratory journeys. Thus people speak of the "migrations" of lemmings, which, as will be shown in the last chapter, are nothing but mere emigrations without return that draw off the periodic overpopulation from certain regions. Paleontologists and zoogeographers also commonly refer to the "migrations" of certain groups or certain species from one continent into another. Nowadays reference is similarly made to the "migration" northward of the Texas armadillo, which, starting from the Mexican frontier and Texas, spread in 75 years over northeastern Oklahoma and Louisiana before crossing the Mississippi valley and advancing into southwestern Arkansas and eastern Oklahoma. In this case the word "migration" becomes synonymous with the extension of the range of a species, and the underlying causes of such a process certainly have nothing in common with those of true migrations.

### THE MIGRATIONS OF WILD MAMMALS

WE know much less about the migrations of mammals than about those of birds. The phenomenon is a rare one among our terrestrial species, and such recent techniques as bat banding and the marking of whales and seals have not as yet afforded all that can be wished for in the way of results. The few instances to be given in this chapter will show, nevertheless, that migrations are not peculiar to birds and fishes and that there is still much to be done before we can describe them precisely or understand their mechanism.

Among terrestrial mammals the best examples of true migration—varying widely in extent, to be sure—are to be found among the large ungulates [1] that inhabit regions in great part undisturbed by man. The most spectacular are the migrations of caribou in the vast northern regions of America. Clarke, Hoare, and Murie have provided some exact information on these movements and have shown how variable they are according to the districts concerned. During the summer the herds occupy the barrens, which they begin to leave as early as July in order to move toward the timber line—that is, usually but not always, toward the south. A temporary return northward is usually witnessed in August and September. During the cold season the animals wander about in their winter zone, and their move-

[1] This is not to say that the ungulates have a monopoly in these seasonal movements, for instances are known in other orders, including the primates. Malbrant and Maclatchy lay stress, for example, on the regularity of the "seasonal migrations that bring the bands together on the same dates and in the same places" in the African Cercopithecidæ (Old World monkeys), especially a mangabey (*Cercocebus albigena*).

ments from place to place may show some regularity. Thus the caribou studied by Clarke went back and forth from east to west or vice versa, whereas the herds observed by Hoare in the Reliance region moved counterclockwise in circles. The caribou set out again between late February and early May and return to the barrens for the summer. The routes followed would seem to be much the same from year to year, and the herds use trails that are quite visible on the ground and from the air. When certain streams are crossed, mass drownings can occur, as witness one mentioned by Clarke that resulted in the death of 525 animals. Under some circumstances males may move in compact bands of 100 to 1,000 head; but this segregation of the sexes is not invariable, as appears from the fact that copulation takes place during the autumn migration, the young being brought forth during the spring migration.

When the American bison was abundant, it carried out impressive migrations, over a more or less circular route, that might result in the herds spending the winter 200 or even 400 miles south of the zone occupied in summer.

The migrations of other species, such as the elk, the Dall sheep, or the mule deer, are much less extended. Russell has carefully studied this last species in the Yellowstone and Yosemite National Parks, where they are not interfered with by human activities. In these two areas the species sojourns successively in summer pasturage of higher altitude, where it spends the season of mild weather, and in a wintering zone, at low altitude, where it arrives in autumn and from which it sets out again in the spring. These summer and winter habitats are not far apart, say from 10 to 60 miles as the crow flies. The first snowfalls on the summer pasturages initiate the fall migration, regardless of the temperature. In spring, on the other hand, the return migration does not occur until several weeks after the snow melts, and the animals are en route only when the growth of vegetation is sufficiently advanced to assure their subsistence at higher altitudes. The period of rut coincides with the fall migration and the beginning of the sojourn in winter quarters; the young are brought forth in late June or early July shortly after the return to summer pasturage. It appears evident that the accessibility of food is a dominant factor in causing these migrations. In Yellowstone Park, for example, there is an especially interesting district, that of the geysers. Although it is situated at an altitude of 7,500 feet, snow does not remain on the ground in winter because of the abundance of hot springs. Now, the approximately 70 mule deer that inhabit this particular region never migrate, remaining there in sedentary fashion the year round. In Manitoba likewise the ample sufficiency of food, the good cover, and the comparatively thin layer of snow on the ground are correlated with a completely sedentary habit of the species.

The aquatic mammals afford several examples of migration on the grand scale, since some of them move periodically between subpolar latitudes and tropical waters. The seasonal abundance of certain whales in certain localities has long been well known to whalers. The gray whale, for instance, is found in numbers from the beginning of winter to the end of spring in the Pacific along the California coast, where it comes to give birth to its young in lagoons and estuaries; at the approach of summer this species returns northward along the coast and spends the summer in the

Arctic Ocean and the Sea of Okhotsk. A similar migration has been observed along the Asian coast, and whales of this species are hunted in winter off the coast of Korea.

No longer ago than 1932 the Discovery Committee succeeded in perfecting a practical method for marking whales. The invention consists of a stainless steel tube about 10 inches in length, engraved on the outside with a serial number, the address of the Colonial Office in London, and a promise of reward to the finder. This tube, contained in a special cartridge, can be fired as a projectile from a special cannon of sufficient power to hit a whale 70 or 80 yards from the boat. The tube buries itself in the animal's blubber without causing a serious wound, and it will be easily found later when the fat is removed on the deck of the factory-ship. From 1932 to 1938—in the course of five whaling-seasons in the Antarctic, that is—668 blue whales, 3,915 fin whales, and 548 humpbacks were marked, and of these 33 (4.94 per cent), 118 (3.01 per cent), and 36 (6.59 per cent), respectively, were recovered later, some of them 4 years after marking. Rayner has made a very careful analysis of these recoveries up to 1939, and this has enabled him to draw the following conclusions: the blue whales met with around South Georgia do not constitute a fixed population, nor do those hunted at the same time off Enderby Land. Thus one individual was caught, 88 days after marking, more than 500 miles southwest of the place where it was marked, and another had traveled, in 32 days, more than 300 miles to the southeast. Some individuals of this species are unquestionably capable of covering very great distances. A blue whale marked in summer off Bouvet Island, for example, was caught the following summer off

South Georgia (about 1,180 miles from its position of the preceding summer). Most of the animals recovered after one, two, three, or four years were taken, however, in the vicinity of the place where they had been marked originally. It is remarkable that no marked blue whale has as yet been recovered in the winter in tropical latitudes, for this species is hunted at that season (to be sure in small numbers) off the West African coast, in the Indian Ocean not far from Madagascar, and northwest of Australia, as well as on the west coast of South America up to Peru and the Equator. But these individuals are mostly young, and it is possible that the winter migration toward warm waters is less clear-cut for this species than it is for the humpback. The fin whale displays migratory behavior similar to that of the blue whale. In summer it frequents the same Antarctic waters, and in the winter it, too, is found at times in African waters. A young individual marked in February 1935 in the Antarctic, at latitude 65° south, was captured on July 1, 1937, off Saldanha Bay in South Africa, 1,900 miles north of the point where it was marked. As in the preceding species, there is a pronounced tendency for marked individuals to return summer after summer to the same locality, although this rule does not always hold. The humpbacks of the Southern Hemisphere would seem to travel immense distances each year. Figure 81 reproduces one of Rayner's charts and shows the regularity of these movements. In summer these whales frequent Antarctic waters and in winter the tropical latitudes (northwest of Australia and Madagascar), where they breed; the following summer they return very faithfully to the localities of the preceding year, and so on year after year. Some segregation even seems to exist

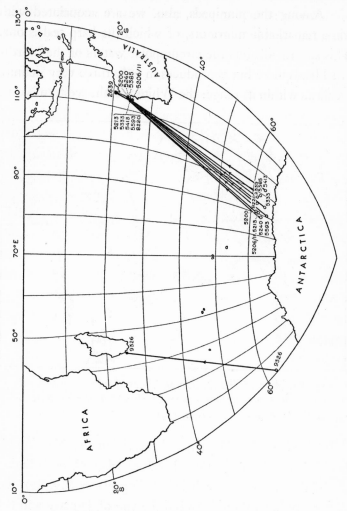

FIG. 81: *The migration of Antarctic humpback whales in the Indian Ocean. Points of marking and recapture of a few individuals. After Rayner, 1940.*

between the different groups (African, West Australian, New Zealand, Chilean, and Atlantic), which would thus tend to be isolated from one another.

Among the pinnipeds, also, we are acquainted with some remarkable migrators, of which the harp seal is one. This species inhabits the circumpolar waters of the Northern Hemisphere but reproduces in only three very definite localities within its range: the White Sea, the western North

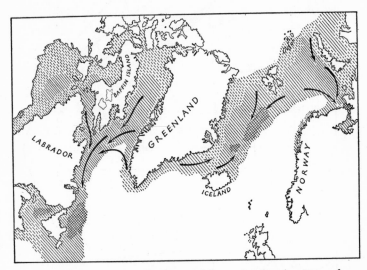

FIG. 82: *Area of distribution and lines of migration toward zones of reproduction (cross-hatched) of the harp seal. After Nansen, in Sivertsen, 1941.*

Atlantic about Jan Mayen, and the vicinity of Newfoundland.[2] A regular migration therefore takes place, bringing the adults in autumn to their breeding-places (fig. 82); the young are born there between the end of January and the beginning of April, and then there is a return migration toward the more northern latitudes, where the summer is spent. In the White Sea Sivertsen marked 171 young seals with numbered aluminum plates attached to their flippers;

[2] One group northwest of the Island and another in the Gulf of Saint Lawrence.

eleven recoveries were made up to 1941, and fig. 83 clearly shows the dispersal of the young animals. In the northern Pacific, Alaska fur seals carry out even more spectacular migrations. This species reproduces only on the Pribilof

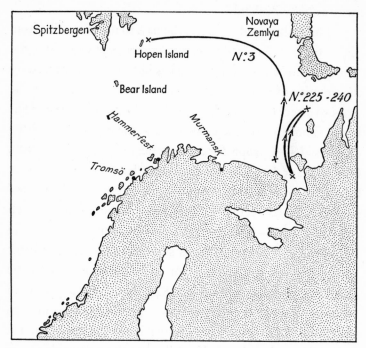

FIG. 83: *Some results obtained from markings used in studying the migrations of the harp seal. Nos. 225 and 240 were captured a year after marking, No. 3 eight years later. After Sivertsen, 1941.*

Islands, 200 miles away from the nearest land, where the animals are to be found from May to November. As winter begins, the females and young undertake a journey of nearly 3,000 miles that brings them to the coast of Southern California where they pass the cold season. The males, on the other hand, spend the winter no farther away than the

Gulf of Alaska and the waters south of the Aleutian Islands. Spring brings both sexes back to the Pribilofs. In the Antarctic the crab-eating seal usually remains all winter near the edge of the ice pack, although it has been reported as far away as New Zealand.

The ability to fly enables the bats to move readily from place to place and facilitates migrations over vast distances. The study of these movements has been much advanced by the practice of banding the animals with incomplete metallic rings so attached to the front limb as not to injure the membrane. The large mouse-eared bat and the noctule have been most used in Europe for systematically planned research. Out of 8,295 large mouse-eared bats banded by Eisentraut between 1932 and 1942, 199 were recovered later, and analysis of these recoveries shows that in the spring—March and early April—this species leaves its winter quarters (in Brandenburg), and flies to its summer stations. The latter are located along the arc of a circle extending from the northwest to the northeast (fig. 84). The distances between winter and summer quarters vary a good deal according to the individuals concerned, the maximum being 160 miles, the minimum less than half a mile, and the average between 20 and 50 miles. Great fidelity to the wintering-locality, even to certain exact spots (such as a particular gallery in a cave), is the rule. Out of 355 large mouse-eared bats banded during the winter of 1932–3 and recaptured during the winter of 1933–4, only three had changed locality. Moreover, some individuals were moved late in the winter from their accustomed winter shelter to another some 90 miles away, where they finished their hibernation, but not one of these returned to this place the next year, although many did return to their accustomed winter quarters.

There were not so many recoveries of the noctule— only 19 out of 1,464 that were banded. But here the distances between winter and summer quarters were much

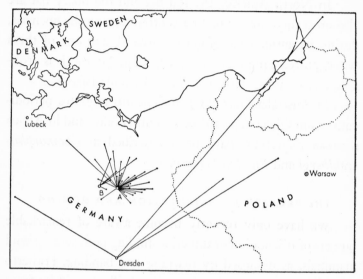

FIG. 84: *Migrations of two groups (A and B) of large mouse-eared bats banded in their winter quarters at Brandenburg, and of four noctules banded in winter at Dresden. After Eisentraut.*

greater, as is witnessed by an individual that was banded at Dresden and recaptured at Kampiai, Lithuania, 470 miles away. An observation made by Bels illustrates again the remarkable ability this species has for making rapid flights over long distances: a noctule banded August 1, 1938, at Haarlem in Holland was recovered on the 29th of the same month near Duffel in Belgium, 90 miles to the south.

The record for distance as the crow flies is held at present by a European pipistrelle, which, banded on June 28, 1939, in the province of Dnepropetrovsk, Russia, was recovered by Buresch on September 8, 1939, near Plovdiv in Bulgaria, at a minimum distance of 720 miles!

In North America the red bat and the hoary bat are also great migrators. The first is often seen on the open sea, during its autumn migration southward, and one of them was captured 240 miles off Cape Cod, in August. It is probable that they regularly reach the Bermuda Islands.

In Australia *Pteropus poliocephalus* migrates periodically from Queensland to New South Wales, and in Africa seasonal migrations have been described in *Epomorphus wahlbergi* and *Eidolon helvum*.

### THE PROBLEM OF ORIENTATION AND HOMING

WE have only recently become aware of remarkable powers of orientation or direction-finding possessed by wild mammals, as disclosed by marking and banding. Hitherto the homing of an individual experimentally moved far from its home range seemed to be an attribute of migratory birds exclusively. Today there is proof that similar phenomena are to be observed in rodents and bats at least. Future studies will show whether these observations, along with the many cases of domestic dogs [3] finding their way home after being

---

[3] Some of these instances of "finding the way home" are truly remarkable. Soulath (*Zeits. f. Tierpsychol.*, Vol. 6, 1944, p. 147) gives, for example, the case of a dog that was taken 20 miles from home by rail in a special compartment for dogs and returned by itself, making use of the railroad track. The same author cites also the case of another animal that returned home by boat, disembarking only at its destination, although the two-hour passage included several other stops. But visible landmarks quite probably play a large part in homing. In this connection Grzimek (*Zeits. f. Tierpsychol.*, Vol. 5, 1943, p. 481) has made interesting ex-

taken a long distance away, into unfamiliar country, represent isolated occurrences or, on the contrary, reveal a more general faculty. For the present we must patiently gather reliable observations while admitting our ignorance of the physiological mechanisms involved.

Let us begin by surveying some well-established facts. Stickel has recently published the results of an ingenious experiment, which should be systematically repeated. This author worked with white-footed mice at the Patuxent Research Refuge in Maryland. He used the following technique: 22.5 acres of forest were selected in a uniformly wooded area, so that the surroundings were everywhere the same and there could be no possibility of different plant formations serving as landmarks for the animals. Further, the selected zone seemed to be uniformly populated with white-footed mice, so that "vacant spaces" or sparsely populated spots were eliminated as sources of different population pressure. In this experimental area Stickel set up three concentric parallel squares measuring 990, 660, and 330 feet on a side respectively and marked by rows of Sherman live-traps set at regular intervals of 55 feet, as indicated in the accompanying diagram (fig. 85). All the mice taken alive in the traps were marked with metallic ear tags before being released.

The homing experiment was performed at three different times. On the 27th and 28th of August, 1946, all the mice captured were set at liberty where they were caught. On the 29th of August those taken in the outer line of traps

---

periments on the horse. Five mares were taken (on foot or in vehicles), *blindfolded*, for distances varying from 3 to 10 miles from where they were bred and into territory unknown to them; under these conditions not one succeeded in returning to the stable.

were transferred to the center of the experimental area—
that is, to a distance of 500 to 700 feet—before release,
whereas the individuals taken in the traps of the two inner
quadrilaterals were released at their place of capture, as before. No trapping was done during the five following days,

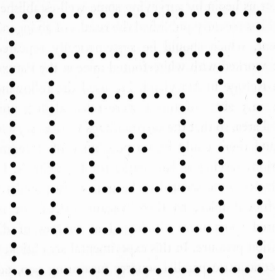

FIG. 85: *Diagram showing the location of traps in Stickel's
experiment.*

so as to leave the population undisturbed before the last
series of trappings, which took place on September 4 to 6.
It will perhaps be supposed that a removal from home of
only 500 to 700 feet would constitute a very slight displacement, but this distance is in reality much beyond the average
normal range of a mouse, which at this season and under
these environmental conditions does not in fact exceed 150
feet for males and 100 feet for females.

The results of this experiment were as follows: out of
27 males thus artificially displaced, 22 (or 82 per cent) re-

turned to their home site where they were recovered between September 4 and 6, two probably returned, one was recaptured 765 feet from its original home range in the wrong direction, and two others were not retaken. Out of 21 females similarly transferred, 13 (or 62 per cent) returned to their home site, one probably returned, another remained near the point of release, and six were not retaken. There were five juvenile individuals that were "displaced" under the same conditions as the adults, none of which were later recaptured. For purposes of comparison, I will mention the fact that 90 per cent of the males and 100 per cent of the females released where they were caught during the first trappings were retaken there during the last period of trapping—which indicates the sensitivity of the method used.

Other authors have also engaged in experimentation of like nature. The Muries, for instance, have obtained some spectacular results. Using the deer mouse, whose individual cruising range is of the order of 100 yards, more or less, they have observed the homing of subjects transported to distances of 100 yards to 2 miles and therefore very probably into unknown territory. More, a young individual of the same species succeeded in regaining its home range after having been carried to a distance of two miles—and that in less than 48 hours! In Austria Wolfgang Schleidt observed the homing of a common redbacked vole from a distance of 700 yards.

Not all rodents would seem capable of such feats. But Hamilton observed the return in less than an hour of a large male meadow vole carried 200 yards from its domicile, and yet this species is of a notably stay-at-home disposition. The same author got positive results with American red squirrels transported more than a mile from their home range, and from eastern chipmunks transported to a distance of 700 paces from their shelters.

The most beautiful experiments in homing, however, have been carried out with bats. The papers of Eisentraut, Norbert Casteret, and Ryberg offer many examples, like those that follow. The last author mentioned obtained many returns of noctules *in a few hours* between Alnarp and Lund (about 6 miles) and between Malmö and Lund (13 miles). The distance between Falsterbo and Lund (28 miles) was covered in 24 hours. The European pipistrelle, on the other hand, was able to accomplish homing flights of only a few miles. The species that at present seems to hold the record for these homing flights is the large mouse-eared bat. In Germany Eisentraut obtained the return of an individual released almost 94 miles away. Casteret has carried out many displacement experiments with the bats of the Tignahustes Cavern in the Hautes-Pyrénées. Several released at 10 miles were already back the next day; out of 65 released at 22 miles, 8 were recovered 3 days later; a few released at 62 miles were back a month later. A few individuals even returned to Tignahustes after having been released at Saint-Jean-de-Luz, 112 miles away from home, on the seashore at Moliets (Landes), 125 miles distant, and at Sète, 165 miles away! It is true that these returns from distant points were very slow and that the large mouse-eared bat is a species that normally accomplishes long journeys, but these performances are remarkable none the less.

How are these mammals able to regain their homes? Visible landmarks unquestionably exist and no doubt they play a predominant part over short distances. It is also probable that they are a factor in migrations. But it must not be forgotten that bats fly almost exclusively at night and that on this account their recognition of topographic features must be limited to twilight hours. Again, it is hard to see what kind of landmarks might be of assistance to small rodents such as deer mice moving about in the uniform, low vegetation of the underbrush. Here the scented trails of their fellows are probably more helpful. There remains the hypothesis of the exploration of unknown territory in chance directions or in a spiral path, until some landmark enables the animal to regain its customary home range. In favor of this explanation is above all the progressive decrease in the percentage of successful returns accompanying increase in distance. This reasoning has validity, and no doubt chance exploration plays a part, as do orientation by visible landmarks and previously familiar scents; but is there not something else?

### CHAPTER 8

# The Social Life of Mammals

IT might be supposed that in the matter of social behavior
two different types of mammals exist: the solitary and the
social. This is not true in reality, for a mammal that is
strictly solitary throughout its life cycle is inconceivable.
There always exists, in fact, a minimum of social relations
between the sexes, at the time of mating, and between
mother and young during the period of nursing, and some
cases are known in which the social relations between individuals are held strictly to this minimum. So it is with the
little eastern chipmunk of North America, a species in
which the male and female become antagonistic no more
than a few minutes after mating and in which the mother
and young are associated only as long as they remain together in the nest and for a week after. There is thus no
lasting mutual attraction between individuals, and there
even seems to be just the opposite of a "need" that would
lead the animal to seek the company of its kind.

Sexual relations and family behavior have been sur-
veyed in preceding chapters, and we now have to consider
interactions between individuals that live permanently in

groups. Without attempting to draw up a classification of mammalian societies, which would of necessity be unsound in the present state of our knowledge, we shall confine ourselves to stating what we know at present about the social behavior of a few species sufficiently studied in this respect, after briefly surveying the means of communication and the social hierarchy.

### MEANS OF COMMUNICATION

MUCH has been written on the "language" of wild animals, but it is only in the course of the last twenty years or so that we have begun to understand the nature and function of the means of intercommunication used by mammals. Observation and experiment have revealed the existence of a great many "signals," not only acoustic but also visual and olfactory, that release a characteristic reaction in the individual perceiving them. These sign stimuli of different kinds (sounds, odors, or mimickings) appear to have well-defined functions in the social life of wild mammals, and if divergences exist between different schools of thought as to the interpretation of the observed facts, the reality and importance of the facts are no longer disputed by anyone.

The *acoustic signals* uttered by mammals are not so pleasing to the human ear as are many of the songs and some of the cries of birds, and so it is not surprising that their systematic study has been undertaken only recently and then for very few species. Although their notation encounters the same technical difficulties as that of bird songs, it has still been possible, in a limited number of cases, to analyze the effects of these sounds on the behavior of members of the group, to discover the circumstances under which they are produced, and to gain some idea of their role in the social life of the species.

The California ground squirrel is a gregarious rodent that has been closely studied in recent years by Linsdale and Fitch. The adult animal apparently utters only one simple chirp, and only when in danger. But Fitch's prolonged observations have shown that this familiar chirp varies significantly in pitch, loudness, and inflection according to the occasion. When a squirrel perceives a bird of prey flying in the vicinity it utters a single short syllable of unusual loudness and carrying quality, a "*cheesk*," and seeks cover. As soon as this signal is perceived by the other squirrels, they pay attention to it and seek their holes while taking up the cry of alarm in turn. If the enemy is a snake, the ground squirrel edges up to it, often coming within a foot or two, examines it, flicks its tail violently from side to side, and gives a peculiar chirp, "*cheet'-ik-irr-irr-irr*," distinctive in its low, vibrating quality and the series of subdued notes following the loud initial sharp note. This chirping and tail-waving of squirrels that have located a snake serves to attract the attention of others in the vicinity. If a man, dog, or coyote constitutes the danger, the signal generally becomes trisyllabic, "*chwee-chu-chuk*." A still different sound is produced when the danger is less immediate —a "*cheesk-isk-isk-isk-isk*," with the final syllables blending in a rapid succession. In the case of a mother with young, the female's agitation in the presence of danger that is not immediately threatening is expressed by the prolonged repetition, at intervals of two or three seconds, of a low, melodious note, "*chwërt*," that is more in the nature of an anxiety symptom than of a signal of alarm. Finally, other sounds, different from the basic chirp, are produced by this species: a low growl that seems to express defiance, a sharp squeal that seems to be a cry of pain and fear, and a high-pitched squeal ending in a trill, given when one squirrel is pursued by others.

Carpenter's researches on the behavior in nature of several species of monkeys afford other examples of auditory signals. The Panama howling monkeys have a vocabulary of at least 15 to 20 different vocalizations, all of which appear to play a very definite part in the behavior of the species. The functions of nine of them seem rather clear. The first is *a voluminous barking roar*, low-pitched and sonorous, uttered by the males of the clan in the presence of an enemy, of a rival clan trespassing upon the territory, or of any other disturbance. It has an inhibiting effect on all activities, such as feeding, locomotion, playing, and so on, and the members of the group prepare for attack or defense. The second signal is a *deep, hoarse cluck*, which may be given in series or singly by the leading male before and during the troop's movements; it initiates progression and controls its direction. The third is a *deep, gurgling sound given in a series* by the adult males in the presence of some disturbing factor; it usually precedes the loud roars but seems to affect only the males and not the females or young. The fourth vocalization is a *wail made on inspiration of air, followed by a groan*, sounded by a female whose young one has fallen; it is repeated until the baby is recovered, and it stimulates the males to utter their loud roar. In these circumstances the fallen baby gives a *series of three notes or little cries* that direct the mother and the males toward it.

Another sound is a *purr* of several seconds' duration which a young individual utters in order to obtain coddling from its mother. Finally, the young at play give *little chirping squeals*. The males of the clan produce two other easily recognizable sounds: a *grunting sound* produced when the young play at fighting and one of them utters a cry, the effect of which is to stop the fight; and a *rapidly repeated grunting* that is heard when the group situation involves something new and strange. The function of this latter sound seems to be to attract the attention of the members.

Studying the lar gibbon, the same observer has similarly described nine types of vocalization that play a part in the co-ordination of the social group. One of them, however, a *series of hoots with rising inflection, rising pitch, increasing tempo, the climax followed by 2 or 3 notes of lower pitch*, is heard under two very different conditions. It is sounded in general when there is competition for territory between two groups, and then it is an obvious manifestation of the behavior of the animals that are vocally forbidding access to their territory. But it is to be heard also when no rival group is present, and Carpenter thinks that in this case it is an expression of excess energy, a type of vocal play. In any event this example indicates that the stereotyped vocalizations of the primates may sometimes have multiple functions, a fact that by no means facilitates their study.

Regarding the chimpanzee, we shall note only that the studies of Yerkes and Learned on captive animals have demonstrated the richness of this ape's vocabulary; young individuals use at least thirty-two different sounds.

Even marine mammals have auditory signals. The bottlenosed dolphins observed in captivity by McBride and

Hebb make use of no less than three different noises: a snapping sound made with the jaws, a whistling, and a barking—all produced under water and transmitted over considerable distances. The white whale, studied by Schevill and Lawrence in the lower Saguenay River (Quebec), has a fairly rich vocabulary: high-pitched resonant whistles and squeals, ticking and clucking sounds, mewing, chirps, bell-like sounds, and even trilling. Kritzler's pilot whale uses five distinct kinds of sounds, including whistling, a sound definitely characteristic of all dolphins, if not of the toothed whales generally.[1]

It would seem that all these sounds are inherited and characteristic of the species concerned, although human languages depend essentially on imitation and tradition. But this does not exclude the possibility that young animals, in contact with adults, may improve their pseudo-language to some extent.

We must recognize, further, the existence of auditory signals other than vocal. The powerful slapping of the tail on the water by beavers is a most efficient alarm signal; and drumming on the ground with the hind paws is a noise produced under little-understood circumstances by many rodents; such, for example, as Shaw's jird, the lesser Egyptian jerboa, and the fat-tailed gerbil. Tail rattling is similarly used by the dusky-footed wood rat.

*Olfactory signals* must play an important part in the daily life of wild mammals, but, unfortunately, it is very difficult for us to appreciate the role of odors because of our own mediocre sense of smell. Cutaneous glands are common

[1] The possible existence of a "sonar system" in cetaceans comparable to that of bats has recently been discussed (see Kellog, W. N., Kohler, R., and Morris, H. N., *Science*, 117:239–43, 1953).

in mammals,[1] and the accompanying text figures borrowed from Pocock's classic studies will give a better idea of them than would dry descriptions. In the ruminants alone this author described and figured pedal glands (fig. 86) between

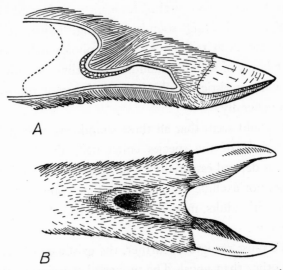

FIG. 86: *Pedal gland of the muntjac*, Cervulus muntjak. *A, median section of the hind foot of young six days old; B, front view of the same foot. After Pocock, 1910.*

the bases of the hoofs, carpal, tarsal, and metatarsal glands whose names alone are enough to show their anatomical positions, and preorbital (fig. 87A and B), inguinal (fig. 87C), retrocornal, occipital, caudal, and preputial glands. Anal glands are common in the carnivores, and the civets have peculiar ones in the perineal region. Some of the secretions of these glands undoubtedly play a part in sexual at-

---

[1] They are the subject of a recent monograph by Schaeffer (1940). It is an odd fact that these glands are lacking in the primates, excepting the marmoset family.

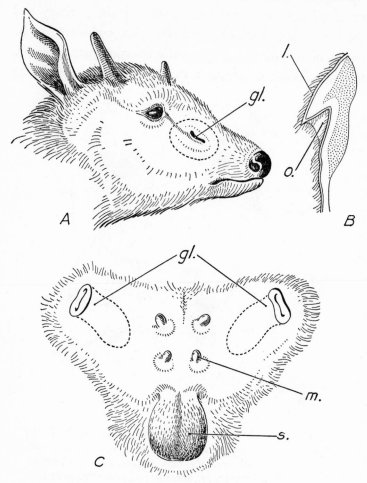

FIG. 87: *Some types of cutaneous glands in the ungulates. A, head of the male* Tetraceros quadricornis; gl., *orifice of the preorbital gland; B, section of this gland; o., orifice; l., flap of skin constituting upper lid of orifice; C, inguinal glands of a male bushbuk: m., nipples; gl., orifices of the glands; s., scrotum. After Pocock, 1910.*

traction,[2] some are employed in marking the territory and the home range (fig. 88), and others are considered to be means of defense. In reality their functions are probably multiple. What is certain is that the scented "trails" and

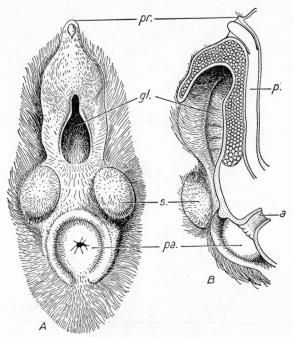

FIG. 88: *Anal gland of the male civet,* Viverra zibethica. *A, inferior view of the anal pouch and glandular area; B, vertical section through the same region. Pa., anal pouch; gl., interglandular space; s., scrotum; p., penis; pr., prepuce. After Pocock, 1915.*

"marks" so important in the lives of wild animals result from the functioning of these glands. Beavers deposit the secre-

<hr />

[2] J. Le Magnen (*Comptes Rendus Soc. Biol.,* Vol. 165, 1951, pp. 851–60) has shown, for example, that the male white rat is able to perceive and distinguish the odors of males and females of its species and to discriminate between a female in heat and one that is not. The behavior of the female with regard to biological odors is, moreover, clearly different from that of the adult male.

tion of their musk glands on hillocks of mud or projecting objects, and California ground squirrels that of their dorsal glands on stones and twigs. Martens and mongooses smear branches or bark with the product of their anal glands; un-

FIG. 89: *Male* Antilope cervicapra *"marking" a twig by depositing on it the preorbital secretion. After a sketch by Hediger.*

gulates often place the thick secretion of their preorbital (fig. 89) or retrocornal glands on certain trees; many Canidæ mark stones, stumps, stakes, and other projecting objects with their urine mixed with the product of their preputial glands; and Enders states that the ocelot marks out its hunting grounds with heaps of excrement that are often of considerable size. It is known also that West African civets do not bury their excrement but on the contrary accumulate it at certain points in the vicinity of which the animals remain for several months. Verheyen, for instance, found a pile of excrement two feet in diameter and two or three inches high in the National Park of Upemba in the Belgian Congo. Vicunas also build up heaps of dung on their home range which may reach eight feet in diameter and a foot in thickness. Pearson often watched a herd of these animals, young and old, approach such piles of excrement and saw individuals go one by one to sniff at the material, add their contributions, and then move off. The oribi antelope, a species in which the pairs are strongly attached to their territory, marks this ârea both with the anteorbital secretion and with urine and feces always deposited in the same places. Male hippopotami also make use of mingled urine and feces to mark certain fixed points in their harem's territory (Hediger). All these odoriferous signals or "signposts" unquestionably play an important part in the everyday life of wild mammals.[3]

*Visual signals* have been studied much less in mammals than in birds. But it is certain that they exist, and all investigations of the hierarchy in social species include men-

---

[3] Linsdale insists, for example, on the importance of smell in mutual recognition among California ground squirrels. When members of the same family are concerned, such as parents and young, the animals sniff at one another's snout, periphery of the mouth, or cheeks. When, on the other hand, two strange males meet, they smell each other's anal region with their tails raised, probably to identify each other and to determine each other's physiological condition through the odorous peculiarities of the anal gland secretion.

Odoriferous signals are important also in direction finding by subterranean mammals, as Godet's observations on the European mole have proved.

tion of characteristic attitudes indicating the rank an individual holds in the society. In many instances it even seems that "threatening" attitudes play a much greater part than real fights.

Certain parts of the fur that sometimes contrast violently in color with the rest of the coat are often made use of as visual signals. The clearest case is that of the "rump

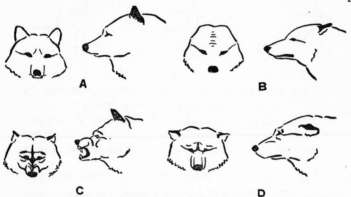

FIG. 90: *Some characteristic expressions of the wolf. A, normal facial expression of an animal of high rank; B, expression of timidity; C, threatening expression; D, suspicious expression. After Schenkel, 1947.*

patches" of the American pronghorn. This animal has long white erectile hairs in the perianal region that are suddenly raised when it is disturbed or frightened; in that state they form two large white rosettes that are visible from a great distance. They probably serve as a "signal of alarm" and as directive marks to other individuals. In a preceding chapter we have described how the European wild rabbit uses the white underside of the tail to attract the female's attention during the nuptial display.

Various positions of the head, ears, and tail, furthermore, have definite meaning. Figures 90 and 91, taken from

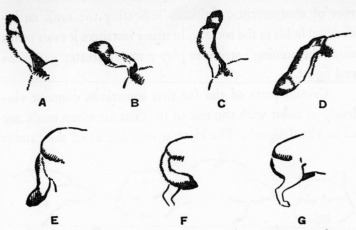

FIG. 91: *The expressive function of tail movements in the wolf. A, self-assurance; B, threatening attitude; C (with wagging sidewise), attitude of intimidation; D, normal; E (with wagging sidewise), attitude of submission; F and G, attitudes of acute discomposure. After Schenkel, 1947.*

Schenkel's recent memoir on expression in wolves, represent examples of this "sign language"; many other instances are given in Antonius's work.

### THE SOCIAL HIERARCHY

IN the year 1913 the naturalist Schjelderup-Ebbe discovered that there exists in flocks of hens a "pecking order," or hierarchic organization, in which the social ranking depends on the number of pecks or blows with the beak given or received, as well as on the aggressive or submissive attitudes assumed by the individual concerned. The many investigations pursued since then, especially by Allee and his students, have demonstrated the existence of analogous phenomena in many species of domesticated animals. Thus the more or less artificial groupings of hens or white rats are not disorderly assemblages but rapidly become organized

*A female marmoset*, Marmosa murina, *carrying her young.*
New York Zoological Society Photo.

*Female Virginia opossum carrying her young.*
Courtesy of American Museum of Natural History.

*An eastern chipmunk hibernating.*
*Courtesy of American Museum of Natural History.*

groups by virtue of the relations of dominance and subordination that are set up among their members.

In what degree are these facts, observed in laboratory rodents or flocks of sheep, peculiar to domesticated species or to life in captivity? How far can they help us toward an understanding of the social component in wild mammals?

To begin with, it is now quite certain that social hierarchies are not peculiar to domesticated animals. This has been shown, for example, by Katz's recent work on the Barbary sheep, carried out on a herd of twelve head—four males, four females, and four young—living in semiliberty on a fenced-in plot of about two acres at the Bronx Zoo in New York. At the beginning of the study, which lasted 53 days, the animals were marked with spots of color in order to make identification easy, and the "rank" of the various members of the group was ascertained as follows: when two individuals were together near the fence of the enclosure awaiting food, they were offered a piece of bread, care being taken to have it equally distant from the two animals. At sight of the bread they moved toward it, but the dominant individual was always the one to get it, after having struck with the head or merely threatened [4] the dominated individual, which thereupon withdrew.

Katz made many repetitions of this test with the various members of the herd and got the following results: Male 1 dominated males 2, 3, and 4; male 2 dominated males 3 and 4; male 3 dominated male 4. Female 1 dominated females 2, 3, and 4; female 2 dominated females 3 and 4; female 3 dominated female 4. Young 1 dominated young 2, 3, and 4;

[4] In the present instance the threat is indicated merely by a sudden twisting movement of the head in the direction of the lower ranking individual.

young 2 dominated young 3 and 4, and young 3 dominated young 4. Further, the males were always dominant with respect to the females, and adults with respect to the young. These results would indicate the existence of a *linear hier-archy* of the simplest kind: Male 1 > male 2 > male 3 > male 4 > female 1 > female 2 > female 3 > female 4 > young 1 > young 2 > young 3 > young 4. This hier-archy or ranking remained very stable throughout the whole course of the tests, since 270 observations out of 272 gave results in conformity with this tabulation.[5] It is note-worthy also that quite apart from this ranking it was always female 1 that acted as leader of the flock when it was fright-ened by the observer's presence, showing quite clearly that the leader of a group is not necessarily the individual high-est in the social scale.

Other examples of hierarchies in wild mammals in cap-tivity are afforded by lions, baboons, and chimpanzees (Yerkes), and even by bottlenosed dolphins.

The second point of importance is the occurrence of unquestionable hierarchies in certain wild species living under natural conditions. Southern's study of the wild rab-bit, for example, shows that the whole social organization of the colony during the period of reproduction is based on the territorialism of the females and the dominance of cer-tain of the males. The latter are usually old individuals that are intolerant of competition from young males; they not only chase them and even compel them to go away to try

---

[5] Hierarchies are not always linear; a common arrangement among birds, for example, is the *triangular hierarchy*, where a subject A domi-nates a subject B while being dominated by a subject C, which is itself subordinated to B. All hierarchies, moreover, undergo change with the passage of time and with the age and physiological state of the subjects. Experimental castration of males reduces their aggressiveness.

their luck in other colonies, but sometimes they fight with them. Southern describes a fight between two males, one of which had ventured too near his rival's mate. After a chase the two adversaries engaged in a furious joust, leaping against each other to a height of three feet. The old dominant males may rule over a section of the warren for several years, as did two animals marked by Southern.

We may consider the existence of a social hierarchy, involving the more or less lasting superiority of certain individuals over others, to be a fairly frequent phenomenon among wild mammals and in no way peculiar to life in captivity. It remains for future research to analyze in detail the relationship between the social hierarchy and territorial behavior, for there seem to be many links between these two manifestations of aggressiveness within the species.

### SOME INSTANCES OF SOCIAL LIFE IN MAMMALS

IT is likely that there are mammals of permanent social habit in most of the orders, and doubtless detailed study of the modes of life practiced by exotic species will in the near future provide many new data on this subject. But at the moment we have exact knowledge regarding only a few species of rodents, pinnipeds, ungulates, and primates, to which we shall now turn our attention.

GREGARIOUS RODENTS. The first instance that comes to mind when mammalian societies are under consideration is that of the beavers. In fact these industrious rodents have been the subject of so many books and articles that one might suppose our understanding of their social organization to be well advanced. Unfortunately it is nothing of the kind, for if more or less fictionalized accounts are many, persevering observations are few, and it is no exaggeration to say that a full-scale study of beaver biology is yet to be undertaken.

Bradt, however, has published a considerable series of observations on the American beaver, which serves as a fortunate corrective of previous efforts (that of Warren, for instance). These observations are of interest because they were based on the study of marked [6] individuals living at liberty and because some of them could be followed up for several years. This work makes it evident that the beaver colony—that is, the group frequenting the same body of water,[7] using the same source of food, and maintaining the same dam or series of dams—most commonly consists of a family group comprising 2 adults, the young of the year, and often those of the preceding year. At the age of two years the young, then approaching maturity, are driven away, and the society is thus limited to 12 individuals at most. For example, 42 colonies studied by Bradt were constituted as follows:

| CONSTITUTION OF COLONIES | NUMBER OF CASES |
|---|---|
| 1 *female* | 1 |
| 1 *female and the young of the year* | 7 |
| 1 *female and the young of the preceding year* | 2 |
| 2 *females and their young of the year* | 1 |
| 1 *male* | 6 |
| 1 *male and* 1 *female* | 6 |
| 1 *male,* 1 *female, and their young of the year* | 9 |
| 1 *male,* 1 *female, and the young of the preceding year* | 2 |
| 1 *male,* 1 *female, their young of the year, and the young of the preceding year* | 8 |

[6] All other marking methods (tagging ears, clipping toenails, etc.) being inconvenient to use for this species, Bradt adopted that of branding the tail with a red-hot iron. Marks so made at various levels on one side or the other or on the upper or under surface last for about one year.

[7] Where, however, they may inhabit more than one house or one burrow.

The history of one of these colonies, followed at House Lake from 1928 to 1933, is especially suggestive. A pair marked in October 1928 had 4 young in May 1929, and 6 others in May 1930, bringing to 12 the number of members of the colony for the latter year. By September of 1931 the 1929 young had disappeared, but 4 of the 6 1930 young remained with the parents and 6 new young were born, the colony thus continuing to consist of 12 members. In May 1932 there were still 12 members: the 2 parents, 6 young a year old, and 4 young of the year. In May 1933 Bradt once again found 12 members: the 2 adults, the 4 1932 young, and 6 newborn of the year. This example shows that the pair of reproducing adults is the nucleus of the social group; in the 42 colonies studied there never was more than one adult male, and his intolerance toward other males of reproductive age explains at once the absence of overlapping in the territories of several colonies and the expulsion of the young when they approach maturity. The males also take the lead in repairing damaged dams, but all the members of the colony share this work. Beaver colonies thus stand as the type of familial societies in which co-operation and co-ordination of activities reach a high degree of perfection.

Almost nothing is known precisely about the social organization of European beaver colonies. We do know that in some localities, where the animals are not in too close contact with man (parts of Norway, the Elbe valley, and Poland, for example), this species is quite capable of building houses and dams like those of the American species. If the Rhone beaver now lives in burrows, it may be in consequence of centuries of contact with civilization; and the case of the female, kept in a park at Parjurade, that before giving birth built a house of branches with a floor and a central opening for escape, shows that under favorable circumstances the characteristic behavior pattern of the species can again be overtly expressed. The colonies of this species are probably constituted like those of its American relatives. Curry-Lindhal, cited by Hainard, believes that in Sweden "a colony consists almost without exception of a single family: parents, young of the year, and young of the preceding year, the latter leaving their parents at two years of age." This at least would indicate close similarity to the American beaver.

It is probable that Alpine marmot colonies also have a family basis. Hainard emphasizes the fact that marmots living in the same place often have the same coat characters, and the fact could be explained by a high degree of inbreeding in small isolated populations. It is not known, however, if the parents live together in the same burrow throughout their active period, nor for how long the young remain with them. It would seem that the co-operative activities of the members of the same colony are decidedly limited, and the existence of sentinels supposed to whistle as a danger signal to their fellows appears to be purely legendary, each animal in reality being very much on the watch.

The mountain vizcachas of Peru also live in colonies of varying size, numbering from 4 to 75 individuals, among the crags of the high Andean regions wherever water is available. Pearson has recently made a careful study of their biology in the valley of Caccachara, at an altitude of more than 15,000 feet. Like the European marmot, the vizcacha is a strictly diurnal and gregarious animal living in burrows that are often no more than crevices among the boulders with little in the way of furnishings. Most of the colonies consist of family groups that vary in constitution during the course of the year. In July, August, and September a majority of the members of the colony are paired, and the family is made up of an adult male and a parous or pregnant female accompanied by one, two, or three young of different ages; [8] the oldest male offspring may be sexually mature yet still living with the family. When œstrus comes on, the female no longer tolerates the presence of the adult male and chases him out of the burrow while continuing to live with her offspring and even with other females. The evicted males may then join a group living in a special burrow or lead a more or less vagrant life. Sexual promiscuity seems to be the rule in the colony; Pearson saw a male attending several females and several males paying court to one female. When gestation begins, the aggressiveness of the females declines, the adult male is tolerated once more in the burrow, and the family group is re-formed. In the colonies he observed Pearson saw no sign of individual or collective territories defended by their "owners." He noted at most that not every part of the colony's area was common ground; certain individuals, pairs, or families were sometimes seen to occupy exactly the same spot week after week. One family, for instance, always took its sun bath on a particular rock that other members of the colony obviously avoided, although the family in possession never showed any signs of defensive behavior.

We have already discussed the social organization of the wild rabbit warren as disclosed in Southern's beautiful

[8] In this species the young are born one at a time, and a female may give birth two or three times a year.

investigation. Here also the element of stability is provided by the females, which raise their young in their burrows and are jealous in their defense. As for the polygamous males, only certain ones succeed in gaining dominion over the warren and mating with the females. Sexual promiscuity is again the rule in this instance.

THE PINNIPEDS. This order includes the eared seals, the walruses, and the true seals, which are mostly gregarious. Only a few seals, in fact, such as the Ross seal, the leopard seal, and the bearded seal, are truly solitary. All the rest of the species live in groups, but the social structure of these groups is not the same in all cases.

In some instances—all the eared seals, the southern elephant seal, and the North Atlantic gray seal—the polygamy of the males involves the formation of harems during the period of reproduction. Thus the Falkland sea lion, carefully studied by Hamilton, lives in vast herds (unorganized, it would seem) when not reproducing. With the coming of the Antarctic summer, however, the breeding and nonbreeding animals separate, but many of the previous season's pups remain with their mothers until the next are born. The nonbreeding animals repair to certain shores, and among them will be found not only immature individuals and some of the previous season's pups but also idle bulls that have not been able to obtain cows. The breeding herd thus consists of harem bulls, pregnant cows about to give birth, virgin cows, and newborn pups. Each male has a definite number of females (9 on the average), which he jealously defends against the sexual approaches of other males and with which he will copulate soon after the young of the preceding year are born. The male does not allow any of the females of his harem to return to the sea before copulation has taken place, but when all the females have been covered, the harem breaks up. Then the males become less aggressive, and they may be seen sleeping or guarding the young. The reproductive season is in full swing during the first half of January, and the dispersal of the harems begins in early February. The existence of such harems during the reproductive period seems to be general among all the eared seals. Those of the Alaska fur seal are well known, and, as we have seen, the two sexes undertake long migrations in order to keep the rendezvous in the Pribilof Islands.

The harems of the southern elephant seal likewise involve the separation of the females into groups when they go ashore to have their young. Those observed by Matthews in South Georgia contained from 2 to 30 females per male, the average being between 12 and 20. Here again the males having adjacent harems fight violently in defense of their property and drive away bachelor bulls that frequent the beach around the edges of the harems. When one of these bachelors approaches, the harem bull throws back his head, roars while inflating his proboscis, and opening his mouth utters a series of muffled bellows. Usually this display of might is enough to scare off the intruder, but sometimes there is a fight. Then, face to face, the two males rear up as high as they can, mouths open and proboscises inflated, trying to tear at each other with their upper canine teeth. If one of the animals loses his balance while fighting, the other throws himself upon the foe, biting him in the back and neck; the wounds thus inflicted may be six inches across, and the eyes and proboscis are often reached. Usually the wounded animal gives up the fight. The females, for their part, accept any male that approaches them and are in no way faithful to their lord and master. With this species, then, as with the eared seals, there is a territory defended by the male during the period of reproduction, and this territory is strictly limited to the harem.

The gray seal is transitional between the polygamous pinnipeds and the gregarious seals that are sexually promiscuous. This species has been closely studied by Darling on the Treshnish Islands and North Rona, off Scotland, and by Davies on Ramsey Island in the Irish Sea. On the latter island it is the males that arrive first at the breeding-grounds, after the first of August. In September they have established their territories and they are on patrol along the beaches where the females are to come and give birth. The latter reach land three days to three weeks before the birth of their young; during this waiting-period they spend most of their time in the water and as a rule take the initiative in prenuptial play with the males. Individuals of the two sexes face each other and touch each other with their front limbs, the female mounts on the back of the male, and the two animals often swim in circles, one behind the other. The young are born in September and October, and the males copulate with the females shortly after the latter give birth. The important point is that several different males rule in succession over the same harem, without there being any relation between the number of females that compose it and the number of males that succeed one another. Thus at Ogof Colomenod, in 1947, there were 24 females, and Davies observed a succession of 4 males within two months and a half. At Aber Mawr, for 12 females, 3 males succeeded one another within three weeks. On another beach (Ogof Thomas Williams) a single male, to the contrary, maintained a harem of 17 females for six weeks and was seen at least twice chasing away a possible rival. Mutual intolerance between males is therefore rather variable according to the case, and real fights are rare. Bertram rightly considers the gray seal to be a species in which polygamy and harem formation are dying out.

All the other species of seals, though mostly gregarious, seem to be sexually promiscuous, and they never form harems of females protected by a male proprietor.

GREGARIOUS UNGULATES. Gregariousness is extremely frequent in the various families of this vast group, and truly solitary species are the exception. The hyraxes or "conys," the elephants, the horse family, the hippopotami, many of the pig family, most of the Bovidæ, the giraffes, the guanacos, the vicunas, and a majority of the deer family live in groups. Unfortunately the social structure of these herds and its seasonal changes through the course of the year remain unknown in most cases, since but few of the species have been studied from this point of view.

In a good many species the males associate with one or several females only at the rutting period. When this is over, they abandon mate or harem and resume solitary life or else form herds made up of males only. The females and young go their way and form herds occupying a well-defined home range and "controlled" by a female leader. The young follow their mothers for a longer or shorter time according to the species, the young males generally departing just before puberty. These matriarchal associations are able to carry out co-ordinated activities, such as even mutual aid.[9]

The red deer is a good example of this type of society. Darling's observations, made in the Highlands of Scotland, have established the fact that in winter the companies of stags and the groups of hinds have separate and distinct home ranges. The range of the females is really their "home" and they have their young there. That of the males, on the other hand, appears for the most part to be merely a winter retreat. In no case are these home ranges defended against intrusion by other members of the species, and when circumstances are unfavorable several groups may even unite. Here, then, there is no question of true territorial behavior.

In summer the deer move up toward the mountaintops, and several herds that occupy separate home ranges in the winter may unite and graze together. The various groups nevertheless retain their independence.

In autumn, at the time of rut, the males enter the "territory" of the females and fight among themselves as they endeavor to establish their harems. At this time the males evidently dominate the females they have rounded up. But this dominance is real in the sexual sphere only, and in case of danger the females come together again in a compact group under its accustomed female leader, as before the harems were formed.

This annual cycle in itself accents the essential role of the female herds, and a deeper study of the facts only goes to confirm this first impression. Whereas the hind groups are organized and always have a leader of female sex and

[9] A striking instance is afforded by the Indian elephants that, according to Sauvel (*Terre et vie*, 1947, p. 29), transported a fatally wounded individual for about forty yards.

reproductive age, the stag companies are less coherent. The latter have no leader, although one individual may fight with the others. An animal may often spend the winter with one group and the summer with another, and the company may sometimes split into age groups. Solitary individuals are generally old, sick, or wounded animals, and it is probable also that some of them are unmated males.

A similar social organization is to be met with again in a good many species of Bovidæ (gaur, kouprey, banteng, ibex, tahr, chamois, Barbary sheep, etc.), in numerous Cervidæ, and apparently in the hippopotami and elephants.

In the American pronghorn the social group is organized as follows: At the end of spring and in the summer the herd consists typically of 1 male, 1 to 8 females, and 2 to 14 young; the "unemployed" males form a group by themselves. At the time of reproduction the females are assembled in harems and the young gather in special bands watched over (?) by an adult female. In winter the two sexes reunite in seasonal bands of 20 to 60 head to spend the cold part of the year together. At the beginning of spring the pregnant females go into temporary isolation to give birth to their young and rejoin the herd only toward the beginning of summer. In the Uganda kob males and females live together in an indiscriminate herd outside the rutting period, but during that period the males form temporary harems. In the Defassa waterbuck the polygynous family with a male leader seems stable throughout the year, and in Albert Park Hoier observed a single male with his harem occupying the same area from 1931 to 1939! Outside the period of rut several harems can live together peaceably.

Wild herds in the horse family (Equidæ), investigated by Antonius, by no means exhibit a uniform structure. Such African species as Burchell's zebra and related forms live in bands of varying size in which the two sexes are mingled indiscriminately except at the time of rut, when the pairs are briefly isolated. These assemblages appear to have no true leader. Grévy's zebra forms only small herds in which the stallions play no permanent or dominant part, and it is the same with the mountain zebra. The wild asses of Nubia and Somaliland form herds of females accompanied by their young and led by a female; the males join them only at the reproductive periods.[1] Among the Mongolian wild asses it is again the females that form the stable element in the herds; during rut the stallions take possession of 3 or 4 females with their foals and protect them against the advances of other males. The herds of wild horses that formerly existed, on the other hand, were to the best of our knowledge controlled and led by a dominant stallion. Thus we can observe again, in this one family, all the gradations between the loose and leaderless assemblages of the zebras, the matriarchal societies of the wild asses, and the patriarchal societies of the true horses.

THE SOCIAL MONKEYS AND APES. Here we find once more a great diversity of organization in social grouping. Some live as families occupying a definite territory, access to which is forbidden to neighboring groups. This is true of the lar gibbon, which is monogamous and forms permanent

[1] Among the Indian wild asses, the herds of females, accompanied by their young, live apart from the males for three months after giving birth.

family groups. Each group typically comprises the two parents, the young of the year, and a variable number of older but still immature individuals. These last are the young of preceding years, and as in this species only one offspring is born every two or three years, the cohesion of the family group would thus appear to be very powerful. Solitary individuals of one sex or the other are also to be met with. These must include not only subjects beyond the reproductive age, but also young individuals that have left their original family group at puberty and are trying to mate and found a new family.

Many species are polygamous and live the year round in troops made up of a variable number of harems. The sacred baboons and the yellow baboons live in bands that seem to be no more than aggregations of harems, each ruled by a dominant male. These males are constantly under the necessity of defending their positions against younger males that are endeavoring to rise in the social scale. Rhesus monkeys also live in harems in which a dominant male rules a variable number of receptive females accompanied by their young. Males that have been unable to set up a harem sometimes live as isolated individuals, but more often in groups. The langurs or common monkeys of India have the same social organization, and the troop defends its territory against rival groups. The same seems to be true of the guenons or common African monkeys, at least in some species. Redtail monkeys live in family groups consisting of 1 male, 1 or 2 females, and 1 or 2 young, or no young. The family party may include 1 or 2 "bachelor" males, but they have no social relationship with the females, though they may have homosexual contacts with other males. When feeding, several family groups may unite, and then separate for sleeping.

The howling monkeys of tropical America form true clans. The clan of the Panama howling monkeys typically comprises 3 adult males, 8 females, 3 dependent infants, and 4 juveniles. This group ranges over a common territory defended by voice and action against the inroads of neighboring clans. No definite hierarchy seems to exist among the males of one clan, and a single female may be covered by several of them in succession. The males of a clan co-operate in defending and leading it, but there is no one individual acting as a permanent leader. Solitary males are to be met with outside these clans, usually isolated, and such males are not old individuals, as a rule, but rather young ones that have left their original clans and are trying to join others.

The spider monkeys of Central America likewise form groups consisting on the average of 2 adult males, 4 females, 2 dependent infants, and 4 juveniles. In these societies the females appear to play a more active role than do the female howling monkeys, and they may take part on occasion in the defense of the group, always in subordination to the males. Unmated males live in bands and are not isolated.

We unfortunately have very little precise knowledge concerning the group structure of anthropoid apes living under natural conditions. In the chimpanzee and gorilla it appears that the typical group is made up of a dominant male, a certain number of less dominant males, and a larger number of females with their young, totaling perhaps 10 to

15 individuals.[2] Solitary males of these two species undoubtedly exist. Probably the orang-utan also forms similar societies. On the west coast of Sumatra Carpenter has, for example, observed a group made up of two adult females with their young and a large adult male.

It would be of great interest to know about the social behavior of the tarsier and the various lemurs, but so far our information on the life of these primitive forms in their natural environment is meager indeed. The tarsier does not seem to be a strictly solitary species. Wharton reports that in the Philippines four may sometimes be found in the same tree, and this hunter captured an adult male and a pregnant female together. The Indian slender loris is usually solitary, and at the most couples may be seen together. Much the same is true of four species of the tropical African galagoes or bush babies, but they are sometimes found during the day collected in sleeping groups and pressed closely together in a hollow tree or old squirrel's nest. On Madagascar the ring-tailed lemur is clearly gregarious, and Rand observed it always in bands of 4 to 15 individuals, the females carrying their babies or followed by their young. The same can be said of *Lemur fulvus*, *L. rubiventer* and the sifaka, though the bands of these species are smaller.

[2] For the gorilla of French Equatorial Africa Blancou gives the average constitution of the group as follows: 1 male leader, 4 adult females, and 8 to 10 immature young and juveniles.

# Mammals and Their
# Environment

MAMMALS are not mere automata functioning apart from their surroundings. Every one of them is more or less closely adapted to its habitat, and its presence, in turn, has repercussions upon the environment. This environment is, in fact, a living complex, the integration of a whole series of factors —climatic, edaphic (properties of the soil), biotic (fauna and flora), and even psychologic [1]—the effects of which combine to make up the specific environment of each animal.

One need not be a naturalist to realize that species are not distributed at random over the surface of the earth. It is wholly unlikely that chamois or Alpine marmots will be

[1] It is fully justifiable to take account of "psychological" factors, along with other factors of ecological and historical nature, in the study of the distribution of species. There is no lack of instances where climatic and biotic influences, taken alone, are insufficient to explain the selection of certain habitats, and it is with good reason that ornithologists appeal in such cases to "subjective" or "psychological" factors that still elude precise and complete analysis. The recent experiments made by Van. T. Harris at the University of Michigan clearly show that laboratory-bred deer mice do have an innate tendency to select particular kinds of objects in the environment. Each of the two subspecies under test exhibited a definite preference for the type of habitat normally occupied in nature.

encountered in western European plains, and there is an equally slight chance of finding moles in a sand dune or red squirrels in a beet field! Each major life zone is made up of a whole series of distinct habitats, and each one of the latter includes many different biotopes or ecological niches supporting a special fauna and flora made up of species that depend, directly or indirectly, upon one another and that compose a kind of community of organisms—a biocœnose —having its own metabolism and undergoing its own evolution.

The ecological requirements of a species are what cause it to inhabit a particular environment. Sometimes these are very strict and sometimes they are not so stringent, and in consequence some species will be highly specialized and others relatively unspecialized; but all have played and are still playing an important part in the evolution of living mammals.

In this chapter we shall go on to examine some aspects of these interactions between organism and environment, never losing sight of the fact that in this field, possibly more than in any other, what we know is only an infinitely small part of what would be important for us to know.

### CLIMATIC FACTORS

CLIMATIC factors come first to mind when we try to understand the peculiarities of the geographical distribution of species. But we soon realize that the climates of the meteorologists are wholly inadequate alone to account for the preference many mammals show for some particular habitat. What are certainly much more important for most living creatures than regional climates, based on annual averages from many localities, are the local *micro-climates* of the various biotopes or ecological niches. For a forest rodent, to take an example, what count are temperature, humidity, and light at ground level and beneath the plant cover, and not the atmospheric conditions in a meteorological shelter six feet above open grassland. And the differences between them are far from slight! The micro-climate in our temperate forests is on the whole even more moderate than that of the open air. The extremes of temperature and humidity are not so great, and the average temperature is lower than outside, the average humidity higher; air currents are very slight, and there is less light. Furthermore, considerable differences exist among the various levels or strata within the forest. The micro-climate of even an ordinary cultivated field is very different from the macro-climate of the region that includes it. As for burrows and soil cavities, they have a climate very much their own, and we have already seen that this peculiarity plays an essential part in the life of small desert mammals.

TEMPERATURE. The great majority of mammals being homoiothermal or "warm-blooded"—that is, animals that can keep their inner or body temperature constant—one might suppose that the temperature of their surroundings is but a secondary factor in their ecology.

It is true enough that many species originating in warm countries easily bear in captivity temperatures much lower than those of their native countries, but this is not to say that these species can live and prosper as well in our climate as at home. It is absolutely necessary for the ecologist to distinguish carefully between *lethal* and *optimal* temperatures. Here are some examples: Among laboratory animals the lower critical temperature [2] is −15° C. for the guinea pig, −25° C. for the white rat, −45° C. for the rabbit, and −160° C. for the dog (Giaja). The upper critical temperature, more easily reached than the lower, is +40° C. in dry air for the white rat and +49° C. for the dog (Adolph). Inside these limits the inner body temperature remains nearly constant whatever that of the surroundings may be; a variation, say, of 12° C. in the latter changing the internal temperature of a mouse by not more than 0.4 of a degree.[3] But within this range of homoiothermic regulation there is for each species a *thermic optimum* that is alone compatible with the normal course of the life cycle. If we compare the growth of genetically identical white mice, some raised at optimum temperature (21°–3° C.) and others at a higher temperature (32° C.)—all conditions being otherwise equal

[2] The term "critical" is applied to temperatures beyond which the temperature regulation of the organism breaks down.

[3] It should be said, however, that on the whole arctic mammals resist cold better than tropical species and indeed show remarkable endurance. The polar foxes of Greenland, for instance, are able to live in the depth of winter on the icecap. Several were seen during the winter of 1950–1 (September to March) around the Central Ice Cap Research Station of the French Polar Expeditions (70°54′N; 40°42′W), at an altitude of 9,000 feet and more than 280 miles from the nearest ice-free land, with the thermometer ranging below −50° C.; during blizzards the animals took shelter in burrows dug in the snow. Ernst Sorge, a member of the Wegener Expedition, made similar observations at "Eismitte," from the 4th to the 22nd of October, in temperatures reaching −52° C. Scholander and his co-workers failed to reach the lower critical temperature for polar foxes subjected experimentally to cold as extreme as −80° C.! The zone of thermoneutrality in these animals is thus very broad, enabling them to endure excessively low temperatures, at least temporarily.

What accounts for this remarkable resistance to cold? The investigators just mentioned have clearly shown that there is no metabolic adjustment to cold in these species and that the phylogenic adaptation to cold or hot climate has taken place only through factors that regulate the heat dissipation, notably the fur and skin insulation. The ability of limbs and feet to get along with little heat supplied from the central body mass is remarkable indeed.

—we find that the growth of the second group is clearly retarded, sexual maturity comes later, and fertility is lower. The second generation will be almost completely infertile, and, furthermore, all animals raised at 32° are more subject to infections than those raised at 21°–3° C. (Mills). Herter made a study of the "thermotactic optimum" for rodents, and even showed that it is almost constant for a given stock because it is hereditary, being transmitted as a dominant character. These optimum temperatures are more important for the ecologist than are the extremes that may be borne temporarily by adults but in any case do not permit the species to thrive and multiply.[4]

Some mammals are but imperfectly homoiothermic and quite unable to carry on their normal activities when the temperature is too low. These are the monotremes, the sloths, and the bats.[5] The duckbilled platypus and the echidna (monotremes) have an inner temperature that varies slowly with the surrounding temperature. According to Martin as cited by Giaja, the body temperature of an echidna rises 4 to 6 degrees when the outer temperature goes from 5° to 30° C. The internal temperature of the South and Central American three-toed sloth, normally about 32° C., falls to 20° C. when that of the surroundings drops to 10 or 15° C. (Britton and Atkinson). This hypothermy is reversible and is accompanied by a state of torpor

[4] The problem of acclimatizing cattle from temperate regions in the tropics raises questions of great interest from this point of view. The various races are not all alike in this respect, and the underlying causes of these differences are by no means fully understood. For a general review of these matters see Dordick, *Acta Tropica*, Vol. 6, 1949, pp. 221–45.

[5] Certain marsupials and armadillos should probably be added to this list.

that may last for hours. Inversely, mere exposure to the sun at 30–40° C. induces a hyperthermy of 40° C. that is quickly fatal. In consequence the sloth family is physiologically restricted to a limited equatorial habitat of very constant temperature. In the bats the internal temperature of the small species normally varies between 34.4 and 40.6° C., according to the degree of wakefulness (Eisentraut), but this temperature falls very rapidly when the animal is at rest and tends to approach the outer temperature. In regions where the winters are cold, bats must therefore migrate or take refuge in caves, attics, or other enclosed places for hibernation.

There has been much debate about the effects produced by environmental temperatures upon certain morphological characteristics, but in some cases the existence of these relations seems to admit of no doubt. Thus it is with the pigmentation of the fur in Himalayan rabbits, which afford a good example of the interaction of genes and environment in the production of the external characteristics of an animal. In this race of rabbits there is certainly a special genetic color factor that exercises its inhibiting effect on coloration only at certain temperatures; cold prevents it from showing its effect, and the result is a peculiar coat color in adults: wholly white except for the tips of the limbs, the ears, and the muzzle, which are pigmented. This pigmentation of the extremities is probably to be explained by the fact that their temperature is lower than that of the rest of the body. If, indeed, a part of the white fur of an adult is shaved off and the animal is kept at a cold temperature during the regrowth of the hair, a pigmented area will develop. Similarly, the young often show a slight general pigmentation of their first fur as a result of the cooling of the nest during the winter.

In this connection it has long been noted, when related forms of the same species inhabiting different climates are compared, that those in cold regions are usually larger than those in warm regions. This seems rather generally true of the vertebrates and is often referred to as Bergmann's law. This law, however, is far from being absolute, and we even know of animals (such as the raccoons) in which the size of different forms becomes smaller as the latitude inhabited by them becomes higher. Stein has recently shown that the size of the European mole decreases with the altitude; a difference in altitude of only 450 yards can entail an appreciable difference in size. In Central Europe, east of the isotherm of $-8°$ C. in January, the large race is replaced by a smaller one. None the less Bergmann's law is valid for many mammals, and it may be verified even within the compass of a single species. In England, for example, house mice living in cold storage plants where the temperature never rises above $-10°$ C. are always much larger than mice of the same species inhabiting houses or wheat stacks (Laurie); a female has been taken in the cold habitat which weighed 40 grams, whereas 30 grams is the maximum for the others. Again, it has been noted that the species of cold regions show a tendency toward shortening of the extremities (Allen's law); feet, tail, and ears are seen to decrease in length as the observer goes northward. The classical instance of this tendency is furnished by the North American hares and rabbits of the genus *Lepus:* the ears of the antelope jackrabbit, living in Arizona, are much longer than those of the more northern snowshoe hare and still more markedly so than those of the arctic hare, living in the far north. The North American foxes show the same tendency.

The most generally accepted explanation of these facts is that the increase in size involves a relative decrease in surface area, which reduces heat loss and aids in maintaining homoiothermy. This explanation is based on experimental evidence. It has been shown that if white rats of homozygous stock are raised, at a high temperature (31 to 33.5° C.), each animal will have in two or three months a longer tail, a more developed scrotum, and less weight than those kept at 15 to 20° C. It is also true that rabbits raised at a high temperature have ears longer than normal (Mills). All this promotes the dissipation of heat.

WATER. In all its forms—gaseous, liquid, or even solid —this element plays an important part in mammalian ecology. This is not surprising, for water is by weight the most important constituent of living matter and the constant movement of water within the organism is a fundamental physiological mechanism.

For land mammals water is first of all an essential element in metabolism. But as regards ecology, the main point is that the various groups do not all have the same requirements, and, what is more, that these requirements can be satisfied in very different ways.

Some mammals drink a great deal and in consequence are practically restricted to habitats that provide free water in sufficient quantity. Many African herbivores, for instance, regularly visit water holes or other sources each day at a fixed hour, often coming from considerable distances.

Other animals, in the absence of a temporary or permanent water supply, drink dew or water running down tree trunks or foliage after a rain. There are still more numerous species that can do without free water for longer or shorter periods, finding enough for their needs in the water content of their animal or vegetable food. This is true of many ungulates, rabbits and their relatives, carnivores, and insectivores. On the other hand certain groups—especially among the rodents—can subsist indefinitely and reproduce on a diet of seeds and other almost anhydrous or waterless plant foods. As is to be expected, these groups are predominant in all the desert regions of the Old and New Worlds. The pocket mice and kangaroo rats of the southwestern United States, for instance, are quite able to live exclusively on seeds that have a water content not exceeding 5 to 10 per cent. On this diet they not only fail to lose weight but even grow normally fat. Under the same conditions the white rat rapidly loses 40 to 50 per cent of its weight and is unable to survive in the end. The pocket mice and kangaroo rats have no reserves of water in their tissues, but they excrete urine twice as concentrated as that of other rodents, which makes for a considerable economy in the use of water (Schmidt-Nielsen). This may be called a true physiological adaptation to desert conditions, but it would be risky to generalize on this basis concerning all the other desert small mammals. The southwestern white-throated wood rat, also native to the desert zones, is able to live in such an environment only because of a special peculiarity in its diet. This rodent cannot subsist on anhydrous seeds alone, but it finds the water it needs in the cactus and other succulent plants that compose up to 44 per cent of its food.

*Atmospheric humidity* is another important ecological factor, particularly for certain species. The small bats, for example, can live only in rather humid air. If the European species are kept in captivity without food or water and with the humidity below 85 per cent, they die in a day or two with their wing membranes partially desiccated. But if the humidity is high, the same species can survive a fast of 30 to 40 days (Nerincx). In the caves used for hibernation the relative humidity is always very high, 75 to 98 per cent. Some insectivores, in particular the moles, also require dampness. Outside their always very humid burrows moles do not live long in a dry atmosphere; in nature they may be forced by prolonged dry spells to emerge from their burrows, and that is quickly fatal.

Variations in relative humidity also affect behavior: the red deer, for example, is extremely sensitive to variations in atmospheric humidity. Although rain has no definite influence on the movements of a herd of deer, a very humid atmosphere reduces travel from place to place, whereas a dry atmosphere has the opposite effect. This is interpreted by Darling as owing to the fact that a warm and humid atmosphere favors the transmission of various scents and is necessary for the proper functioning of the olfactory apparatus. The California ground squirrel retires to its burrow if the humidity of the air is too low or too high (Linsdale). The fact is that a certain optimum humidity is required by all the rodents, and it is noteworthy that whenever the relative humidity is measured inside burrows, a rather high and almost constant figure is obtained.

There are some morphological peculiarities which have been attributed to atmospheric humidity. It is, in fact, rather commonly true that in a group of related forms the coat color darkens as the humidity of the habitat increases; this has been noted in North American insectivores (certain moles), rodents (lemmings), and carnivores. It may be that the enlargement of the tympanic bullæ (rounded projections below the ears) of desert mammals is also correlated with the dryness of the habitat (Heim de Balsac). The cavities of these bullæ are said to contain air of very high humidity, which may check dehydration of the middle ear and the fluid it contains, but this suggestion has still to be investigated experimentally. The occurrence of enlarged bullæ in some marine Cetacea does not accord well with this idea, and in some cases at least the bullæ could act as resonators, facilitating the perception of vibrations in soil or water.

Snow and ice constitute an important and complex ecological factor for mammals living in cold regions. When the winter snow reaches a certain depth, it seriously interferes with the feeding of herbivores and impedes the locomotion of even the largest species. But, on the other hand, it is a poor conductor of heat, and this property helps many species in their struggle to survive low atmospheric temperatures. Arctic hares often let themselves be covered by falling snow and in this way find shelter from the cold. In Siberia there are voles which dig their burrows under deep snow and succeed in remaining active all winter and breeding under these conditions (Formosov). In summer the coolness of glacier snow attracts certain ungulates and hares that come to the locality to get relief from the biting insects that swarm at that season on the tundras.

All the direct or indirect effects of water which we have just been reviewing are, in brief, dependent under natural conditions upon the annual rainfall. It is not surprising, therefore, that certain isohyetal lines (indicating equal precipitation) should coincide with the distributional limits of certain forms of animal life. In the Mediterranean region of the Old World the isohyetal line 200 marks a threshold that warm-blooded desert vertebrates scarcely cross and beyond which to the southward Berber or North African components of the fauna cannot live (Heim de Balsac). In east European Russia the distributional limit of the wild boar corresponds approximately with the limit of winter snow cover 20 to 30 inches deep (Formosov). Further detailed study of mammalian ecology will doubtless bring to light more data of this kind.

As for the aquatic mammals, we are but poorly informed about their tolerance of varying physico-chemical characteristics of the water in which they live, but it is probably rather wide. We do know that the manatee lives equally well in fresh, brackish, and salt water, and that seals in captivity do very well in river water. Along the coasts of Europe the common seal lives in salt water as well as in brackish water (Baie de Somme), and it may even ascend rivers.[6] On the other hand, the European otter, primarily a fresh water species, readily enters salt water in search of fish, as has been observed in Scandinavia, Scotland, Brittany (Sept Iles), and even Morocco.

LIGHT. This factor, still little studied, affects the ecol-

---

[6] In Canada a local subspecies (*Phoca vitulina mellonæ*) of the common seal even lives in a fresh water lake in Ungava (New Quebec), known as Seal Lake; it has probably been evolving there, landlocked, since the last Glacial Period; that is, for about 5,500 years (Doutt, *Ann. Carnegie Museum*, Vol. 29, 1943, pp. 61–125). Two distinct forms of the ringed seal inhabit the fresh water lakes Ladoga and Saina in Finland. A well-marked species of seal (*Phoca sibirica*) is found in Lake Baikal.

ogy of mammals in many ways. Daily variations in light intensity are fundamental to the nycthemeral or day-and-night rhythm of most species. Diurnal mammals become active at sunrise or sometimes a little before, as do Godet moles (fig. 92). Their activities go on all day and come to an end

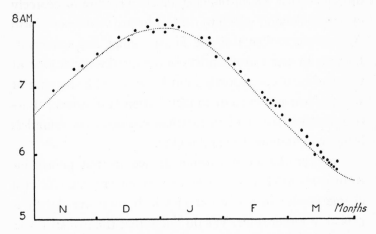

FIG. 92: *Variations in the time at which daily activity begins for the European mole, from November to March, in the vicinity of Rennes, Brittany. Time of sunrise is indicated by the dotted curve. After Godet.*

at twilight. The California ground squirrel will serve as another example. From June to August in Hastings Reserve (California) the squirrels emerge from their burrows between 5.40 and 6 a.m. They carry on their various activities all day long, with maximum intensity always around 8 or 9 a.m. and 4 p.m. They go back underground between 6.40 and 7.30 p.m. These data represent only an average, of course, for other factors, especially temperature and humidity, may modify this timetable. In January the few that do not hibernate come out toward noon to warm themselves in the sun, returning to their burrows by five o'clock at the latest. The strong propensity for sunbathing shown by this species, even in very warm weather, is explained by Linsdale as a method for getting rid of ectoparasites. Twilight and nocturnal species have a contrasting rhythm of activity. The European badger, for example, carefully studied by Neal, does not emerge from its burrow until after sundown, and the time of emergence in summer is later than in autumn or spring. Other factors, such as temperature and periods of full moon, may cause slight variations in this rhythm, but intensity of sunlight remains dominant.

Variations during the month in the intensity of light at night must probably be taken into account, at least in connection with strictly nocturnal species. Harrison observed in the giant forest rat of Malaysia, for example, that the rate of pregnancy showed a bimonthly rhythm that appeared to be in phase with the moon, and which suggested that the greatest number of conceptions occurred near the time of the full moon. Nothing of the kind is found in diurnal rodents of the same region, and Harrison believes that the onset of the period of bright moonlight near the time of full moon has some stimulating effect on conception.

*Variation through the year* in the length of the days may be even more important, and its effect upon the reproductive period and the molting cycle has already been proved, at least in certain species.

Artificial lengthening of the day can cause the gonads to mature out of season in some mammals. The experiment was performed by Bissonnette on the ferret, from October to March, and he observed an increase in the size of the testes during this period, which is normally the time of testicular involution. Spermatozoa were produced by the experimental animals three months earlier than would ordinarily be the case. In the field vole reduction of the photoperiod from 15 to 9 hours prevents normal reproduction (Baker and Ranson). But many mammals reproduce in the fall rather than in the spring; that is, at a time when the length of day or photoperiod is decreasing regularly. Now, it appears that these species also can react to an experimental change in the photoperiod, and Bissonnette has been able to show that in the goat an artificial reduction in length of day stimulates reproductive activity, whereas an increase is inhibitory. Other evidence in favor of the importance of variation in the length of daily illumination is afforded by the change in the reproductive period experienced by species native to the Northern Hemisphere which are transferred to ecologically comparable regions in the Southern Hemisphere. In Scotland the stag has its rutting period in September and October, but in New Zealand this occurs in March and April; that is, in the austral autumn. The American gray squirrel, introduced into South Africa by Rhodes around 1904, reproduces there in the austral spring and summer (October to January), whereas in North America and in England the reproductive period of the species is from January to July. Factors other than light must be concerned in tropical species, for a seasonal rhythm of testicular activity clearly exists in some forms, such as the flying foxes (*Pteropus*), despite the uniform length of the day in low latitudes.

The influence of variations in the photoperiod on the molting cycle appears equally probable, for certain species at least. This has been discussed above (page 125), and here

Adult long-eared bat. Photograph by Ernst Krause. Courtesy of Dr. M. Eisentraut.

Young long-eared bat three days old. Compare the ears and the front limbs with those of the adult in the next picture. Photograph by Ernst Krause. Courtesy of Dr. M. Eisentraut.

*A harem of Alaska fur seals, Pribilof Islands.*
*Note the male, the pregnant females, and the few young.*
*Photography by Dr. Arétas.*

we shall only call attention to a few pertinent experiments. Artificial reduction of the photoperiod has been known to bring on an out-of-season molt in two North American Mustelidæ, the Bonaparte weasel and the long-tailed weasel. In the first species the white winter coat followed the brown summer pelage, whereas in the second a light-brown coat spotted with white on the feet was obtained. Artificial lengthening of the day also induced molting in these two species, with a return to the summer coloration. Yet there is great variability from one animal to another in this respect (Bissonnette and Bailey). In the snowshoe hare Lyman has been able to prevent the appearance of the white coat in autumn by exposing the animals to artificial light for 18 hours per day; the same treatment, given in January to animals in winter white, resulted in the appearance of the brown summer coat. It is even possible to keep the hares in dark fur the year round, if the photoperiod is held constantly at 18 hours; but if the illumination is reduced to 9 hours a day, the change to white fur occurs, even when the temperature remains at 21° C.! All these results, along with those of Novikov and Blagodatskaia on the Siberian varying hare (see page 126), are proof of the influence of variations in the daily photoperiod upon the molting cycle, but some species seem to be more sensitive to such changes than others.

ALTITUDE. A good deal is known about the physiological changes produced by altitude (and particularly by artificial reduction in barometric pressure) on man, the dog, and the laboratory rodents. Undoubtedly one of the most important is the increase in the number of red corpuscles in the circulating blood, which adapts the organism to the reduced oxygen pressure that makes all effort distressing to man at high altitudes.

Now, there exist in mountainous regions, and especially on the high plateaus of the Andes and of Central Asia, a number of mammalian species that appear to be remarkably well adapted to these habitats, peculiar as they are. On this account the physiology of these animals is of very special interest, and it seems odd that so few works have been devoted to them.

In 1936 Hall, Dill, and Barron published some observations they made in the Andes on three typical mammals of high altitudes, the llama, the vicuna, and the vizcacha. The first has been domesticated and used as a beast of burden by the natives for thousands of years. The second is a wild species, capable of running at a speed of 30 miles an hour at an altitude of more than 15,000 feet, which these physiologists were privileged to study. Their observations were made on a very tame individual that had been in captivity for some time. As for the vizcachas, the individuals used as standard samples had been captured at an altitude of 12,000 feet.

The researches of Hall and his associates showed that the hemoglobin of these three species has a much greater affinity for oxygen (oxygen capacity) than the hemoglobin in rabbit and sheep blood. This peculiar character, an important advantage for life at high altitudes, would seem to be *hereditary*, since these same authors have also found it in four llamas in the Boston Zoo, three of which were born in that city and the fourth in Hamburg! Furthermore, if we make a comparative study in the sheep and llama of the variation with altitude in the number of red corpuscles per cubic millimeter of blood, we find a great difference between the mammal of the plain and the mammal of the mountain. In the sheep there are 10,530,000 red blood corpuscles per cubic millimeter at sea level and 16,000,000 at 16,050 feet, whereas practically no variation is observable in the llama (11,430,000 at sea level and 11,100,000 at 16,050 feet).

Is this lack of variation in corpuscle number with altitude in mountain species a fact of general application? It is still too soon to say with certainty, but in support of such a view must be counted Kalabuchov's observation when he transferred to Moscow (altitude 490 feet) twelve long-tailed field mice caught at 5,200 feet in the Caucasus. After seven months at the lower altitude their red-cell count per cubic millimeter had not changed materially, continuing to register between 9,500,000 and 10,600,000.

### EDAPHIC FACTORS

THE nature of the soil affects the distribution of mammals in two ways: indirectly, through vegetation whose characteristics depend in large measure upon soil differences, and directly, where fossorial species that spend most of their lives under ground are concerned. We shall mention here only a few examples of the second, or direct, type of soil influence, which has so far been studied only incidentally.

Subterranean rodents and insectivores do not live indiscriminately in any kind of soil, and the difficulties encountered in keeping them in captivity are not all concerned with feeding. They must have proper soil, and the texture of the soil, directly affecting its water and gas content, is possibly more important than its chemical composition.

The observations of Schaerffenberg and of Godet demonstrate the importance of soil aeration in the case of the European mole. This animal cannot live long in captivity if it is confined in wooden boxes containing earth, but it can be kept alive for months if cages of metal screen are used or if the wooden cages are liberally perforated on all sides and filled with fibers of wood. Godet even believes that to provide good aeration is the essential function of the complex system of concentric galleries surrounding the nest. In nature this species invades various biotopes, but a hard and stony soil stops it. Pavlinine's recent marking experiments have shown, for example, that railroad ballast is for this animal a more difficult obstacle to pass than is a stream of water.

Another significant soil factor is humidity. Common voles in France commonly favor clayey, calcareous soils, neither too light nor too heavy and above all not too moist. The Sierra pocket gophers marked by Ingles lived during the summer in meadows where the water table was more than 4.3 feet below ground, exploring the more humid zones only when their nests happened to be located near-by in dryer soil. On the approach of winter the gophers migrated to better-drained land that did not freeze and thus allowed the animals to continue their activities during the less favorable season; the following spring they returned to the meadows. Thus the species carefully avoids damp soils, and a strip of wet ground, even though a narrow one, may form an impassable barrier.

Even for ungulates the soil may constitute an important factor in limiting their geographical distribution. Essential minerals may be insufficient or lacking altogether in some soils, with the result that deficiency diseases cause the rarity or even the extinction of particular species in certain localities. Domesticated cattle furnish good examples of this. When the soil of the region where they are raised is too poor in phosphoric acid and calcium phosphate, disorders due to phosphoric deficiency appear (called aphosphorose), indicated by such symptoms as perversion of the appetite with tendencies toward bone eating, abnormalities in gait, broken bones that are spontaneous or caused by the slightest impact, sexual apathy and disturbances of the œstrus cycle, and so on. Raising stock is practicable in such regions only if the phosphorus content of the soil is artificially increased.

### BIOTIC FACTORS

THE relations of mammals with the living environment —the fauna and flora of their habitats—are multifarious; some are secondary, others of dominant influence, but all deserve close study, for they bring us into direct contact with the complex interrelations between the animal and its animal and plant environment.

PHYTOBIOTIC FACTORS. Plants may influence the distribution of mammals in many ways. Species with highly specialized diets cannot occur at all in a given locality unless the particular plants they eat grow there. Koalas without eucalyptus trees are inconceivable, as are giant pandas without bamboo. But we have seen that narrowly specialized diets are the exception, and so, for most mammals, the relations with the plant environment are more complex.

In some cases trees are practically indispensable, if only

for locomotion. Sloths find it extremely difficult to travel on the ground, and many monkeys and apes are truly at home only among the branches of trees.[7] The same can be said of the European red squirrel, whose existence is closely bound up with that of trees, and this is true of many other tree-dwelling rodents.

More important in many instances is plant cover. Here what the animal seeks primarily is a type of vegetation—whose precise composition may be a matter of comparative indifference—that affords a certain microclimate and some degree of solitude. Cover is certainly important for many small mammals, and it probably is for many ungulates, however varied their diets. Hediger lays emphasis on the fact that many of them retire to chew the cud in some sheltered retreat where they habitually spend a part of each day.

It would be foolish to try to treat this subject too systematically in the present state of our knowledge. What is unquestioned is that we often observe the presence of a species in a given plant formation, and its disappearance when that formation changes, quite apart from any human intervention. Hubert's study of changes in the fauna of large mammals on the plain south of Lake Edward (in the Belgian Congo) since it was made a part of Albert National Park provides an excellent example. Two thirds of this plain of 1,200 square kilometers consists of a savanna of low grasses, geographically and ecologically isolated on all sides. It forms a kind of cut-off, terminal portion of the distributional area proper to the savanna species; in particular, the topi, the Uganda kob, and the reedbuck. These antelopes

[7] Examples are common among the primates, and Hediger bases interesting deductions on them with reference to keeping such animals in captivity.

probably reached this area from the east by way of the narrow passage between Lake George and the Ankola Mountains, a passage now closed by forest growth. The isolation of this enclosed savanna area is completed by the vast Congo forest on the west, the mountains on the south, and Lake Edward on the north. In 1931 this enclosed plain supported a population of large mammals, whose density by species was about as follows:

*Topis*   10,000 head, or 12 per sq. km.[8] of low-grass savanna
*Kobs*   15,000 head, or 24 per sq. km. of low-grass savanna
*Reedbucks*   1,000 head, or 2 per sq. km. of low-grass savanna
*Defassa waterbucks*   1,000 head, or 1 per sq. km. of the whole plain
*Bushbucks*   1,000 head, or 1 per sq. km. of the whole plain
*Wart hogs*   1,000 head, or 1 per sq. km. of the whole plain
*Lions*   250 head, or 1 per 5 sq. km. of the whole plain
*Spotted hyenas*   300 head, or 1 per 4 sq. km. of the whole plain
*Leopards*   100 head, or 1 per 12 sq. km. of the whole plain
*Hippopotami*   4,000 head, or 3 per sq. km. of marshes, high grasses, and forest galleries
*Cape buffalos*   2,000 head, or 3 per 2 sq. km. of marshes, high grasses, and forest galleries
*Giant forest hogs*   200 head, or 1 per 6 sq. km. of marshes, high grasses, and forest galleries
*Elephants*   150 head, or 1 per 8 sq. km. of marshes, high grasses, and forest galleries

In 1932–3 clouds of grasshoppers descended on the plain, denuding the grazing-grounds and covering the surface of streams and ponds with a floating carpet of decaying insects (with the result that much river life was killed; at one time 12 hippopotamus bodies were seen floating in Rutshuru River!). In 1932 cattle-pest raged and killed 500 to 600 buffalo and many wart hogs, without affecting the antelopes. And finally, since the land was made part of the

[8] One square kilometer equals about 38/100 of a square mile.

reservation the customary seasonal brush fires were forbidden and only those occurred which were set by lightning.

All this entailed a rapid change in the vegetation of the plain, and its effects on the fauna of large mammals soon became evident. Observers noted a large decrease in the numbers of antelopes and members of the pig family (1,200 topis in 1940 replacing 10,000 in 1931, 3,000 kobs replacing 15,000, and so on) and a corresponding decrease in carnivores (lions, hyenas, hunting dogs). On the other hand the number of elephants and hippopotami increased considerably (500 elephants and 6,000 hippopotami in 1940), while the buffalos remained unchanged. Hubert has no doubt that the changes in vegetation were the primary cause of these faunistic changes; the abolition of brush fires would appear to have been especially important. The effect of these fires is to favor the growth of a tender grass that many herbivores are fond of; moreover, when the periodical fires are abolished, the natural grazing-grounds are taken over by thickets of scrub growth, and plains species have to give way to animals of the bush. In further support of his thesis, Hubert calls attention to the observations made at Tanganyika by Swynnerton during a "no burning" experiment. Here it was found that the impala antelopes were the first herbivores, four years later, to desert completely the experimental "block" in which the grasses had not been burned over. Later on, as the change in vegetation proceeded toward its climax (dense bush), other species gradually left the region—first the roan antelopes and the giraffes, then the elands. The topis and Thomson's gazelles, very numerous on the neighboring plains that were burned over annually as before, did not enter the plain where burning was prohibited. Cape buffalos and elephants, on the contrary, continued to be very much at home there.

These examples show how the fauna of a region changes when the vegetation is modified, and they clearly illustrate the close interdependence of all the elements of the biocœnose, or biotic community. For the decrease in herbivorous mammals entails not only that of the carnivores that prey on them but also, for example, that of the many dung-feeding insects whose life cycle centers in the bulky droppings of the ungulates.[9] Breaking an important link in this great chain of interactions may thus have far-reaching consequences upon the fauna of a whole region.

The mammals play an essential part, furthermore, in the support and evolution of certain plant formations. In England Summerhayes has investigated the changes in natural vegetation brought about through the agency of the field vole. In this research he compared, between 1932 and 1939, the vegetation of control plots with that of others enclosed with fine wire netting that extended 20 inches below the surface so as to prevent voles from entering at all. The results were clear; absence of the animals favored the dominant plant species, increased their vigor, and was accompanied by an almost complete disappearance of mosses. In this particular case, therefore, the activities of the rodents promoted the existence of a larger number of plant species,

[9] Some of these insect species may even disappear. In France a dung beetle, *Aphodius cervorum*, lives in red deer droppings, and this species vanished from the forest of Saint-Germain along with the deer. In the forest of Fontainebleau the decrease in the deer population made this species of *Aphodius* turn to rabbit dung. Will it be able in this way to survive the complete disappearance of the deer?

especially the less dominant ones. Formosov, again, emphasizes the essential role played by mammals in the evolution of the Eurasian steppes. Fossorial or digging rodents, such as the boback marmot and the little souslik, work over enormous quantities of earth, bringing it from depths of as much as 15 feet to the surface where it forms numerous mounds. This earth is quite different in composition from the surface soil. It is richer in mineral salts but is poorer in humus and it is less alkaline, and on it springs up a special vegetation somewhat like that of deserts, which persists until the soil of the mounds has gradually become like the adjoining soil. The xerophytic plants then colonize newly built mounds, and so the cycle continues. In this case the rodents exert a clearly conservative influence, retarding the natural succession of plant formations.

In general the rodents of fossorial habits have a considerable effect, in some regions, upon the evolution of soils. Grinnell has attempted to estimate the amount of earth brought to the surface each year by the pocket gophers of Yosemite National Park, in California, and he arrives at a figure of about 8 tons per acre. Again, Ellison gives an average of 5 tons per acre for the northern pocket gopher in Utah. Formosov also gives large figures for the little souslik of the steppes between the Don and the Volga, estimating the amount of earth collected in mounds on the surface at 100,000 cubic yards per square mile! This means that a very considerable mixing and aeration of the soils has been accomplished. But it all implies some danger to the soils concerned, for under certain conditions such extensive undermining promotes the erosion that sometimes alters the biotope radically.

ZOOBIOTIC FACTORS. We have already referred in passing to the relations between animal species living in the
same habitat. And in the next chapter we shall discuss the
interrelations between predators and their prey (lynx and
snowshoe hare, carnivores and ungulates, etc.), as well as
the influence of certain pathogenic organisms on the dynamics of wild populations. We shall therefore do no more
here than give some information on the ecological importance of certain blood-sucking insects, on the problem of
symbiosis or commensalism, and on the question of interspecific competition.

The blood-sucking insects, in particular the Diptera
or two-winged flies, play a very considerable part in the
ecology of the ungulates. In analyzing the behavior of red
deer in Scotland, Darling lays stress on the role of the
Tabanidæ (horseflies and deerflies) as a determining factor
in certain seasonal movements. The most dreaded fly
(*Hæmatopota pluvialis*) is especially active in bright sunlight on calm, warm days, with maximum activity between
the hours of ten and four; this is when it attacks the deer,
covering them with bites on face and feet (Darling counted
the bites at an average rate of 30 per minute!). These bites
are so painful that the deer leave the lowlands and ascend to
higher levels in late June, when the flies begin to appear in
numbers. Sdobnikov studied the reindeer living at large on
the tundras of arctic Russia, and he, too, emphasizes the
ecological importance of the Diptera, represented in his case
by 9 species of Tabanidæ, 4 Culicidæ (mosquitoes), and
some Simuliidæ (black flies); the last are especially partial
to the blood-filled young horns of the animals, and when
the flies are numerous the horns fail to attain normal size and

may even become deformed. Two endoparasitic flies, *Cephenomyia nasalis* and *Œdemagena tarandi*, are also important in reindeer ecology, especially the first, whose larvæ (sometimes numbering a thousand in a single animal!) may bring the host to exhaustion. Several observers in the American Arctic regard mosquito attacks as the determining factor that starts the caribou migrations; this, however, is a doubtful matter.

The blood-sucking Diptera are important for ungulate ecology in regions other than the cold North. As is well known, the African tse-tse fly, carrier of certain protozoan blood-parasites (trypanosomes) that cause animal disease, can prevent the breeding of large mammals in some localities and thus directly modify the habitat in general. Thomas mentions certain parts of Uganda, for example, where the densely populated pasturage was beginning to show the effects of overgrazing and erosion. After the decimation of the cattle by trypanosomiasis, the vegetation recovered and in three years the grass grew a yard high. In the valley of the Kidepo River, along the boundary between the Sudan and Uganda, the stratum of herbaceous plants reached a height of six feet some years after a similar epidemic. Such an alteration of the habitat has, of course, a direct effect on the composition of the fauna with respect to small mammals as well as large ones.

The detailed study of the reciprocal relations between certain species for mutual benefit (called mutualism, symbiosis, or commensalism) should be worth undertaking. But in any case the association of cattle egrets and oxpeckers with the larger ungulates, wild and domesticated, is an established fact. Verheyen has actually seen antelopes, when visited by oxpeckers, stand still, slightly separate their legs, and elevate their tails as if to facilitate the work of these birds.[1] Percival reports that when a rhinoceros is asleep, it is easy to approach it if no oxpeckers are on it but difficult if the birds are there. He adds that they would give the alarm when perched on a rhinoceros but not when they were doing their pecking on cattle. The well-known British ornithologist Moreau, who made a special study of the redbilled oxpecker in East Africa, feels that it is perfectly justifiable in this case to speak of symbiosis.

Another curious case of commensalism is the association, in tropical Africa, of the ratel or honey badger and a bird, the honey guide (*Indicator indicator*). These two vertebrates gain appreciable benefit from their common exploitation of wild bee nests, and Verheyen has recently stated precisely how their association works. The honey guides have the habit of uttering a series of characteristic calls when in the presence of any mammal, even a man; if a ratel hears these calls, it follows the bird and soon discovers the bee tree. What is most remarkable is that the ratel seems evidently capable of evoking the bird's calls by putting itself in plain sight of the bird and whistling softly. But the whole procedure cannot be considered obligatory, for in India the honey badger is quite capable of locating wild bee nests without the aid of a honey guide.

The association between the hippopotamus and a fish (*Labeo velifer*) that nibbles at the abundant organic detritus on the amphibious mammal's hide is not unlike the associa-

---

[1] The tendency of cattle egrets (*Bubulcus*) to associate themselves with mammals is so strong that Hediger reports seeing them perch, in captivity, on South American capybaras, which are rodents. (See the photograph by Hediger in *Wild Animals in Captivity*, 1950, fig. 26b).

tion between oxpecker birds (Buphagidæ) and big game in the savannas.

In certain cases the commensalism is less intimate, as when, for example, it is the burrow of a digging animal that attracts other species living in it. In Europe the burrows of the badger often harbor foxes, rabbits, or rats. In Africa aardvark holes are fancied by wart hogs, porcupines, mongooses, and many other small mammals, and on the high Peruvian plateaus guinea pigs may frequently live in tunnels dug by tuco-tucos.

*Interspecific competition*, finally, is a matter of great importance in the history of wild populations.

According to the observations of certain ornithologists, it would seem that two species having the same ecology are never found in a given biotope. It is likely that this is true of the mammals also, but in our present state of ignorance about their biology it would be quite visionary to attempt to establish the validity of this hypothesis. But two forms need not have exactly the same ecology to come into competition. Cases indisputably exist where two species, differing more or less in ecology, have entered into competition, one more or less completely eliminating the other in the end or forcing it into a small section of its former range. This has happened with the black rat and the brown rat in central and western Europe since the eighteenth century. It is a known fact that the black rat preceded the brown rat in the countries of this region. We are sometimes given to suppose that the former has been known in Europe only since the Middle Ages, but in fact its remains have been found in lake dwelling sites, in the Magdalenian deposits of Frankenland Cave in Bavaria, and in the Pleistocene of Bohemia, Austria, and Hungary; its antiquity may therefore be greater than has been thought. The brown rat, on the other hand, has undoubtedly appeared more recently in these regions. It would seem to have come from Central Asia at the beginning of the eighteenth century, crossing the Volga in 1727. Next it invaded Germany, where it was reported in 1750, reaching Paris in 1753, Norway in 1762, Spain in 1800, and Switzerland in 1809. By way of seaports it got to Copenhagen in 1716, England in 1728–9, and the eastern United States in 1775; thence it moved westward to reach Wyoming in 1919 and Montana in 1923. It arrived on the coast of Morocco with the French troops, reaching Marrakech only in 1934. The reasons for the brown rat's success are no doubt various. More aquatic and more subterranean than the black rat, it multiplies in seaports, industrial sections, city sewers, storehouses, and slaughterhouses. Thus it was favored by the increasing industrialization brought on by western civilization, and furthermore its high fertility assures rapid multiplication in any favorable environment. The black rat, on the contrary, climbs more than its relative, and so more readily inhabits the upper floors of houses and attics; it is more likely to frequent residential sections, small villages, and even the countryside far from human habitation. These differences in ecology explain why the two species are sometimes encountered in the same localities but in different niches, the black rats in the attic and the brown rats in the cellar and the drains. Thus, in Morocco, according to Laurent, the two species occupy quite distinct biotopes; the brown rat has invaded the industrial sections of seaports, but is otherwise rather rare in cities, being absent from those sections in which the black rat rules supreme. The latter also ranges into the farmhouses and encampments of the countryside and as far as the oases to the southward, where it may be found even in the tops of palm trees. In India the black rat is again the dominant species of the interior, the brown rat having colonized only the main ports at present. There is competition between these two species, therefore, in spite of their ecological differences,[2] the changes brought about by the industrialization of the modern world having obviously favored one species above the other.

Another possible though not yet certain example of interspecific competition is afforded by the common European red squirrel and the American gray squirrel in England. The latter has been introduced on various occasions since 1828, but only since 1889 has it become firmly established in several localities. In 1930 it was reported as already inhabiting a total area of about 9,920 square miles. Since that time it has extended its distributional area still farther, so that it covered 18,688 square miles in 1935 and 21,120 in 1937. In 1944–5 its progress was still continuing. Since this spread of the introduced species was accompanied, from 1904 to 1914, by a corresponding decrease in the native species, the "competition" of the gray squirrel was forthwith regarded as being to blame. As a matter of fact the two species have rather different ecologies. As Middleton has clearly shown, the European squirrel is strictly bound to coniferous forests and a moderately specialized diet, whereas the gray squirrel frequents parks and both deciduous and mixed forests, and its diet is but very slightly selective. The

[2] And even *because* of them. It was these small ecological differences that *preadapted* the brown rat to the environmental changes effected by widespread industrialization.

fact remains, nevertheless, that wherever the American squirrel gains a foothold, the native squirrel seems to disappear. In 1946 Shorten reported that after the two species had been present in the same zones for 15 years, the native species tended to die out. Here again there would seem to be competition between the two species, in spite of the differences in ecology. It is for the future to decide whether this is the true explanation of the facts or whether they are due, on the contrary, merely to coincidence. In Australia competition between prolific introduced species, such as the rabbit and the rat, and the small native marsupials is resulting in an alarming decrease in the abundance of many of the marsupial species.

# The Structure
# and Dynamics of
# Natural Populations

THE interest of naturalists in the study of wild or natural populations is something comparatively new, for at the beginning of this century very little attention was paid to the structure and dynamics of natural populations, and the difficulties in the way of their study seemed insurmountable. Two very different points of view have been influential in bringing about the complete change of opinion which marks our time.

In the first place, the advance of applied zoology has given increased urgency to the development of accurate census-taking methods applicable to species of economic importance, and without such techniques it was useless to try to check on the efficiency of game-management methods. Thus it was that specialists in wildlife management were led to concern themselves more and more with census techniques, and, as regards the vertebrates at least, they have played a prominent role in perfecting the methods used in field work.

In the second place, and more recently, theoretical considerations about the modes of evolution have given a new impetus to this type of research. As a result of the work of such geneticists as R. A. Fisher, J. B. S. Haldane, and Sewall Wright, population size has emerged as one of the essential factors in evolution. Indeed, as George G. Simpson justly writes, "it is populations, not individuals, that evolve," and when a new character appears by mutation, its chances of survival and spreading through the population vary with the size of the population. Without going into details,[1] we may say that in a large population, where mating occurs at random, the chances that a mutation will become established depend first of all on its selective value. In small populations, on the contrary, the influence of selection is much reduced and that of chance tends to prevail.

Thus the qualitative and quantitative study of populations has at once practical utility and theoretical interest. This study has hardly been sketched out as yet for the wild mammals, but what we know is already promising.

### THE TECHNIQUES OF POPULATION STUDY

IT is not easy to ascertain the number of any one species living on a given area. Let it be said at once that none of the methods in current use is rigorously accurate, for all include more or less important sources of error, but the essential point is to be aware of them and to make sure that

---

[1] On this subject see G. G. Simpson's books and the *Principles of Animal Ecology* by Allee, Emerson, Park, Park, and Schmidt. The recent work of Paavo Vaipio ("Evolution at the population level with special reference to game animals," *Papers on Game Research*, Helsinki, Vol. 5, 1950, pp. 1–176) contains numerous mammalogical examples, particularly details on the *cervina* type of moose and the Samson fox, and their evolution in Finland.

the technique used is adapted to the case under consideration. Thus an approximation will be obtained that is sufficiently close to the truth to be used in making valid comparisons.

A direct *census* of all the individuals of any one species
inhabiting a given region is rarely possible with mammals.
It has been attempted at times with large ungulates living in
open country (savannas, tundras) by the use of aerial photography at low altitude. In this way it was possible to
enumerate, for example, herds of caribou in migration in the
Canadian barrens or of pronghorns in the southwestern
deserts of the United States. This method, however, is useful only in very exceptional cases, and furthermore fails to
provide any idea of the structure of the population studied.

In most cases it is necessary, then, to infer the composition of a population from that of a sample wisely chosen
from that population. But precisely in this choice of a representative sample lies the difficulty. When a protozoologist
wishes to know how many paramecia there are in a liter of
culture medium at a given time, he needs only to stir up the
liquid and then draw off a tenth of a cubic centimeter in a
pipette where, under the microscope, he counts directly the
number of infusorians in this random sample. Repeating this
operation twenty or thirty times and multiplying the average number of paramecia per cubic centimeter by the volume of the nutrient liquid, he will be able to estimate with
extreme exactness the number of individuals present in the
culture. Things are not so simple when it is a matter of
knowing how many sewer rats there are in a city district or
how many squirrels inhabit a tract of woodland. Choosing
the sample to study will then require a profound knowledge

of the habits and ecology of the species, if the population sample is to be truly representative of the total population.

The population sample once chosen, it remains still to count it and ascertain its composition. Theoretically it would be enough to catch and count all the component individuals, but this is often impossible and sometimes undesirable. Resort must then be had to various indirect methods that ought not to be used uncritically.

The marking method is the one in most common use, at least for small mammals. The procedure is as follows: In the selected area traps [2] are uniformly set out in a grid pattern over the surface under study. During a first period of trapping (Period 1), all the animals captured are released after being marked in some way (punching holes in the ears, clipping off certain toes, and so on). After enough time has elapsed for the marked individuals to redistribute themselves throughout the whole population, a second series of trappings is made (Period 2). At this time some animals are captured that were marked during Period 1 and others that have not been taken previously. Now, let us assume that the probability of an animal's being caught is the same, whether it has been marked or not. If we let M represent the number of individuals marked during Period 1, R the number of individuals marked during Period 1 and recovered during Period 2, $n$ the total number of individuals (marked or not) taken during Period 2, and $x$ the total population during Period 1, we can then write:

[2] The traps are of course the kind that captures the animal alive and uninjured. For further practical details see, for example: Blair, W. F., 1941. Techniques for the study of mammal populations, *Jour. Mammal.*, 22:148–57; Blair, W. F., 1941. A simple and effective live trap for small mammals. *Jour. Wildlife Manag.*, 5:191–3; Chitty, D. and Shorten, M., 1946. Techniques for the study of the Norway rat (*Rattus norvegicus*). *Jour. Mammal.*, 27:63–78.

$$\frac{M}{x} = \frac{R}{n}, \text{ whence: } x = \frac{M \times n}{R}$$

Of course this method is valid only under certain conditions. The interval between Periods 1 and 2 must be so short that in the meantime no significant change has been effected in the composition of the population, especially by death or immigration. Further, the behavior of marked individuals must be exactly like that of those not marked and their mortality rate must be the same.[3] Additional technical information will be found in the papers of Jackson (1939), Davis (1948), and Hayne (1949). Hayne also gives two new methods for correcting in some degree the inaccuracies of the Lincoln index.

To estimate the number of individuals of a species inhabiting a given area is not enough; the composition of that population according to age and sex must also be ascertained. If it is relatively easy to determine the sex (except in young individuals), as much cannot be said for age.

Very often it is possible at best to classify the animals in two large categories—adults and immature—according to the degree of development of the secondary sex characters. This division, crude as it may be, still has the advantage of indicating the proportion of reproductive individuals in the total population, a matter of great biological significance.

In some cases, however, age determinations can be made much more precisely. Ungulates whose horns consist

---

[3] In some species the marked subjects become more wary of the traps, and the anesthetic used by some investigators to facilitate clipping off the toes may increase the death rate of marked individuals. It is common, finally, for males to be more easily trapped than females at the breeding-season. All these sources of error must be taken into consideration and allowed for in the interpretation of results.

of a bony axis covered with a permanent corneous sheath (chamois, ibex, bighorn, etc.) have their age inscribed, so to speak, on their heads. The growth of the horns is stopped or much retarded in winter, and this temporary interruption of

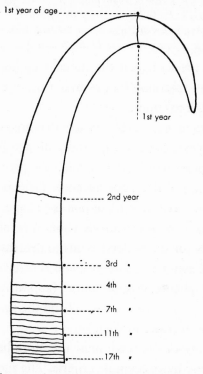

FIG. 93: *Diagram showing the positions of the age rings on a chamois horn from a male 18 years old. After Couturier.*

growth is indicated by an "age ring," a distinct transverse streak with loosened edges that is generally much less conspicuous than the "ornamental rings" with which it is often confused. Figure 93, taken from Couturier's monograph, represents an actual example in which this method is applied to the chamois. We see that in this species the horns lengthen very rapidly during the first two years and much more slowly thereafter. Thus the horns grow on the average

*from 2½ to 7 inches in length during the second year,*
*from 7 to 8¼ inches in length during the third year,*
*from 8¼ to 8¾ inches in length during the fourth year,*
*from 8¾ to 9 inches in length during the fifth year,*
*from 9 to 9¹⁄₁₆ inches in length during the sixth year,*
*from 9¹⁄₁₆ to almost 9¼ inches in length during the seventh year.*

Beyond the sixth year the annual lengthening does not exceed a small fraction of an inch, but the age rings remain distinct enough to count.

In the ungulates having antlers that are regularly shed whole each year, there are naturally no age rings, and the antlers cannot be used in determining the precise age of the animal. In the red deer, for instance, there is no complete correlation between number of points and age. On the other hand the height of the pedicels (bony protuberances that serve as bases for the antlers) tends to decrease as the buck gets older. Each year they become shorter and broader, while the roughened disk or "burr" (appearing in the third year) that lies between the pedicel and the shaft or "beam" of the antler increases in diameter.

The study of the teeth must therefore be undertaken, as it will suppy more accurate criteria. The age at which the milk teeth and the permanent teeth appear has been determined for a number of species in captive individuals or others marked at birth and living at large, and this method has been used in studying progressive wear of the molars and premolars in adults. The following table, taken from Severinghaus's recent work on the Virginia deer, illustrates the results obtained and show the changes occurring in the dental formula from birth to age two:

| First week | $\dfrac{0-0-0-0}{4-0-0-0}$ |
|---|---|
| From 1 to 4 weeks | $\dfrac{0-0-2-0}{4-0-2-0}$ |
| From 4 to 10 weeks | $\dfrac{0-0-3-0}{4-0-3-0}$ |
| From 10 weeks to 7 months | $\dfrac{0-0-3-1}{4-0-3-1}$ |
| From 7 months to 13 months | $\dfrac{0-0-3-2}{4-0-3-2}$ |
| From 13 months to 24 months and more | $\dfrac{0-0-3-3}{4-0-3-3}$ [4] |

Each of these age classes except the first can be divided into subclasses, and it is possible to distinguish eleven subclasses between thirteen months and ten and a half years, based on the shedding of the milk teeth and the growth and wear of the permanent teeth. Similar work seems not to have been done with such care on other species, but Baumann's recent volume on Swiss mammals contains a series of remarkable photographs showing age criteria, established in much the same fashion, for the roebuck and the stag.[5]

Age determination is still more difficult in small mammals. During the growth period it is possible, through com-

[4] Each dental formula shows the upper teeth above the line and the lower teeth below it. The figures represent the numbers of teeth present on one side of each jaw, in the following order: incisors, canines, premolars, molars.

[5] Scheffer, V. B. (Growth layers in the teeth of Pinnipedia as an indication of age. *Science*, Vol. 112, 1950, pp. 309–11) has presented proof that in certain pinnipeds the growth of the canine teeth is retarded in summer, and this is indicated by visible annual marks. And Laws (*Nature*, Vol. 169, 1952, pp. 972–3) has also succeeded in determining the age of sea elephants through the use of cross sections of the canines.

parison with subjects of known age, to estimate the age of an individual by its weight, size, or degree of development of certain of its organs. Various methods are based on this principle. The age of the beaver, the Canadian otter, and many Mustelidæ (weasels, minks, etc.) has been estimated according to weight, size, and the structure of the baculum or penis bone (Friley, Popov). But this mode of reckoning is rather crude and at most permits the classification of individuals as young of the year, immature, young adults, and

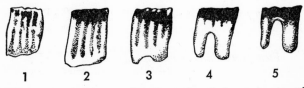

1      2      3      4      5

FIG. 94: *Appearance of the first molar of the common red-backed vole at various ages: 1, at eight weeks; 2, at two months; 3, at seven months; 4 and 5, in "old" individuals. After K. Zimmerman, in Ijsseling and Scheygrond.*

adults. The age of the Levant vole has been estimated (from 25 to 150 days) according to the progressive increase in the weight of the lower jawbone, which varies from 80 to 340 milligrams (Bodenheimer); and that of another, the field vole, according to the length of the row of molars, which, in the upper jaw, increases from 4.78 to 6.56 millimeters (Sperber). It must never be forgotten, however, that two rodents of the same species can reach the same size at different ages, if their diets are very different in quantity and quality. Nevertheless, when individuals of a single population are compared, estimates of age so obtained have some relative value.

Tooth wear can be used in some instances to gain an idea of the age of rodents. Figure 94, taken from Zimmerman, illustrates this point in the case of the common red-backed vole; it is obvious that the appearance of the first lower molar is quite different in animals of 8 weeks, 6 months, and 7 months, and in "old" individuals.

For whales and seals investigators have made rather large-scale counts of the corpora lutea in the ovaries of females in order to get some idea of the animals' ages. It is a fact that in these mammals the successive corpora lutea leave easily identifiable scars in the ovary. Since most of these species are monœstrous, it is sufficient to count the number of old corpora lutea to ascertain the number of years that have passed since reproduction began. In Weddell's seal, for example, only one annual offspring is born, beginning at age three, and so an ovary showing traces of four old corpora lutea will be that of a female aged 4 + 3 years. For the whalebone whales Ruud has suggested counting the growth zones on the baleen plates.

The best method of studying longevity in most wild mammals, as in most birds, will therefore be to mark young individuals, as soon as possible after birth. The investigator will then be in a position to know the exact age of every marked individual that is recovered later, and if the observations are sufficiently numerous, it will be possible to construct a life table for the population concerned.

### POPULATION STRUCTURE

THE total number of individuals of a species inhabiting a given area is in itself a datum of interest to the ecologist. We have already pointed out, however, that this figure is not enough and to understand the dynamics of populations one must know the structure by ages and sexes of the population studied. The work involved has not been done as yet in satisfactory fashion for a single wild species, but we have at our disposal some preliminary "soundings" that can aid future research.

STRUCTURE BY AGES. Knowledge of the length of life of the various members of a population is of first importance. It enables us to calculate the percentage of individuals of the various age classes in that population and also, as we have said, to construct life tables for it, if the data are sufficient, with a statement of the death rate and life expectancy of each age class.

So far we have very few data on the longevity of wild mammals under natural conditions. In the course of his study of the wolves in Mount McKinley National Park in Alaska, Murie collected methodically all skulls (or skull fragments) of bighorns killed by disease or large carnivores. He found 829 skulls in all, and, thanks to age rings on the horns and to dental indications, he was able to determine the ages of 645 animals at the time of death. Murie got the following results:

| | | | |
|---|---|---|---|
| *lambs* | 41 skulls | *animals aged 8 years* | 48 skulls |
| *young of the year* | 117 skulls | *animals aged 9 years* | 79 skulls |
| *animals aged 2 years* | 10 skulls | *animals aged 10 years* | 92 skulls |
| *animals aged 3 years* | 9 skulls | *animals aged 11 years* | 88 skulls |
| *animals aged 4 years* | 9 skulls | *animals aged 12 years* | 64 skulls |
| *animals aged 5 years* | 23 skulls | *animals aged 13 years* | 1 skull |
| *animals aged 6 years* | 34 skulls | *animals aged 14 years* | 3 skulls |
| *animals aged 7 years* | 37 skulls | | |

These figures show that it is especially the young and the old animals that succumb to diseases (mostly necrotic stomatitis and actinomycosis or "big jaw" in the present instance) and to the attacks of predators (wolves and bears). Moreover, the average longevity—that is, life expectancy at birth—seems rather great (of the order of 7 years). It would seem somewhat unwise, however, to attempt the construction of a life table on these few figures, as Deevey tried to do. On the one hand the sample consists of only 645 individuals of both sexes, which is very meager, and on the other hand the probability of finding skulls, or parts of skulls, in the open is smaller for lambs than for adults or old animals with less fragile bones and with durable and very conspicuous horns.

We also have some quantitative data for another ungulate, the chamois, thanks to Couturier's hunting-records. Making use again of the age rings, this hunter-naturalist was able to determine the ages of 526 chamois of both sexes over a year old, killed by him in the French Alps and the Pyrenees; this total number comprised the following:

| | | | |
|---|---|---|---|
| *animals in their 2nd year* | 133 | *animals in their 11th year* | 14 |
| *animals in their 3d year* | 72 | *animals in their 12th year* | 7 |
| *animals in their 4th year* | 85 | *animals in their 13th year* | 4 |
| *animals in their 5th year* | 74 | *animals in their 14th year* | 4 |
| *animals in their 6th year* | 43 | *animals in their 15th year* | 3 |
| *animals in their 7th year* | 29 | *animals in their 16th year* | 3 |
| *animals in their 8th year* | 23 | *animals in their 17th year* | 1 |
| *animals in their 9th year* | 17 | *animals in their 18th year* | 1 |
| *animals in their 10th year* | 12 | *animals in their 19th year* | 1 |

The proportions of the various age classes in this sample should not be very different from what they are in the entire population. The fact is that from the third year on the horns are of considerable length, and it is exceedingly difficult, at more than 100 yards, to be sure of the age of the animal one is firing at. The make-up of this sample should therefore be rather close to that of a true random sample.[6] As with the bighorns, those figures indicate a higher death rate in young and old animals than in mature adults.

As for the small mammals, there are some reports on these also which indicate in every instance an extremely short mean length of life, always much below the potential longevity.

In the course of his study of wild brown rats on a Maryland farm, Davis marked 1,036 individuals from March 1946 to March 1947; 366 were recovered later, alive or dead. Analysis of the recaptured animals showed that only 5 per cent of the rats had reached one year of age (as contrasted with a potential longevity of about 3 years!). Of 100 born in early spring, 74 are still living in spring, 60 in the summer, 54 at the end of summer, 27 at the beginning of autumn, 15 at the end of autumn, and about 5 in the winter. The turnover rate of the age classes [7] is therefore extremely high; as for the percentage of adults, that remains rather constant (48 to 52 per cent) throughout the year, excepting in early spring (when it is 71 per cent).

The Levant voles of Palestine seem likewise to have a very short mean length of life. Bodenheimer's study of the age-class distribution of 550 skulls taken as a sample from owl pellets gave the following results:

[6] Except perhaps for the animals in their second year, whose proportion in the total population is probably larger than their percentage in this sample.

[7] The *turnover period* of the age classes may be defined as the time needed for all the individuals of an age class to disappear completely; certain authors prefer to use the time needed for 95 per cent of the individuals of an age class to disappear, that is, the 5 per cent *survival time*.

| | | | |
|---|---|---|---|
| *animals aged less than 25 days* | | *animals aged 100 days* | 98 |
| 11 | | *animals aged 150 days* | 60 |
| *animals aged 35 days* | 52 | *animals aged more than 150* | |
| *animals aged 50 days* | 129 | *days* | 30 |
| *animals aged 70 days* | 170 | | |

Thus 16.3 per cent of these voles caught by barn owls had survived for more than 100 days, and only 5.4 per cent of them had passed the age of 150 days! This result is verified by observations made in the field; Bodenheimer reports that it is rare to collect individuals aged more than 100 days, although the potential longevity is two and one half years for the female and three for the male! Only the litters born at the beginning of the dry season have any chance of surviving in the summer, and practically no adults born at the beginning of winter are still alive the following summer. So it is that the surviving population is much reduced when the period of high fertility arrives toward the end of autumn.

The little sousliks or Asiatic ground squirrels of the northern Caucasus marked by Kalabuchov are similarly very short-lived on the average (a little under a year). Out of 4,627 individuals marked (3,329 of them newborn), 113 were later recovered, 34 the same year, 53 a year after, 24 two years after, and 2 three years after the marking. At the reproductive period a little souslik population would therefore be constituted somewhat as follows:

| | |
|---|---|
| *young of the year* | 76 per cent |
| *adults aged one year and more* | 24 per cent |

Among the adults 61 per cent are aged one year, 7.4 per cent two years, and 0.6 per cent three years and more.

Blair has also published some observations on average longevity and the death rate under natural conditions of several North American rodents and insectivores. His results agree closely with those already given; the deer mouse lives on the average 4.88 ± 0.20 months, the white-footed deer mouse 4.64 ± 0.22 months, and the meadow vole 4.23 ± 0.22 months.

We have no accurate statistics for bats, age at the time of banding not being known. But Eisentraut reports a regular yearly disappearance of 40 per cent of the individuals marked.

The high mortality of small mammals in nature and their low average longevity (as compared to their potential longevity) are certainly due to ecologic factors and not to physiological causes.

The fact is that if populations of species related to those just mentioned are kept in captivity under favorable conditions, very different survivorship curves are obtained. The white rats of Wistar stock (an albino form of the brown rat), raised by Wiesner and Sheard, had an average longevity of 693.1 ± 7.33 days for females and 669.4 ± 3.57 days for males, which is to say that their length of life was considerably greater than that of their wild cousins of the Maryland farm studied by Davis. The same is true of the field voles raised by Ranson and Leslie at Oxford. The survivorship curve of this colony (fig. 95) shows a high mortality during gestation (21.07 per cent) [8] and the first two weeks of life after birth (14.20 per cent). After weaning, the mortality is low for about 14 weeks and then rises

[8] The prenatal mortality can be even greater in wild populations. In the English wild rabbit, up to 60 per cent of the litters conceived may be lost and the embryos resorbed.

again until the 64th week; the oldest animals attain the age of 96 weeks. Thus a survivorship curve that approaches a convex form is obtained in experimental populations, if by rigorous control of rearing-conditions the injurious effects of variations in temperature, overpopulation, predation, parasitism, and food shortage are prevented.

Some supplementary information on length of life of

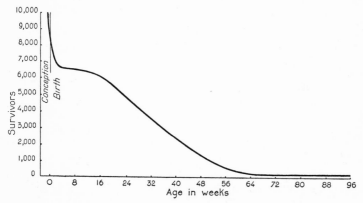

FIG. 95: *Survivorship curve for the field vole, showing the number of survivors out of an original population of 10,000 embryos. Redrawn from Ranson.*

marked individuals in nature will be found in the papers of Burt and of Linduska. It all goes to confirm the low average length of life of species possessing nevertheless a much higher potential longevity.

STRUCTURE BY SEXES. Reliable data on the respective proportions of the sexes at birth and in adulthood in populations of wild mammals are scarce indeed. Some data on the sex ratio of adults is certainly to be found in the literature, but most of them are unreliable, the probability of capture being usually not the same for males and females.

An unequal sex ratio at birth would seem to be the rule in certain species. The European red deer is a good example of this. Miller found 162 males and 109 females when he examined 271 embryos taken as a sample from the uteri of the animals (in Scotland). At birth the proportion of males is smaller but still exceeds that of females; equality should be reached toward the second year of life, according to Darling, and among adults, the same author states, there should be 35.6 per cent of males, as against 64.4 per cent of females. Male mortality would thus be always higher than that of females.

In the muskrat 58.1 per cent of males at birth (Errington) and 56 per cent among the adults (Dozier and Allen) have been found. In the American beaver the embryonic sex ratio seems to be about equal (Bradt), just as in the American red fox (52.93 per cent of males in the week following birth [Johanssen]), the little brown bat (50.6 per cent of males at birth [Griffin]), the European field vole (50.89 per cent of males at birth [Ranson]), the harp seal (51 per cent of males among the young [Dorofejev]), and so on. Among adults equality of the sexes appears to be the rule in the small mammals: 50.9 per cent of males in the mountain vizcacha, of which nine complete colonies were collected by Pearson; 49.2 per cent of males in the eastern cottontail rabbit (Gerstell); 47.9 per cent of males in the wild rabbit in England (Southern), and so forth.

As for the polygamous ungulates, we have already said that females are generally more numerous than males in the adult population. Thus, after the complete extermination of the population of mule deer inhabiting the Stanislaus forest in California—an extermination caused by epidemic foot-

and-mouth disease—Leopold identified 48 per cent as males and 52 per cent as females in a total of 22,362 individuals.

Definite variations in the sex ratio at birth in different populations of one and the same species (or at different seasons of the year in the same population) have been brought to light in certain cases. In his study of different house mouse populations in England, for example, Laurie found that in houses and stores the sex ratio of the mice was 51.83 per cent of males, as against 50.43 per cent in flour storehouses, 48.19 per cent in cold-storage plants, and 48.19 per cent in wheat stacks.

## THE PHYSIOLOGY OF POPULATIONS

STABLE populations in the wild state are probably much less common than classical notions of the "balance of nature" would lead us to believe. Every change in the birth rate or in the death rate has its repercussions on the structure of a population, and factors capable of effecting such changes are very numerous, as we shall see.

FACTORS INFLUENCING THE BIRTH RATE. There would seem to be many of these factors, but the main ones may be grouped, at least for the time being, under three chief heads: age of mother, maternal diet, and season of the year.

The age of the mother is surely an important factor that would repay closer study. The following figures by Leslie and Ranson for the field vole raised in optimum conditions show that in this animal the fertility of the females is highest between the ages of 12 and 50 weeks. In the first pregnancies the number of young per litter is less than in

| AGE OF THE MOTHER IN WEEKS | NUMBER OF LITTERS | NUMBER OF LIVING YOUNG | AVERAGE LIVING YOUNG PER LITTER |
|---|---|---|---|
| 4 | 12 | 37 | 3.03 |
| 12 | 43 | 156 | 3.62 |
| 20 | 36 | 133 | 3.70 |
| 28 | 25 | 93 | 3.72 |
| 36 | 14 | 42 | 3.00 |
| 44 | 7 | 22 | 3.14 |
| 52 | 2 | 4 | 2.00 |
| 60 | 0 | 0 | |
| 68 | 1 | 3 | |

later ones; very old females remain fertile but in diminished degree. In the Levant vole the fertility of the females continues until death, but it is at its height between the ages of 150 and 450 days.

Diet has a predominant influence on the fecundity of females. The following example, drawn from Bodenheimer's work on the Levant vole of Palestine, will be enough to show its importance. Bodenheimer compared the fertility (as indicated by the number of young born during 1,000 days of mated life) of females subjected to widely different diets. His results follow:

*Standard diet* 73  
*Wheat and water* 18  
*Wheat, barley, and carrots* 75  
*Carrots alone* 18  
*Meat, wheat, and water* 0  
*Meat alone* 0  

These figures show how decisive the effect of a change in diet can be; but the researches of the Jerusalem school are to be credited also with showing that certain food plants have a peculiarly powerful influence upon the fertility of rodents. As long ago as 1934 the Friedmans demonstrated the presence in certain plants (alfalfa, corn, and oats) of a substance of gonadotropic effect that is active in the rabbit (but not in the rat), and Mendelssohn was able to increase the summer fertility of Levant voles by feeding them hempseed. What is the mode of action of these substances of vegetable origin on the fecundity of small wild herbivorous mammals? We do not know as yet, but their existence raises an interesting problem in ecology.

The fecundity of Levant voles is affected also by certain physical factors. Continuous lighting or a constant temperature of 35° C. over several generations has a clear inhibiting effect on fertility, whereas permanent darkness or differences in relative humidity produce no effect. Such observations should be repeated on many species. We must always bear in mind that an ecologic factor may very well have no apparent effect on an adult and yet be decisive for the future of the species if it affects its fecundity.

It is probably a combination of the above mentioned ecological factors with many others still to be studied that causes the seasonal variations in fecundity manifested by a single population, as well as the variations in fecundity of different populations of the same species. There is no lack of examples to illustrate the reality of these facts. Thus Maximov recorded from 1940 to 1943 the average number of embryos per female of the common vole in central Russia in different months of the year, and obtained the following figures:

MONTHS/AVERAGE NUMBER OF EMBRYOS PER FEMALE

| | | | |
|---|---|---|---|
| *January–February* | 5.6 | *July–August* | 6.7 |
| *March–April* | 6.1 | *September–October* | 5.3 |
| *May–June* | 6.1 | *November–December* | 5.4 |

In the Levant vole of Palestine the most numerous litters were observed, on the contrary, from November to May, and the least numerous from June to October.

As for variations in fecundity between different populations of the same species, there is no doubt that they certainly also exist. In his study of the reproduction of house mice living in different biotopes in England, Laurie reports that the average number of litters per year is 5.52 in human habitations, 7.97 in flour warehouses, 10.22 in corn ricks, and 6.68 in cold-storage plants. The average number of young per litter is 5.6 except in the cold-storage plants, where it is 6.37. The brown rat manifests great geographical diversities; in England a female bears litters averaging 7.8 young; in San Antonio, Texas, they average 7.9, and in Baltimore 9.9. The number of litters per year also varies: 6 litters a year on the average in Baltimore and only 3 to 4 litters in Massachusetts.

FACTORS AFFECTING THE MORTALITY RATE. Many small mammals are endowed with noteworthy powers of reproduction.[9] Each female field vole, raised in favorable circumstances, bears on the average 5.75 litters of 3.5 living young. Under such conditions, according to the calculations of Leslie and Ranson and assuming that the birth and death rates remain constant,[1] a population would increase its numbers tenfold in six months! According to Bailey, the female meadow vole can reproduce from the age of 25 days and

[9] Potential reproductive capacity means the maximum number of descendants that a population of individuals belonging to the same species could have under ecologically and physiologically optimal conditions; it is of course a purely theoretical concept, but the effective reproductive capacity (meaning that observed in fact) is still considerable.

[1] A thing that *never* happens in practice.

have up to 17 litters of 6 to 8 young in one year! These few figures give some idea of the enormous fecundity of certain small mammals and bring home to us the importance of the mortality factors that are its counterbalance in nature.

These factors may be classed in two main categories: those which depend upon density of population and those which are independent of it. The first category (disease, predation, intraspecific competition) is of especial ecologic interest, for on it depends the maintenance of the population at an appreciably constant level.

In a stable population the percentage of diseased individuals appears to be small, at least in the adults.[2] Elton, Ford, and Baker, studying the morbidity of the long-tailed field mice of Bagley Wood, near Oxford, obtained the following figures for the parts of the body more commonly affected:

| PART AFFECTED | NUMBER EXAMINED | NUMBER DISEASED | PERCENTAGE DISEASED |
|---|---|---|---|
| Blood (cultures) | 468 | 0 | 0 |
| Liver | 989 | 25 | 2.6 |
| Lungs | 475 | 2 | 0.4 |
| Alimentary canal | 719 | 2 | 0.3 |
| Spleen | 719 | 1 | 0.1 |
| Skin of legs (mite scab) | 924 | 102 | 11.1 |
| Skin (lesions) | 1,156 | 1 | 0.1 |

It is evident that as a whole the population is in perfect health, although the occurrence of 41 species of parasites (bacteria and viruses not included) has been reported in this species.

Research on such parasitic micro-organisms as *Salmo-*

[2] Infant mortality, very high in most species, is perhaps more commonly due to disease.

*nella, Mycobacterium, Pasteurella, Rickettsia,* and *Lepto-spira,* in the organs of 55 Levant voles in Ganigar (Palestine), gave only negative results in 1938, according to Bodenheimer, and agglutination tests were positive in only two cases for *Salmonella Kentucky,* in one case for *S. ærtrycke,* and in one case for *S. enteridis.*

From time to time, however, extremely violent epidemics occur, and these may entail the death of a great many individuals: rabies in the carnivores (wolves, coyotes), Bang's disease or infectious abortion (ungulates), tularemia, salmonellosis, and plague in rodents, and so on. Some of these epizootics or animal epidemics may destroy almost entirely the fauna of a whole continent, as witness the great epidemic of bovine plague that began in Egypt in 1885 and spread progressively toward the south (Somaliland, 1887; the Congo and Nyasaland, 1892; Zambezi, 1895) to reach the Cape in 1897. It crossed the continent from north to south in ten years and killed several hundred thousand buffalos and antelopes, in addition to six million head of cattle.

The exact part played by predation in the dynamics of wild mammalian populations remains to be determined. Most of the older naturalists believed that predators (carnivorous mammals, birds of prey, and the like) had an essential role in holding certain populations of very prolific species at a constant level. As a matter of fact, this does not seem to be true in most cases. The barn owl, for example, is the chief predator on the Levant vole in Palestine, and the remains of one or sometimes two individuals of this species are found in one regurgitated pellet out of two. Now, this owl exploits a hunting-terrain of more than 9 square miles on the average around its nest—that is, an area supporting at least 25,000 voles; as one hardly finds more than 600 pellets under each nest, it is highly probable that the proportion of these voles destroyed by owls is insignificant.

Most modern ecologists, such as Bodenheimer, Elton, and Errington, agree in regarding the predation of the higher vertebrates as a mortality factor of secondary importance, and in all cases quite insufficient in itself to explain large numerical fluctuations.

In the case of the wild ungulates, however, whose fecundity is much lower than that of the rodents, predation may be more important in keeping a population at an approximately constant level. The story of the deer inhabiting the Kaibab plateau in Arizona, as told by Léopold, is very significant in this connection. At the beginning of the present century this plateau of 127,000 acres supported an apparently stable population of about 4,000 head; a certain number of pumas, wolves, and coyotes lived at its expense. From 1907 to 1917 six hundred pumas were killed, then 74 more from 1918 to 1923, and finally 142 from 1924 to 1939. The wolves were completely exterminated in 1926, and the coyotes were also pretty well hunted out, since about 3,000 were killed from 1907 to 1923 and 4,388 from 1923 to 1939. The result of this tremendous slaughter of predatory animals was soon evident. From about 4,000 in 1905, the deer increased to almost 60,000 in 1920 and reached 100,000 in 1924. The effects of such overpopulation were not slow in making themselves felt, for a given environment cannot support an unlimited number of individuals of the same species; beyond a certain threshold—the carrying capacity of the habitat—there are not enough food resources to provide normal nutrition, and food shortage begins to cause trouble, especially in the unfavorable season. This is what happened on the Kaibab plateau, and the number of deer decreased from 100,000 in 1924 to 40,000 in 1925, then to 30,000 in 1929, to 20,000 in 1931, and to about 10,000 in 1939. In this case, then, a certain equilibrium did exist between the ungulate population, the carnivore population, and the plant formations of the region; man by his intervention upset this equilibrium to the great disadvantage of the species that on the contrary he intended to protect. Correlated fluctuations in the relative numbers of lions and antelopes have also been observed in the Rwindi-Rutshuru plain, south of Lake Edward in the Belgian Congo. From 1920 to 1930 the number of topi antelopes increased greatly, while the number of lions diminished as a result of intensive hunting carried on from 1918 to 1929. It is well, therefore, not to generalize too widely, one way or the other, as to the meaning of the few facts now known. It may very well be that predation is a negligible mortality factor for the small rodents [3] but an important one for the ungulates.

It would seem that there has been much exaggeration of the importance of natural accidents, floods, brush fires, etc., which are mortality factors independent of population density. The observations made by Stickel in comparing the density of a population of the white-footed deer mouse before and after a severe flood show that this had hardly any unfavorable effect at all. Those of Currier on the wood-

[3] Even in the case of the small rodents predation may sometimes be important in small and more or less isolated populations. McCabe and Blanchard mention the spectacular destruction of a local population of *Peromyscus* (deer mice) by a series of weasel raids, suggesting that predation pressure may sometimes descend with sudden and catastrophic force.

chuck tell the same story. The duration of the abnormal period seems to be more important than its apparent severity; an example is furnished by Errington's investigation of the effect of a prolonged and extremely severe drought in Iowa during the summer of 1934 and during the years 1936–7, which were also more than normally dry. He states that when the marshes are beginning to dry out a majority of the muskrats remain on their home ranges. It is only when the drought persists and the drying-out advances that one sees an increase in emigration and in the aggressiveness of both sexes, with fights carried on by both adults and young when the emigrants try to invade the territories of muskrats still at home. Prolonged drought thus has complex effects; it sets off an emigration that in turn brings on an increase in intraspecific competition while augmenting the risk of capture by predators and the chances of death by starvation.

POPULATION CYCLES.   One of the most fascinating problems raised by the study of population dynamics in nature is certainly that of population cycles. It is, in fact, very rare for a single species to remain equally common from year to year in a given region; but the fluctuations in population density which are the rule can in many cases be attributed to some evident modification of the environment —often under the direct influence of man and his methods of cultivation. Here the quantitative variations have no set periodicity, and their causes are generally easy to discover. Quite different, on the other hand, are the *cyclical fluctuations* of a whole series of species living sometimes in regions where man's activity hardly makes itself felt. The fact that they exist is undeniable, and long before the detailed studies undertaken in the last fifty years, these cycles—above all in northern zones, where they are most clearly manifested—had impressed themselves on the imagination of naturalists and even of the public at large.

It would be misleading to draw up, at present, a list of the mammals composing populations that periodically undergo large numerical fluctuations; the number of such species is in fact considerable, and it continues to increase as our knowledge progresses.[4] Not all have the same interest, to be sure, and only the species on which we have numerous records, covering a sufficiently long period, can be of any use in analyzing this phenomenon. Such species are the lemmings, certain voles, the American snowshoe hare, the muskrat, the lynx, and some foxes and other fur-bearing animals.

Table 8, based on data from Collett, Elton, Siivonen, and Kalela, shows, by way of example, the years of maximum abundance of lemmings, voles, and foxes in various parts of Scandinavia. "Lemming years" have in fact been recognized since time immemorial in these regions. Ordinarily the Norway lemming is a small, nocturnal, and retiring rodent inhabiting the plateaus and mountains of the peninsula. In some years it is extremely rare, and one hardly ever sees a hole or a dropping to betray its presence; but in other years it swarms in extraordinary numbers. Now active in full daylight, it sets out on long journeys, sometimes in enormous swarms, bursting out from its natural habitat and invading plains and valleys. This emigration does not usually

---

[4] It is equally difficult, furthermore, to name the species that certainly do not manifest cycles of abundance; of all the mammals of North America, only one would qualify: the beaver!

**Table 8.**—*Comparison of maximum years of abundance of some Scandinavian species of mammals (According to data from Collet and Elton, completed by Siivonen and Kalela)*

| SOUTHERN NORWAY | | | SWEDEN | CENTRAL AND NORTHERN NORWAY | | | NORTHERN FINLAND |
|---|---|---|---|---|---|---|---|
| Lemmings[a] | Voles,[b] etc. | Foxes[c] | Lemmings[a] | Lemmings[a] | Voles,[b] etc. | Foxes[c] | Lemmings[a] |
| 1862–3 | 1863 | | 1862–3 | | | | 1862–3 |
| 1866 | | | | | | | |
| 1868–9 | | | 1868 | | | | |
| 1871–2 | 1872 | | 1872 | | 1872 | | 1871–2 |
| 1875–6 | 1876 | | 1876–7 | 1876 | 1876 | | 1875–6 |
| | | | | 1878 | | | |
| 1879–80 | | 1880 | | 1880–1 | 1880 | 1880 | |
| 1883–4 | 1882–4 | 1884 | 1883–4 | 1883–4 | 1882–3 | 1884 | |
| 1887–8 | 1888 | 1887 | | | 1887–8 | 1888 | |
| 1890–1 | 1891–2 | 1892 | 1890–1 | | 1890–1 | 1891–2 | 1891 |
| 1894–5 | 1894–5 | 1895 | | 1895 | 1894–5 | 1896 | 1893–5 |
| 1897 | 1897 | 1899 | | | 1897 | 1899–1900 | 1897 |
| 1902–3 | 1902 | 1903 | 1902–3 | 1902–3 | 1902–4 | 1903 | 1902–3 |
| 1906 | 1906 | 1907 | 1906–7 | 1906 | 1906–7 | 1907 | 1907 |

[a] The lemmings are *Lemmus lemmus*.
[b] Under "voles, etc." are included *Myopus schisticolor, Microtus agrestris, Clethriomys glareolus, C. rutilus,* and *C. rufocanus.*
[c] The foxes are *Vulpes vulpes.*

309

**Table 8.**—(*Continued*)

| 1909–10 | 1909 | 1910 | 1911 | 1911–12 | 1910–12 | 1911 | 1911 |
|---|---|---|---|---|---|---|---|
|  |  | 1915 | 1916 |  | 1914 | 1915 |  |
| 1918 |  | 1918 | 1919 | 1918–9 |  | 1920–1 |  |
| 1920 | 1920 | 1921 |  |  |  | 1924 | (1926) |
| 1922–3 |  | 1926 | 1922–3 | 1922–3 | 1926–7 | 1926 | 1930 |
| 1926–7 | 1926–7 | 1930(?) | 1926 | 1926 | 1930–1 | 1930(?) | (1934) |
| 1930 |  |  | 1929–30 | 1929–31 | 1934 |  | 1937–8 |
| 1933–4 | 1934 |  | 1934 | 1933–4 |  |  | 1941–2 |
| 1938 | 1938 |  | 1937–8 | 1938 |  |  |  |
| 1941 | 1941–2 |  | 1940–1 |  |  |  |  |

310

take place in compact groups and serried ranks, the lemmings most often traveling one by one, though in the same direction; it is only when they come to some obstacle—stream, lake, or seashore—that they collect in bands. Then they hurl themselves *en masse* into the water, swimming straight ahead and landing by chance on rocks, islets—even on the nets and boats of fishermen—and drowning by tens of thousands. Off Trondheim in 1868 a "shoal" of lemmings was seen that was so vast a steamer took a quarter of an hour to pass through it! It should be added that the Norway lemming is not the only mammal to multiply rapidly in "lemming years." As the table shows, a close relative, *Myopus schisticolor*, and several species of voles are abundant at the same time, as well as the ptarmigans or grouse, which are also plant feeders, and the foxes and certain birds of prey that live on small rodents.

Another good example of the population cycle with regular periodicity is furnished by the snowshoe hare and the Canada lynx, whose synchronous cycles have been very carefully studied by MacLulich, Elton, and Nicholson. It is well known that the fur trade is one of the rich resources of Canada; this trade is for the most part centralized in the great companies that buy skins from the trappers. Now, the records of these companies, sometimes going back for two hundred years—particularly those of the Hudson Bay Company—have been kept remarkably up to date, and make it possible to follow the annual fluctuations in abundance of the fur-bearing animals. This unique source of written information has been extensively turned to account by the authors just mentioned, and has been completed by very careful investigations in recent years. This enables us to recognize the years of abundance and of rarity in a certain number of species. To take one example, the snowshoe hare was especially abundant [5] in 1856, 1864, 1875, 1886, 1895, 1904, 1914, 1924, and 1934. During these "good years" the Company took in an average of 115,000 rabbit skins, as compared with about 10,000 in "bad years." It can be seen that these variations in abundance are of great amplitude. From 1932 to 1935 MacLulich endeavored further to estimate the populations of the snowshoe hare in various places in Ontario; his estimates show that in a period of maximum abundance the density of this species may reach more than 3,400 per square mile, as against only one in a period of extreme rarity! There are also some local variations during each maximum period, from one district to another. During the 1934 peak in Ontario, the rabbits did not attain their maximum abundance everywhere at once, and the same can be said for the phase of rarity. This simple fact is of some importance, as we shall soon see.

The population cycles of the Canada lynx have a periodicity that corresponds very well to that of the rabbits, which, by the way, form one of its basic foods in the cold season. A glance at fig. 96, borrowed from Elton and Nicholson's recent work, will be convincing. The coefficient of correlation between the numbers of the two species, as calculated by MacLulich, is +0.55 with a probable error of ±0.05. Field naturalists, for their part, have long since noted that the abundance and the rarity phases of these two species are synchronous. During a seven months' trip through the Athabaska River valley, Seton encountered

[5] The dates refer to the last year of maximum abundance in each case, immediately preceding the sudden reduction in numbers.

thousands of lynxes hunting desperately for any prey, after the enormous reduction in rabbit population that marked the years 1906–7. A dozen lynxes, half-dead from hunger, were veritable living skeletons, and the carcasses of a dozen others were found in the woods. In this example, as in the

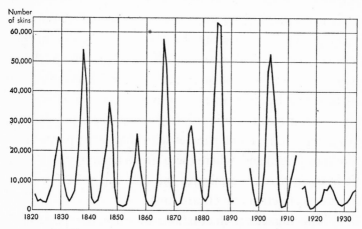

FIG. 96: *Fluctuations in the abundance of the Canadian lynx in the Northern Department of the Hudson Bay Company, from 1821 to 1934. After Elton and Nicholson.*

preceding, the population cycles of predators correspond with those of their prey.

It would be easy to multiply examples; the populations of many Microtinæ fluctuate with some regularity: the common vole in France, southern Germany, and Russia, the field vole in England, the mountain and meadow voles in the United States, the Levant vole in the Near East, and so on. For all these rodents, of small size but high fecundity, the periodicity of the cycles is short, 3 to 5 years as a rule, as in the lemmings dealt with above. For species of larger size and lower fecundity the periodicity is slower, 9 to 11 years

**313**

(10 on the average), as in the snowshoe hare and the musk-rat.[6] As for the predators, these would seem, whatever their size, to model their cycles on those of their prey. The Scandinavian foxes fluctuate in parallel with the lemmings, and the Canada lynxes in time with the snowshoe hares on which they feed. Furthermore, this is not peculiar to carnivorous mammals; the snowy owl of boreal America undergoes changes in abundance timed with those of the lemmings it hunts. The arctic fox, again, offers still more convincing evidence that the population cycles of predators are wholly determined by those of their principal prey. In the American or European Arctic this fox, which feeds primarily on lemmings, has a cycle parallel with that of its prey. But in western Greenland, where there are no lemmings and where it lives on hares, ptarmigans, and fish, this same fox shows no cyclic fluctuations (Braestrup).

The numerical fluctuations in carnivore populations would seem clearly to depend only on those of the basic element in their diet, that is, the small rodents. But how are the rodent fluctuations to be explained? Hypotheses are not wanting, but it must be admitted that none of them is fully satisfactory. That there is a close correspondence between the 9–11-year cycles and those of sunspots has long been thought. We know that the number of sunspots varies from year to year and that it regularly attains a maximum every

[6] The existence of two types of cycles with different periodicity, "lemming type" and "lynx type," is not admitted, however, by all authors. Siivonen thinks, for example, that all the cycles have a fundamental periodicity of about three and a half years; but Kalela is not of this opinion. Palmgren on his part holds that these short-term fluctuations can be explained perfectly well by random fluctuations of various environmental factors capable of acting on fecundity, and by the influence of the density of population in the preceding year upon the growth of this same population during the year that follows.

eleven years approximately. It might be supposed with logic that the resulting periodic changes in solar radiation cause climatic changes that can react on vegetation and, indirectly, on the fecundity of herbivores. But it seems impossible at present to take this hypothesis seriously. MacLulich minutely analyzed the numerical fluctuations of the snowshoe hare in Canada and was unable to find any correlation between the sunspot cycle and the cycles of the hare and lynx. Between 1856 and 1934 there were 8 maxima of abundance in the hares and only 7 maxima in the sunspots; the average length of the cycles was 9.7 years for the hares and 11 years for the spots. And it must not be forgotten that there always exists, during the period of one maximum, some degree of asynchronism in different districts. This lack of simultaneity may be very considerable, since during the peak of 1934 the maximum abundance of hares was reached in 1931 in some parts of southwest Ontario, in 1933 in the south, in 1934 in the north of this same province, and in 1935 in some other counties. It is the same with the lynx; from 1751 to 1925 there were 18 maxima of abundance in the lynxes as against only 15 in the sunspots, and the average length of the cycles was again 9.7 years for the animals and 11 years for the spots. In spite of its immediate appeal, therefore, this seductive theory cannot account for the observed facts.

It has also been supposed that rodent population cycles could be explained by the varying incidence of certain diseases whose ravages would increase with the rise in population density and as the inhabitants of overpopulated areas became less resistant physiologically because of malnutrition. Here again the hypothesis is seductive—but the facts have not confirmed it. There has been much search for pathogenic bacteria that might account for the brutal slaughter that follows immediately upon the years of abundance. Various germs have indeed been found in some species during the period of decrease, but none of them seems able to be held responsible for the deaths *en masse* that are observed. What is still more striking is that in a great many instances autopsy has revealed no pathogenic germs at all. Findlay and Middleton, for example, studied field voles that were collected in England, during the declining phase of their outbreak, and that died in the laboratory after a period of lethargy followed by convulsions. These investigators could find no pathogenic bacteria in the animals' tissues and had to attribute the observed casualties to the presence of a protozoan (*Toxoplasma*) in the brains of some individuals. Hamilton likewise, studying population cycles in the meadow vole of the Ithaca region in New York, observed that his animals died of convulsions after a more or less prolonged period of torpor. He was no better able to demonstrate the presence of pathogenic germs, although the hypothesis of a virus disease could not be excluded.

Still more remarkable are the observations of Green and his co-workers on the snowshoe hare in Minnesota. Only a few deaths could be attributed to infectious diseases during the phase of rapid decline in population. Most of the hares died, on the contrary, of convulsions or fell into a coma after a characteristic phase of torpor. Autopsy showed atrophy and fatty degeneration of the liver, decrease in liver glycogen, and congestion of the brain, adrenals, thyroid, and kidneys, with slight hemorrhages at times; before the animals died it was possible to demonstrate a hypoglycemia or deficiency in their blood sugar, which intravenous injections of glucose would correct, at least temporarily. These symptoms led Green and his collaborators to conclude that the mass deaths of the American hare during the declining phase of its population cycle are due to a true shock disease and not to an infectious malady.

All these facts suggest at the moment another possible explanation for the cycles of abundance in rodents. At the beginning of the cycle, when the population is very sparse, the survivors find themselves in the midst of very favorable ecological conditions; their small number assures them food in plenty, and this results in a higher fertility of the females, probably accompanied by a decrease in the mortality of the young. Thus Hamilton showed that in the course of the cycle in the meadow vole the length of the reproductive period and the number of young per litter increased during the phase of increasing population. The progressive increase in number of individuals that results from this multiplies the opportunities for immediate mating after giving birth. Finally, the number of litters per year increases progressively, and—in this particular case at least—reproduction goes on even during the winter.

The population, therefore, is bound to grow by degrees, and so much the faster as species of early maturity, rapid gestation, and numerous litters are in question. The habitat must soon be overpopulated and its carrying capacity exceeded; the food resources of the environment remaining limited, they will soon become insufficient, and the effects of the shortage will begin to make themselves felt. Competition between individuals will in consequence become stronger, and the animals' resistance to diseases and parasites will diminish; emigration movements will get under way, and this stirring of the population will add to the causes of disequilibrium.[7] All this does not fail to influence the physiology of the animals profoundly. Fasting, cold, muscular fatigue, repeated pregnancies, and many other physical and psychic factors at last set off within the mammalian organism deep-seated changes that may lead to a phase of exhaustion during which any new stress may have fatal effects.

We can then conceive of a population of individuals subjected, from the very fact of their constantly increasing density, to conditions more and more difficult, being brought little by little into that exhausted state of the pituitary-adrenal system that marks the terminal phase of what some pathologists have called the phenomena of adaptation. This is the moment when mass death occurs, as an effect of factors that would normally entail no serious consequences. Christian believes, for example, that the revival of the genital functions, stimulated through the medium of the anterior pituitary by the lengthening of daylight in spring, would be the drop that makes the glass run over. This genital revival would be a factor sufficient to bring on, in an excessive population that has already borne the rigors of winter with distress, the phenomena of shock brought to

[7] In the muskrat mere overpopulation tends to reduce the fertility of the females through the mediation of a whole series of ecological, physiological, and psychological factors. In the same way a reduction in fertility has been recorded at the beginning of the breakdown or declining phase in the Levant vole by Bodenheimer and Dvoretzky. McCabe and Blanchard insist, for their part, on the extreme sense of environmental specificity, far beyond our perception, shown by their deer mice, and also on the fact that this sense is combined with the faculty of easy, unaided death as a natural resource or alternative. This interesting hypothesis, which would explain the emotional deaths of captured or displaced small mammals, deserves to be more deeply studied.

light by Green and his co-workers. Thus the carrying capacity of the habitat would in some sense determine the level of population beyond which the multiplication of individuals only serves to amplify the causes of stress. With this ceiling surpassed, the organisms are quickly brought to a state of psycho-physiological exhaustion that suddenly ends in the death of a majority of individuals. The situation being then reversed, the cycle can begin again.

This working hypothesis, recently defended by Christian, calls for factual confirmation. But at present some data seem to favor it, especially the striking analogy that exists between the state of fatal shock, demonstrated by Green and his students in the snowshoe hare, and the exhaustion stage of the adaptation syndrome as defined by Selye.

Cycles of abundance in various species, the mechanism of which is still far from being cleared up, would seem, therefore, to be more and more clearly the result of multiple and complex phenomena, giving expression on the quantitative plane to interactions between population and environment.

### GROWTH AND DECLINE OF POPULATIONS

POPULATIONS, like individuals, are in a state of perpetual change, and their stability is only apparent. But we are seldom able to study the growth or the decline of wild populations under natural conditions.

We can certainly take for granted that when a few individuals have succeeded in colonizing in one way or another a "new" territory that suits them, they will rapidly increase in number. But questions arise: How will the multiplication take place? To what degree of density will the increase proceed, and in what rhythm? What will happen later, since the carrying capacity of the habitat is limited? There are many such questions to which we should like to find answers based on facts of observation.

Some preliminary material for comparison is furnished us by laboratory studies on experimental populations of fruit flies (Drosophila), protozoans, and bacteria. In these cases experiment has shown that a population in a limited environment may increase in a logistic fashion, which means that the curve representing the increase in number of individuals is characterized by slow initial growth, then rapid growth, and then stability at the upper asymptote. But we have already seen that under natural conditions this stability is more theoretical than real, for even the species that are not subject to the large cyclic fluctuations studied in the preceding pages manifest seasonal fluctuations and annual oscillations expressing the annual variations in food, shelter, and other environmental factors. When the asymptote is once reached, moreover, stability will be conceivable only if the population is properly adjusted to the environment and if the conditions remain stationary. Under opposite circumstances the experiment tends to show that the fluctuations around the asymptote will be very brief or even be lacking and a crash will immediately follow the production of the maximum population. In fact the production of even one generation beyond a certain critical population level overshoots the maximum capacity that the environment can support.

In spite of the rarity and difficulty of observing such facts under natural conditions, it seems very probable that much the same is true for wild mammals. Scheffer's re-

markable study of the rise and fall of the reindeer population of the Pribilof Islands is a very suggestive example.

In the fall of 1911, the U. S. government placed 21 does
and 4 bucks on St. Paul Island, to provide the native resi-
dents with a sustained source of fresh meat. The planting
was an immediate success, and in the following spring 17
fawns were born. During the succeeding 40 years the herd
was kept under observation and regularly counted.
Throughout this period the reindeer were kept in a semi-
wilderness environment, subjected to little hunting pressure,
and they were completely free of attack by predators. No
epidemic of disease was observed. Under such conditions
the evolution of this population is a most instructive study
(fig. 97).

The herd began to increase slowly: 25 in 1911, 284 in
1921, 472 in 1931. From this date on, the growth was extremely rapid: 532 in 1932, 684 in 1933, 834 in 1934, 1,185
in 1935, 1,425 in 1936, 1,753 in 1937, and 2,046 in 1938. But
after this date there was a cataclysmic decline in the number
of reindeer: 1,227 in 1940, 240 in 1946, 120 in 1948, 60 in
1949, and only 8 in 1950.

How are we to interpret such an evolution? It would
seem that the dominant cause was overpopulation. As long
as the herd did not exceed a few hundred head, the lichens
(chiefly the taller, shrublike forms of *Cladonia* and *Cetra-
ria*) that served in winter as emergency rations for the
reindeer kept pace with the demand. But when the herd
continued to increase, this was no longer true. These lichens
require a certain amount of time to recover after grazing,
and during this period the reindeer have to seek food elsewhere. It seems clear that on an average range 33 acres is

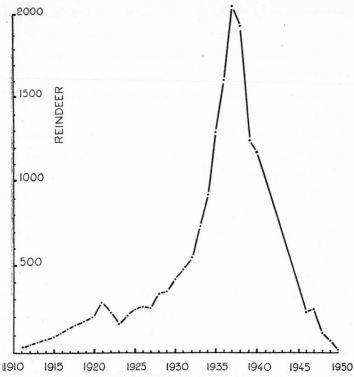

FIG. 97: *Reindeer population of St. Paul Island (Pribilofs) from 1911 to 1950. Each dot represents the combined number of reindeer killed for food and spared, or, in years when no animals were killed, the number counted at the end of the year. Redrawn from Scheffer, 1951.*

the minimum year-long grazing-area requirement for each reindeer. Now, at the peak population in 1938, there were only 11 acres of suitable grazing-land for each animal instead of 33, which means that the reindeer population was at least three times the carrying capacity of the range.

This undernourishment happened to coincide with winters more cold than usual, which accentuated the critical nature of the situation. Winter mortality became very high, and the herd decreased at a catastrophic rate. It is certainly possible that an unfavorable sex ratio may have hastened this decline in later years, but overpopulation was to all appearances the dominant factor.

The case of the deer of the Kaibab plateau is another instance of this phenomenon (see p. 305); here it was the removal of predators that set off a rapid multiplication of the deer, beyond the carrying capacity of the winter food supply of the range. The outcome was again a rapid decline in the population.

As we bring this study to an end, we are impressed once again with the crucial import of the dynamic aspect of vital phenomena. Evolution and change are truly in process at once on the plane of the individual and on that of populations.

As an individual every mammal is manifestly in constant change. At birth it begins a life cycle that will conduct it through the successive stages of growth, maturity and, in the end, senility. At each of these stages not only its morphological characteristics will undergo change, but also some of its physiological peculiarities, and above all its behavior. All this will at once affect the individual and the more or less complex society of which it is an integral part. Actually the living being—in every respect—never remains the same for long.

Populations are also in constant evolution, and it is with good reason that population dynamics have been much studied in recent years; population changes unquestionably play a primary part in the evolution of the living world.

Through the steady interplay of heredity and environment, populations become adapted more or less successfully to the ever changing conditions of their habitats. One of the aims of this book has been to show how situations that are apparently most stable are in reality subject to incessant fluctuation.

We may assert with little fear of being mistaken that great things can be expected from a careful study of the daily life of wild mammals. Far from being a mere hobby, it will in all probability throw an instructive light upon the biology of our own species.

# Taxonomic List of Species, with Common Names

ORDER MONOTREMATA
    *Tachyglossus aculeatus*     = Australian spiny anteater
    *Ornithorhynchus paradoxus* = Platypus
ORDER MARSUPIALIA
  Family Didelphidæ
    *Didelphis marsupialis*     = Virginia opossum
    *Didelphis paraguayensis*   = South American opossum
    *Marmosa isthmica*     = Isthmian marmosa
    *Marmosa cinerea*     = Murine opossum
    *Philander philander*     = Woolly opossum
  Family Dasyuridæ
    *Dasycercus cristicauda*   = Crest-tail pouched-mouse
    *Dasyurus viverrinus*     = Marsupial cat
  Family Myrmecobiidæ
    *Myrmecobius fasciatus*   = Marsupial banded anteater
  Family Phalangeridæ
    *Trichosurus vulpecula*   = Silver-gray opossum
    *Cercaërtus nanus*     = Pigmy opossum
    *Petaurus breviceps*     = Sugar glider
    *Phascolarctos cinereus*   = Koala
    *Schoinobates volans*     = Greater glider-opossum
  Family Phascolomidæ
    *Phascolomis hirsutus*     = Common wombat
  Family Macropodidæ
    *Bettongia lesueur*     = Lesueur's rat kangaroo

| | |
|---|---|
| *Bettongia cuniculus* | = Tasmanian rat kangaroo |
| *Macropus canguru canguru* | = Great gray kangaroo |
| *Macropus canguru major* | = Forester kangaroo |
| *Macropus rufus* | = Red kangaroo |
| *Protemnodon eugenii* | = Dama padamelon |
| *Setonyx brachyurus* | = Short-tailed wallaby |
| *Potorous tridactylus* | = Dark rat kangaroo |
| *Wallabia rufogrisea* | = Brush wallaby |

ORDER INSECTIVORA

Family Tenrecidæ
*Tenrec ecaudatus* = Tenrec

Family Erinaceidæ
*Erinaceus europæus* = (European) hedgehog

Family Soricidæ
| *Blarina brevicauda* | = Short-tailed shrew |
| *Crocidura leucodon* | = Bicolor white-toothed shrew |
| *Neomys fodiens* | = European water-shrew |
| *Sorex araneus* | = Common shrew |

Family Talpidæ
| *Condylura cristata* | = Star-nosed mole |
| *Talpa europæa* | = European mole |
| *Scalopus aquaticus* | = Eastern mole |

ORDER CHIROPTERA

Family Noctilionidæ
*Noctilio leporinus* = Fish-eating bat

Family Rhinolophidæ
| *Rhinolophus ferrumequinum* | = Greater horseshoe bat |
| *Rhinolophus hipposideros* | = Lesser horseshoe bat |

Family Desmodontidæ
*Desmodus rufus* = Vampire bat

Family Vespertilionidæ
| *Barbastella barbastellus* | = Barbastelle |
| *Eptesicus fuscus* | = Big brown bat |
| *Eptesicus serotinus* | = Serotine |
| *Lasiurus borealis* | = Red bat |
| *Lasiurus cinereus* | = Hoary bat |
| *Myotis daubentoni* | = Daubenton's bat |
| *Myotis grisescens* | = Gray myotis |
| *Myotis keenii* | = Keen bat |
| *Myotis lucifugus* | = Little brown bat |
| *Myotis myotis* | = Large mouse-eared bat |
| *Myotis mystacinus* | = Whiskered bat |

| | |
|---|---|
| *Myotis sodalis* | = Indiana myotis |
| *Myotis subulatus* | = Small-footed myotis |
| *Nyctalus noctula* | = Noctule |
| *Pipistrellus pipistrellus* | = European pipistrelle |
| *Pipistrellus subflavus* | = Eastern pipistrelle |
| *Plecotus auritus* | = Long-eared bat |
| Family Molossidæ | |
| *Tadarida cynocephala* | = Florida free-tailed bat |

ORDER PRIMATES

| | |
|---|---|
| Family Lemuridæ | |
| *Lemur catta* | = Ring-tailed lemur |
| Family Indridæ | |
| *Propithecus verreauxi* | = Sifaka |
| Family Daubentoniidæ | |
| *Daubentonia madagascarien-sis* | = Aye-aye |
| Family Lorisidæ | |
| *Arctocebus calabarensis* | = Golden potto |
| *Loris tardigradus* | = Slender lori |
| *Perodicticus potto* | = Potto |
| *Galago senegalensis₁* | = Senegal bush baby |
| Family Tarsiidæ | |
| *Tarsius spectrum* | = Tarsier |
| Family Cebidæ | |
| *Alouatta palliata* | = Panama howling monkey |
| *Ateles geoffroyi* | = Red spider monkey |
| Family Callithricidæ | |
| *Callithrix jacchus* | = Common marmoset |
| Family Cercopithecidæ | |
| *Cercopithecus ascanius sch-midti* | = Redtail monkey |
| *Cercopithecus cephus* | = Mustached white-nosed monkey or guenon |
| *Macaca mulatta* | = Rhesus monkey |
| *Macaca sinica* | = Toque monkey |
| *Papio cynocephalus* | = Yellow baboon |
| *Papio hamadryas* | = Sacred baboon |
| *Papio porcarius* | = Chacma baboon |
| *Presbytis entellus* | = Langur |
| Family Pongidæ | |
| *Gorilla gorilla* | = Gorilla |
| *Hylobates concolor* | = Black gibbon |

| | |
|---|---|
| *Hylobates lar* | = Lar gibbon |
| *Pan paniscus* | = Lesser chimpanzee |
| *Pan troglodytes* | = Chimpanzee |
| *Pongo pygmaeus* | = Orangutan |

ORDER EDENTATA

Family Myrmecophagidæ

| | |
|---|---|
| *Myrmecophaga tridactyla* | = Giant anteater |
| *Tamandua tetradactyla* | = Three-toed anteater |

Family Bradypodidæ

| | |
|---|---|
| *Bradypus tridactylus* | = Three-toed sloth |
| *Cholœpus hoffmanni* | = Two-toed sloth |

Family Dasypodidæ

| | |
|---|---|
| *Dasypus novemcinctus* | = Texas armadillo |
| *Priodontes giganteus* | = Giant armadillo |

ORDER PHOLIDOTA

Family Manidæ

| | |
|---|---|
| *Manis crassicaudata* | = Indian pangolin |
| *Manis javanica* | = Sumatra pangolin |

ORDER LAGOMORPHA

Family Leporidæ

| | |
|---|---|
| *Lepus alleni* | = Antelope jackrabbit |
| *Lepus americanus* | = Snowshoe hare |
| *Lepus arcticus* | = Arctic hare |
| *Lepus californicus* | = Blacktail jackrabbit |
| *Lepus europœus* | = European hare |
| *Lepus timidus* | = Varying hare |
| *Oryctolagus cuniculus* | = European wild rabbit |
| *Sylvilagus floridanus* | = Eastern cottontail |

ORDER RODENTIA

Family Sciuridæ

| | |
|---|---|
| *Atlantoxerus getulus* | = Barbary ground squirrel |
| *Citellus beecheyi* | = California ground squirrel |
| *Citellus pygmæus* | = Little souslik |
| *Citellus tridecemlineatus* | = Thirteen-lined ground squirrel |
| *Cynomys ludovicianus* | = Blacktail prairie dog |
| *Glaucomys volans* | = North American flying squirrel |
| *Marmota bobak* | = Boback marmot |
| *Marmota marmota* | = Alpine marmot |
| *Marmota monax* | = Woodchuck |
| *Ratufa indica* | = Indian giant squirrel |
| *Sciurus carolinensis* | = American gray squirrel |

| | |
|---|---|
| *Sciurus fremonti* | = Fremont chickaree |
| *Sciurus hudsonicus* | = American red squirrel |
| *Sciurus niger* | = Eastern fox squirrel |
| *Sciurus vulgaris* | = European red squirrel |
| *Tamias striatus* | = Eastern chipmunk |

Family Geomyidæ

| | |
|---|---|
| *Geomys bursarius* | = Plains pocket gopher |
| *Thomomys monticola* | = Sierra pocket gopher |
| *Thomomys talpoides* | = Northern pocket gopher |

Family Heteromyidæ

| | |
|---|---|
| *Dipodomys agilis* | = Pacific kangaroo rat |
| *Dipodomys ingens* | = Giant kangaroo rat |
| *Dipodomys merriami* | = Merriam kangaroo rat |
| *Dipodomys ordii* | = Ord kangaroo rat |
| *Dipodomys venustus* | = Santa Cruz kangaroo rat |
| *Perognathus fasciatus* | = Wyoming pocket mouse |

Family Castoridæ

| | |
|---|---|
| *Castor canadensis* | = American beaver |
| *Castor fiber* | = European beaver |

Family Pedetidæ

| | |
|---|---|
| *Pedetes cafer* | = Spring haas |

Family Cricetidæ. Subfamily Cricetinæ.

| | |
|---|---|
| *Cricetus cricetus* | = Hamster |
| *Mesocricetus auratus* | = Golden hamster |
| *Neotoma albigula* | = White-throated wood rat |
| *Neotoma fuscipes* | = Dusky-footed wood rat |
| *Oryzomys palustris* | = Rice rat |
| *Peromyscus boylei* | = Brush mouse |
| *Peromyscus leucopus* | = White-footed mouse |
| *Peromyscus maniculatus* | = Deer mouse |
| *Sigmodon hispidus* | = Hispid cotton rat |

Family Cricetidæ. Subfamily Microtinæ.

| | |
|---|---|
| *Arvicola terrestris* | = Water vole |
| *Clethrionomys gapperi* | = Boreal red-backed vole |
| *Clethrionomys glareolus* | = Common red-backed vole |
| *Dicrostonyx grœnlandicus* | = Greenland collared lemming |
| *Dicrostonyx hudsonicus* | = Hudson Bay collared lemming |
| *Lemmus lemmus* | = Norway lemming |
| *Lemmus trimucronatus* | = Brown lemming |

| | |
|---|---|
| *Microtus agrestis* | = Field vole |
| *Microtus arvalis* | = Common vole |
| *Microtus guentheri* | = Levant vole |
| *Microtus montanus* | = Mountain vole |
| *Microtus nivalis* | = Snow vole |
| *Microtus ochrogaster* | = Prairie meadow vole |
| *Microtus pennsylvanicus* | = Meadow vole |
| *Ondatra zibethica* | = Muskrat |
| *Phenacomys longicaudus* | = Red tree mouse |
| *Synaptomys cooperi* | = Lemming mouse |

Family Cricetidæ. Subfamily Gerbillinæ.

| | |
|---|---|
| *Gerbillus (Dipodillus) dasyurus* | = Wagner's gerbil |
| *Gerbillus gerbillus* | = Lesser Egyptian gerbil |
| *Meriones shawi* | = Shaw's jird |
| *Pachyuromys duprasi* | = Fat-tailed gerbil |

Family Spalacidæ

| | |
|---|---|
| *Spalax leucodon* | = Lesser mole rat |

Family Muridæ

| | |
|---|---|
| *Acomys cahirinus* | = Cairo spiny mouse |
| *Apodemus sylvaticus* | = Long-tailed field mouse |
| *Cricetomys gambianus* | = African giant rat |
| *Lemniscomys barbarus* | = Zebra mouse |
| *Micromys minutus* | = Harvest mouse[1] |
| *Mus musculus* | = House mouse |
| *Rattus manipulus* | = Manipur rat |
| *Rattus mülleri* | = Giant forest rat |
| *Rattus norvegicus* | = Brown (Norway) rat |
| *Rattus rattus* | = Black rat |

Family Gliridæ

| | |
|---|---|
| *Dryomys nitedula* | = Forest dormouse |
| *Eliomys quercinus* | = Garden dormouse |
| *Glis glis* | = Fat dormouse |
| *Muscardinus avellanarius* | = Common dormouse |

Family Zapodidæ

| | |
|---|---|
| *Zapus hudsonicus* | = Meadow jumping mouse |

Family Dipodidæ

| | |
|---|---|
| *Dipus ægyptius* | = Lesser Egyptian jerboa |
| *Dipus sagitta* | = Northern three-toed jerboa |
| *Stylodipus tellum* | = Thick-tailed three-toed jerboa |

Family Hystricidæ
    *Hystrix indica*             = Indian crested porcupine
Family Erethizontidæ
    *Erethizon dorsatum*       = American porcupine
Family Hydrochœridæ
    *Hydrochœrus hydrochœrus* = Capybara
Family Dasyproctidæ
    *Dasyprocta punctata*      = Agouti
Family Chinchillidæ
    *Lagidium peruanum*       = Mountain vizcacha
Family Capromyidæ
    *Myocastor coypus*        = Nutria
Family Ctenomyidæ
    *Ctenomys brasiliensis*     = Tuco tuco
Family Echymyidæ
    *Pröechimys semispinosus*  = Spiny rat
ORDER CETACEA
  Suborder Odontoceti
    *Delphinapterus leucas*    = White whale
    *Hyperoodon rostratus*    = Bottlenosed whale
    *Orcinus orca*            = Killer whale
    *Physeter catodon*        = Sperm whale
    *Tursiops truncatus*      = Bottlenosed dolphin
  Suborder Mysticeti
    *Balæna mysticetus*       = Greenland right whale
    *Balænoptera borealis*    = Finback whale
    *Balænoptera musculus*   = Blue whale
    *Balænoptera physalus*    = Fin whale
    *Megaptera nodosa*       = Humpback whale
    *Rachianectes glaucus*    = Gray whale
ORDER CARNIVORA. SUBORDER FISSI-
  PEDIA.
  Family Canidæ
    *Alopex lagopus*          = Arctic fox
    *Canis latrans*           = Coyote
    *Canis lupus*             = Wolf
    *Lycaon pictus*           = African hunting dog
    *Vulpes bengalensis*      = Bengal fox
    *Vulpes corsak*          = Corsak fox
    *Vulpes fulva*           = American red fox
    *Vulpes regalis*         = Northern plains red fox
    *Vulpes vulpes*          = European red fox

Family Ursidæ
*Melursus ursinus* = Sloth bear
*Thalarctos maritimus* = Polar bear
*Ursus americanus* = Black bear
*Ursus arctos* = Brown bear
*Ursus horribilis* = Grizzly bear

Family Procyonidæ
*Ailuropoda melanoleuca* = Giant panda

Family Mustelidæ. Subfamily Mustelinæ.
*Gulo gulo* = Wolverine
*Martes pennanti* = Fisher
*Martes zibellina* = Sable
*Mustela cicognanii* = Bonaparte weasel
*Mustela erminea* = Stoat (ermine)
*Mustela frenata* = Long-tailed weasel
*Mustela nivalis* = Weasel
*Mustela putorius* = Polecat
*Mustela vison* = Mink
*Pœcilictis lybica* = Lybian striped weasel

Family Mustelidæ. Subfamily Mellivorinæ.
*Mellivora capensis* = Honey badger

Family Mustelidæ. Subfamily Melinæ.
*Meles meles* = European badger

Family Mustelidæ. Subfamily Mephitinæ.
*Conepatus inca* = Andean skunk
*Mephitis macroura* = Hooded skunk
*Mephitis mephitis* = Striped skunk
*Spilogale putorius* = Prairie spotted skunk

Family Mustelidæ. Subfamily Lutrinæ.
*Enhydra lutris* = Sea otter
*Lutra canadensis* = American otter
*Lutra lutra* = European otter

Family Viverridæ. Subfamily Viverrinæ.
*Viverra civetta* = West African civet

Family Viverridæ. Subfamily
   Hemigalinæ.
  *Chrotogale ownstoni*      = Indo-Chinese civet
Family Viverridæ. Subfamily
   Herpestinæ.
  *Herpestes urva*      =Crab-eating mongoose
  *Herpestes vitticolis*      = Striped-necked mongoose
Family Hyænidæ
  *Crocuta crocuta*      = Spotted hyena
  *Hyæna hyæna*      = Striped hyena
  *Proteles cristatus*      = Aardwolf
Family Felidæ
  *Acinonyx jubatus*      = Cheetah
  *Felis leo*      = Lion
  *Felis manul*      = Pallas's cat
  *Felis mearnsi*      = Ocelot
  *Felis pardus*      = Leopard
  *Felis viverrina*      = Fishing cat
  *Lynx canadensis*      = Lynx

ORDER CARNIVORA. SUBORDER PIN-
  NIPEDIA.
Family Otariidæ
  *Callorhinus alascanus*      = Alaska fur seal
  *Otaria byronia*      = Falkland sea lion
Family Odobenidæ
  *Odobenus rosmarus*      = Walrus
Family Phocidæ
  *Cystophora cristata*      = Hooded seal
  *Erignathus barbatus*      = Bearded seal
  *Halichœrus grypus*      = Gray seal
  *Hydrurga leptonyx*      = Leopard seal
  *Leptonychotes weddelli*      = Weddell's seal
  *Lobodon carcinophagus*      = Crab-eating seal
  *Mirounga leonina*      = Southern elephant seal
  *Monachus monachus*      = Monk seal
  *Ommatophoca rossi*      = Ross seal
  *Phoca grœnlandica*      = Harp seal
  *Phoca hispida*      = Ringed seal
  *Phoca vitulina*      = Common seal

ORDER TUBULIDENTATA
Family Orycteropidæ
  *Orycteropus afer*      = Aardvark

ORDER PROBOSCIDEA
Family Elephantidæ
 *Elephas maximus*     = Indian elephant
 *Loxodonta africana*    = African elephant

ORDER SIRENIA
Family Trichechidæ
 *Trichechus latirostris*    = Florida manatee

ORDER PERISSODACTYLA
Family Equidæ
 *Equus asinus somalicus*   = Somali wild ass
 *Equus burchelli*      = Burchell's zebra
 *Equus grevyi*       = Grevy's zebra
 *Equus hemionus hemionus* = Mongolian wild ass
 *Equus hemionus khur*    = Indian wild ass
 *Equus zebra*       = Mountain zebra
Family Rhinocerotidæ
 *Diceros bicornis*     = Black rhinoceros

ORDER ARTIODACTYLA
Family Suidæ
 *Hylochœrus meinertzhageni* = Giant forest hog
 *Phacochœrus æthiopicus*   = Wart hog
 *Sus scrofa*       = Wild boar
Family Tayassuidæ
 *Tayassu angulatus*    = Peccary
Family Hippopotamidæ
 *Chœropsis liberiensis*    = Pigmy hippopotamus
 *Hippopotamus amphibius*   = Hippopotamus
Family Camelidæ
 *Camelus bactrianus*    = Camel
 *Lama vicugna*      = Vicuna
Family Cervidæ
 *Alces americana*     = Moose
 *Capreolus capreolus*    = Roe deer
 *Cervus canadensis*     = Elk
 *Cervus elaphus*      = Red deer
 *Odocoileus hemionus*    = Mule deer
 *Odocoileus virginianus*    = White-tailed deer
 *Rangifer caribou*     = Caribou (reindeer)
Family Giraffidæ
 *Giraffa camelopardis*    = Giraffe
Family Antilocapridæ
 *Antilocapra americana*   = Pronghorn

Family Bovidæ. Subfamily
    Bovinæ.
  *Bison bison*               = American bison
  *Boocercus eurycerus*    = Bongo
  *Bos banteng*            = Banteng
  *Bos gaurus*             = Gaur
  *Bos sauveli*            = Kouprey
  *Syncerus cafer*        = Cape buffalo
  *Taurotragus oryx*      = Eland
  *Tragelaphus scriptus*    = Bushbuck

Family Bovidæ. Subfamily
    Hippotraginæ.
  *Addax nasomaculatus*   = Addax
  *Adenota kob thomasi*   = Uganda kob
  *Alcelaphus caama*     = Cape hartebeest
  *Connochætes gnou*     = Wildebeest
  *Damaliscus korrigum*    = Topi
  *Hippotragus equinus*    = Roan antelope
  *Hippotragus niger*     = Sable antelope
  *Kobus defassa*        = Defassa waterbuck
  *Redunca redunca*      = Reedbuck

Family Bovidæ. Subfamily
    Antilopinæ.
  *Æpyceros melampus*    = Impala
  *Antidorcas marsupialis*   = Springbok
  *Gazella dama*         = Dama gazelle
  *Gazella granti*        = Grant's gazelle
  *Gazella thomsonii*     = Thomson's gazelle
  *Litocranius walleri*     = Waller's gazelle
  *Ourebia ourebi*       = Oribi

Family Bovidæ. Subfamily
    Caprinæ.
  *Ammotragus lervia*     = Barbary sheep
  *Capra ibex*           = Ibex
  *Hemitragus jemlahicus*   = Tahr
  *Ovibos moschatus*     = Muskox
  *Ovis canadensis*      = Bighorn sheep
  *Ovis dalli*           = Dall sheep
  *Rupicapra rupicapra*    = Chamois

**335**

# General Bibliography

IN THIS general bibliography are listed only the comprehensive works indispensable to the mammalogist and the special monographs to which frequent reference has been made in this book. The latter may prove useful as models for the reader who wishes to undertake research of his own. Their study cannot be too highly recommended.

### Morphology and Generalities

CABRERA, A. (1922). *Manual de Mastozoologia*. Madrid, Barcelona. 440 + 12 pp. A splendid manual, unjustly neglected.

WEBER, M. (1927–8). *Die Säugetiere*. Jena, 2nd ed.; Vol. 1, xv + 444 pp., Morphology, with H. M. DE BURLET; Vol. 2, xxiv + 898 pp., Systematics, with O. ABEL. A real classic, unfortunately out of print. Extensive bibliography.

### Classification

GRASSÉ, P. P., ed. (in press). *Traité de zoologie*. Vol. XVII. *Mammifères, Systématique*. Paris, Masson. Concisely describes every living genus. Well illustrated.

SIMPSON, G. G. (1945). "The Principles of Classification and a Classification of Mammals." *Bull. Amer. Mus. Nat. Hist.*, Vol. 85, xvi + 350 pp. The most up-to-date classification of the mammals. Includes a list of all recent and fossil genera and gives their distribution in space and time.

### Ethology and Behavior

BREHM, A. (1912–16). *Brehms Tierleben. Die Säugetiere*. 5th ed., revised by L. HECK and M. HILZHEIMER. Leipzig, 4 vols. with many black and colored plates. The best comprehensive work on the life of the mammals; this edition has been extensively revised as compared with previous editions.

HAMILTON, W. J., JR. (1939). *American Mammals: Their Lives, Habits, and Economic Relations*. New York, McGraw-Hill, xii + 434 pp. An excellent modern book; North America is viewed as extending from the Isthmus of Panama to the Canadian Arctic; bibliographies appended to the chapters.

HEDIGER, H. (1950). *Wild Animals in Captivity: an Outline of the Biology of Zoological Gardens*. London, Butterworths, ix + 207 pp. English translation, revised, of the German edition of 1942; bibliography.

HEDIGER, H. (1951). *Observations sur la psychologie animale dans les parcs nationaux du Congo Belge*. Bruxelles, 196 pp. Completes the preceding. A thought-provoking book.

KRUMBIEGEL, I. (1930–1). *Mammalia*. In *Biologie der Tiere Deutschlands*, Parts 31 and 32, 377 pp. One of the best general books on mammal biology, but strictly limited to the species of the German fauna; extended bibliography.

### Ecology

ALLEE, W. C., EMERSON, A. A., PARK, O., PARK, T., and SCHMIDT, K. P. (1949). *Principles of Animal Ecology*. Philadelphia and London, Saunders, xii + 837 pp. The best modern comprehensive survey of animal ecology; indispensable for all ecologic research; extended bibliography. Does not make unnecessary a careful reading of the following classics.

BODENHEIMER, F. S. (1938). *Problems of Animal Ecology*. London, Oxford University Press.

DICE, L. R. (1952). *Natural Communities*. Ann Arbor, Univ. Michigan Press, x + 547 pp., fig.

ELTON, C. (1927). *Animal Ecology*. London, Sidgwick and Jackson.

HESSE, R., ALLEE, W. C., and SCHMIDT, K. P. (1951). *Ecological Animal Geography*. Second edition. New York, Wiley, xiii + 715 pp.

### Evolution

HUXLEY, J. (1943). *Evolution, the Modern Synthesis*. London and New York, numerous English editions and one American edition. A rich compendium of facts set forth by a zoologist especially interested in the vertebrates; large bibliography.

MAYR, E. (1942). *Systematics and the Origin of Species*. New York, Columbia University Press, xiv + 334 pp. A classic.

SIMPSON, G. G. (1949). *The Meaning of Evolution: a Study of the History of Life and of its Significance for Man.* New Haven, Yale University Press, xv + 364 pp. A brilliant synthesis of modern evolutionary theory, written by one of the best contemporary mammalogists; will serve as an introduction to the earlier and more technical work of the same author, *Tempo and Mode in Evolution,* 1944, New York, Columbia University Press, xviii + 237 pp.

### Faunistic Works

We list below some recent comprehensive works useful in identifying the species occurring in certain countries. Many of these books also contain biological data. Some of them do not enable users to identify the small mammals with certainty, and then it is necessary to refer to taxonomic monographs, especially ELLERMAN's *The Families and Genera of Living Rodents,* London, 1940–9, 3 volumes.

### The European Fauna

BARRETT-HAMILTON, G. E. H. (1910–21). *A History of British Mammals,* continued by M. A. C. HINTON. Twenty-one parts have been published. Unfortunately not completed; only the micromammals are covered in the parts that have appeared.

BAUMANN, F. (1949). *Die freilebenden Säugetiere der Schweiz.* Bern, Hans Huber, xiv + 492 pp. Rich anatomical iconography; bibliography.

CABRERA, A. (1914). *Mamiferos.* Fauna iberica, Madrid, xviii + 441 pp., 12 pls.

HAINARD, R. (1948–9). *Les Mammifères sauvages d'Europe.* Neuchâtel and Paris, Delachaux et Niestlé, 2 volumes, 268 and 273 pp., 54 plates. Essentially biological; a small but lively book, full of original observations.

IJSSELING, M. A., and SCHEYGROND, A. (1950). *De Zoogdieren van Nederland.* Zutphen, Thieme, 2nd edition revised, viii + 544 pp., 87 plates, 301 figs. A model of national faunal work; much biological information; extensive bibliography.

MATTHEWS, L. H. (1952). *British Mammals.* London, Collins. A good introduction, but a complete, up to date, and biologically minded natural history of British mammals remains to be written (the same is true for the French and German faunas).

MILLER, G. S. (1912). *Catalogue of the Mammals of Western Europe.* London, British Museum, xv + 1019 pp., 213 figs. Fundamental for taxonomy; this volume is not a mere catalogue, as it contains keys and descriptions.

### The Asiatic Fauna

By way of introduction, the reader should consult the excellent small manual by G. H. H. TATE (*Mammals of Eastern Asia*, New York, Macmillan, 1947, xiv + 366 pp.). Biological information is unfortunately very slight. On the other hand one will find many ethological data in a small book by S. H. PRATER (*The Book of Indian Animals*. Bombay Nat. Hist. Soc., no date given, xxxii + 263 pp., 176 plates). For more technical study, the following are to be consulted:

ALLEN, G. M. (1938–40). *The Mammals of China and Mongolia*. New York, American Mus. Nat. Hist., 2 volumes.

ELLERMAN, J. R., and MORRISON-SCOTT, T. C. S. (1951). *Checklist of Palaearctic and Indian Mammals, 1758–1945*. London, British Museum, 810 pp. The basic checklist for Eurasia and North Africa; covers all of Asia except the Malay Peninsula and the Malay Archipelago, already covered by CHASEN, F. N., "A Handlist of Malaysian Mammals" (*Bull. Raffles Mus.*, No. 15, 1940).

OGNEV, S. I. (1928–50). *The Mammals of Eastern Europe and Northern Asia*. Moscow, 7 volumes. In Russian; still unfinished.

POCOCK, R. I. (1939–41). *Mammalia*. Fauna of British India, including Ceylon and Burma. London, 2 volumes. Unfortunately not finished.

### The African Fauna

ALLEN, G. M. (1939). "A Check List of African Mammals," *Bull. Mus. Comp. Zool.*, Vol. 83, 763 pp. The basic catalogue.

HILL, J. E., and CARTER, T. D. (1941). "The Mammals of Angola, Africa," *Bull. Am. Mus. Nat. Hist.*, 78:1–211, pls. 1–17. Strictly systematic.

MALBRANT, R., and MacLATCHY, A. (1949). *Faune de l'Équateur africain français*. Tome 2. *Mammifères*. Paris, Lechevalier, 323 pp., 28 pls. Taxonomy and biological notes; a very useful volume.

ROBERTS, A. (1951). *The Mammals of South Africa*. Cape Town, xlviii + 700 pp., 78 pls. Strictly taxonomic.

SCHOUTEDEN, H. (1948). "*Faune du Congo Belge et du Ruanda-Urundi*," Vol. 1. *Mammifères*. Tervuren, *Ann. Mus. Congo Belge*, viii + 331 pp. Strictly systematic; unfortunately lacks biological data.

VERHEYEN, R. (1951). *Contribution à l'étude éthologique des mammifères du Parc National de l'Upemba*. Bruxelles, Institut des Parcs Nationaux du Congo Belge, 161 pp., 20 pls. One of the best books on the biology of African mammals.

### The North American Fauna

ANTHONY, H. E. (1928). *Field Book of North American Mammals*. New York, Putnam, xxvi + 625 pp., 32 pls. Primarily systematic. The only general manual for identifying North American species and subspecies. For several states this book may be replaced to advantage by local faunistic works, such as Burt (Michigan), Hall (Nevada), etc.

Burt, W. H., and Grossenheider, R. P. (1952). *A Field Guide to the Mammals, giving field marks of all the species found north of the Mexican boundary.* Boston, Houghton Mifflin, xxi + 200 pp., 32 pls., range maps, and text figures. A very useful guide for field identification of species (no subspecies); without biological data.

Hamilton, W. J., Jr. (1943). *The Mammals of Eastern United States: an account of recent land mammals occurring east of the Mississippi.* Ithaca, Comstock.

Cahalane, V. H. (1947). *Mammals of North America.* New York, Macmillan, x + 682 pp. Primarily biological; useful bibliography.

### The Neotropical Fauna

Cabrera, A., and Yepes, J. (1940). *Mamiferos sud-americanos. Vida, costumbres y descripcion.* Buenos-Aires, Comp. Argentina de Editores, 370 pp., 78 colored plates. Excellent general work; taxonomy and biology.

Enders, R. K. (1935). "Mammalian Life-histories from Barro Colorado Island," Panama. *Bull. Mus. Comp. Zool.,* 78:385–502, 5 pls. A "must" for every visitor to the Island.

Goldman, E. A. (1920). "Mammals of Panama." *Smithsonian Misc. Collections,* Vol. 69, No. 5, 309 pp., pl.

Goodwin, G. G. (1945). "Mammals of Costa Rica." *Bull. Am. Mus. Nat. Hist.,* 87:271–474, 50 figs. Unfortunately without many biological data.

Osgood, W. H. (1943). "The Mammals of Chile." *Field Mus. Nat. Hist., Publ. Zool.,* Vol. 30, 268 pp. Strictly taxonomic.

Pearson, O. P. (1951). "Mammals in the Highlands of Southern Peru." *Bull. Mus. Comp. Zool.,* 106:117–176, 8 pls. A stimulating study of a very peculiar habitat.

### Australia, Indonesia, the Pacific

Carter, T. D., Hill, J. E., and Tate, G. H. H. (1946). *Mammals of the Pacific World.* New York, Macmillan, xvi + 227 pp. General introduction.

Troughton, E. (1947). *Furred Animals of Australia.* New York, Scribner, xxvii + 374 pp., 25 colored pls. Taxonomy and biology.

### Selected Biological Monographs on Species and Groups

The following monographs are not of similar scope nor of equal value, but all can prove helpful to the field worker.

## Monotremes and Marsupials

BURRELL, H. (1927). *The Platypus.* Sydney, vii + 227 pp., pl. Should be supplemented by Fleay's paper (see page 353).

HARTMAN, C. G. (1952). *Possums.* Austin, Univ. Texas Press, xiii + 174 pp., 104 figs.

## Insectivores

GODET, R. (1951). "*Contribution à l'éthologie de la taupe (Talpa europæa)*." *Bull. Soc. Zool. France*, 75:107–128.

HERTER, K. (1938). *Die Biologie der europäischen Igel.* Leipzig. Monographie der Wildsäugetiere, No. 5, 222 pp.

## Bats

ALLEN, G. M. (1939). *Bats.* Cambridge, Harvard University Press, x + 368 pp. The best general work on the biology of bats. Bibliography.

EISENTRAUT, M. (1937). *Die deutschen Fledermäuse, eine biologische Studie.* Leipzig. Monographie der Wildsäugetiere, No. 2, 184 pp. Excellent digest of the author's researches.

EISENTRAUT, M. (1945). "*Biologie der Flederhunde (Megachiroptera).*" *Biologia Generalis*, 18:327–435.

RYBERG, O. (1947). *Studies on bats and bat parasites.* Stockholm, Svensk Natur., xvi + 330 pp., 55 pls. Useful complement for the preceding works, with extended bibliography.

## Primates

CARPENTER, C. R. (1934). "A Field Study of the Behavior and Social Relations of the Howling Monkeys." *Comp. Psychol. Monographs*, Vol. 10, No. 2, 168 pp., 16 pls. A model of its kind, like the following monographs by the same author.

CARPENTER, C. R. (1935). "Behavior of Red Spider Monkeys in Panama." *Jour. Mammal.*, 16:171–180.

CARPENTER, C. R. (1940). "A Field Study in Siam of the Behavior and Social Relations of the Gibbon (*Hylobates lar*)." *Comp. Psychol. Monographs*, Vol. 16, No. 5, 212 pp., 19 pls.

HADDOW, A. J. (1952). Field and laboratory studies on an African monkey, *Cercopithecus ascanius schmidti*. Matschie. *Proc. Zool. Soc. London*, 122:297–394, 3 pls. The first thorough monograph on an African monkey.

RUCH, T. C. (1941). *Bibliographica Primatologica: A Classified Bibliography of Primates Other than Man.* Part 1. *Anatomy, embryology, and quantitative morphology; physiology, pharmacology, and psycho-*

*biology; primate phylogeny and miscellanea.* Springfield (Ill.), Thomas, xxvii + 241 pp. An indispensable working-tool.

YERKES, R. M. (1943). *Chimpanzees: A Laboratory Colony.* New Haven, Yale University Press, xv + 321 pp., 63 pls.

YERKES, R. M., and YERKES, A. W. (1929). *The Great Apes: A Study of Anthropoid Life.* New Haven, Yale University Press, xix + 652 pp. This work, like the preceding, is of the greatest importance for the field naturalist, although it is based essentially on observations made on captive animals and in the laboratory.

### Edentates

BRITTON, S. W. (1941). "Form and Function in the Sloth." *Quart. Rev. Biol.,* 16:13–34, 190–207.

TABER, F. W. (1945). "Contributions on the Life History and Ecology of the Nine-banded Armadillo." *Jour. Mammal.,* 26:211–226.

### Rodents

CRIDDLE, S. (1930). "The Prairie Pocket Gopher," *Thomomys talpoides rufescens." Jour. Mammal.,* 11:265–280.

EIBL-EIBESFELDT, I. (1950). "*Beiträge zur Biologie der Haus- und der Ahrenmaus nebst einigen Beobachtungen an anderen Nagern." Zeits. für Tierpsychol.,* 7:558–587.

FITCH, H. S. (1948). Ecology of the California Ground Squirrel on Grazing Lands. *Amer. Midl. Natur.,* 39:513–96. Completes Linsdale's monograph.

HAMILTON, W. J., JR. (1934). "The Life History of the Rufescent Woodchuck *Marmota monax rufescens." Ann. Carnegie Mus.,* 23:85–178.

HATT, R. T. (1929). "The Red Squirrel: its life history and habits, with special reference to the Adirondacks of New York and the Harvard forest." *Roosevelt Wild Life Annals,* Vol. 2, No. 1, 145 pp.

LINSDALE, J. M. (1946). *The California Ground Squirrel. A record of observations made on the Hastings Natural History Reservation.* Berkeley, University of California Press, xi + 475 pp. A somewhat confused monograph, but one full of facts.

LINSDALE, J. M., and TEVIS, L. P., JR. (1951). *The Dusky-footed Wood Rat, a record of observations made on the Hastings Natural History Reservation.* Berkeley, University of California Press, vii + 664 pp., fig. An even more confused monograph, so overdetailed that it is sometimes difficult to disentangle the more important facts.

McCABE, T. T., and BLANCHARD, B. (1950). *Three Species of Peromyscus.* Santa Barbara, Rood Associates, v + 136 pp., fig.

MOHR, E. (1950). *Die freilebenden Nagetiere Deutschlands und der Nachbarländer.* Second ed., revised. Jena, Fischer, vii + 162 pp., fig.

PEARSON, O. P. (1948). "Life History of Mountain Vizcachas in Peru." *Jour. Mammal.,* 29:345–373.

SOUTHERN, H. N. (1948). "Sexual and Aggressive Behavior in the Wild Rabbit." *Behaviour,* 1:173–194. A splendid study, to be supplemented by the article published in *Ann. Appl. Biol.,* Vol. 27, 1940, p. 509.

WARREN, E. R. (1927). *The Beaver.* Baltimore, Williams and Wilkins, xx + 177 pp., pl.

### Cetaceans

MACKINTOSH, N. A. (1946). "The Natural History of Whalebone Whales." *Smithsonian Report,* pp. 235–264. Appeared also in *Biol. Reviews,* Vol. 21, No. 2. Survey of modern works with bibliography.

McBRIDE, A. F., and HEBB, D. O. (1948). "Behavior of the Captive Bottlenose Dolphin, *Tursiops truncatus." Jour. Comp. Psychol.,* 41:111–23.

### Pinnipeds

BARTHOLOMEW, G. A., JR. (1952). "Reproductive and social behavior of the northern elephant seal." *Univ. Calif. Publ. Zool.,* 47:369–472, pls. 38–57.

BERTRAM, G. C. L. (1940). "The Biology of the Weddel and Crabeater Seals, with a study of the comparative behavior of the Pinnipedia." London, *Brit. Graham Land Exped. 1934–37, Sci. Reports,* 1:1–139, 10 pls.

DARLING, F. F. (1947). "The Life History of the Atlantic Grey Seal." In *Natural History in the Highlands and Islands.* London, Collins, pp. 217–31.

DAVIES, J. L. (1948). "Observations on the Grey Seal (*Halichœrus grypus*) at Ramsey Island, Pembrokeshire." *Proc. Zool. Soc. London,* 119:673–92, 2 pls.

HAMILTON, J. E. (1934). "The Southern Sea Lion, *Otaria byronia* (De Blainville)." *Discovery Reports,* 8:269–318, pls. 1–13.

MATTHEWS, L. H. (1929). "The Natural History of the Elephant Seal." *Discovery Reports,* 1:233–56, pls. 19–24.

### Carnivores

FISHER, E. M. (1939). "Habits of the Southern Sea Otter." *Jour. Mammal.,* 20:21–36.

MATTHEWS, L. H. (1939). "The Bionomics of the Spotted Hyaena, *Crocuta crocuta* Erxl." *Proc. Zool. Soc. London,* 109:43–56, pls. 1–4.

MURIE, A. (1944). "The Wolves of Mount McKinley." Washington, *Fauna of the National Parks of the U.S.,* No. 5, xx + 238 pp.

NEAL, E. (1948). *The Badger.* London, Collins, xv + 158 pp., 24 pls. Excellent monograph.

SCHMIDT, F. (1943). *Naturgeschichte des Baum- und Steinmarders.* Leipzig, Monographie der Wildsäugetiere, No. 10, 258 pp., 32 pls.

### Ungulates

BENINDE, J. (1937). *Zur Naturgeschichte des Rothirsches.* Leipzig, Monographie der Wildsäugetiere, No. 4, vii + 223 pp.

BUECHNER, H. K. (1950). "Life History, Ecology, and Range Use of the Pronghorn Antelope." *Amer. Midland Nat.,* 43:257–354.

COUTURIER, M. A. J. (1938). *Le Chamois, Rupicapra rupicapra* (L.) Grenoble, Arthaud, xi + 857 pp., 103 pls.

DARLING, F. (1937). *A Herd of Red Deer. A study in animal behavior.* Oxford Univ. Press, x + 215 pp., 7 pls.

MURIE, O. J. (1951). *The Elk of North America.* Washington, Wildlife Management Institute, 376 pp., pl.

### Mammalogical Journals

At present there are only three journals devoted exclusively to the study of the mammals. These are, in order of establishment:

*Journal of Mammalogy,* published quarterly by the American Society of Mammalogists; in publication since 1920. The present editor is Dr. W. R. Eadie, Fernow Hall, Cornell University, Ithaca, N. Y.

*Zeitschrift für Säugetierkunde. Im Auftrage der Deutschen Gesellschaft für Säugetierkunde,* Berlin. In publication since 1926, but this journal ceased publication in 1943. A new quarterly journal, *Säugetierkundliche Mitteilungen,* commenced publication in Munich in January 1953.

*Mammalia. Morphologie, biologie, systématique des Mammifères,* Paris, 55, rue de Buffon. In publication since 1936.

The annual mammalogical bibliography is published in Section 18 of the *Zoological Record,* published by the Zoological Society of London, Regent's Park, London N.W. 8, England.

# Special Bibliographies

## Chapter 1

BARTHOLOMEW, G. A., JR., and CASWELL, H. H., JR. (1951). "Locomotion in kangaroo rats and its adaptive significance." *Jour. Mammal.*, 32: 155–9.

BOURDELLE, E. (1934). *"Les allures de la giraffe, en particulier le galop."* *Bull. Mus. Nat. Hist. Nat.* Paris, 1934:329–39.

DOR, M. (1937). *La morphologie de la queue des mammifères dans ses rapports avec la locomotion.* Paris, 184 pp., 8 pls.

EISENTRAUT, M. (1936). *"Beitrag zur Mechanik der Fledermausfluges."* *Zeits. Wiss. Zool.*, 148:159–88.

GALAMBOS, R., and GRIFFIN, D. R. (1942). "Obstacle avoidance by flying bats: The cries of bats." *Jour. Expr. Zool.*, 89:475–90.

GAWN, R. W. N. (1948). "Aspects of locomotion of whales." *Nature*, 161:44–6.

GRIFFIN, D. R., and GALAMBOS, R. (1941). "The sensory basis of obstacle avoidance by flying bats." *Jour. Exp. Zool.*, 86:481–506.

HARTRIDGE, H. (1945). "Acoustic control in the flight of bats." *Nature*, 156:490–1.

HATT, R. T. (1932). "The vertebral columns of ricochetal rodents." *Bull. Amer. Mus. Nat. Hist.*, 68:599–738, pl.

HOWELL, A. B. (1944). *Speed in animals; their specialization for running and leaping.* Chicago, Univ. of Chicago Press.

IRVING, L. (1939). "Respiration in diving animals." *Physiol. Reviews*, 19: 112–34.

IRVING, L. (1942). "The action of heart and circulation during diving." *Trans. New York Acad. Sci.*, 5(2):11–16.

IRVING, L., SCHOLANDER, P. F., and GRINNELL, S. W. (1941). "The respiration of the porpoise *Tursiops truncatus.*" *Jour. Cell. Comp. Physiol.*, 17:145–68.

IRVING, L., SCHOLANDER, P. F., and GRINNELL, S. W. (1942). "Signification of the heart rate to the diving ability of seals." *Jour. Cell. Comp. Physiol.*, 18:283–97.

IRVING, L., SCHOLANDER, P. F., and GRINNELL, S. W. (1942). "The regulation of arterial blood pressure in the seal during diving." *Amer. Jour. Physiol.*, 135:557–66.

PARRY, D. A. (1949). "The swimming of whales and a discussion of Gray's paradox." *Brit. Jour. Exp. Biol.*, 26:24–34, 2 pls.

SANDERSON, I. T. (1940). "The mammals of the North Cameroons forest area." *Trans. Zool. Soc. London*, 24:623–725, pls. 1–22.

VESEY-FITZGERALD, B. (1947). "*Les fonctions sensorielles des chauves-souris.*" *Endeavour*, pp. 36–41, 2 pls.

### Chapter 2

BUYTENDIJK, E. J. J. (1920). "*L'odorat du chien.*" *Archives néerl. Physiol.*, pp. 434–57.

CAHALANE, V. H. (1942). "Caching and recovery of food by the Western fox squirrel." *Jour. Wildlife Management*, 6:338–52.

COWAN, I. McT., and BRINK, V. C. (1949). "Natural game licks in the Rocky Mountain national parks of Canada." *Jour. Mammal.*, 30: 379–87.

DEGERBÖL, M. (1927). "Do moles (*Talpa europæa* L.) store up worms?" *Videnskab. Meddelel. Dansk naturhist. Foren.*, 84:195–202.

DITMARS, R. L., and GREENHALL, A. M. (1935). "The vampire bat, a presentation of undescribed habits and review of its history." *Zoologica*, 19:53–76, pls. 5–7.

DUNN, L. H. (1933). "Observations on the carnivorous habits of the spear-nosed bat, *Phyllostomus hastatus panamensis*, Allen, in Panama." *Jour. Mammal.*, 14:188–99.

DUSI, J. L. (1949). "Methods for the determination of food habits by plant microtechniques and histology and their application to cottontail rabbit food habits." *Jour. Wildlife Management*, 13:295–8, pl. 10.

EISENTRAUT, M. (1950). "*Die Ernährung der Fledermäuse (Microchiroptera).*" *Zool. Jahrb.*, 79:114–77.

HARDY, G. A. (1949). "Squirrel cache of fungi." *Canad. Field Naturalist*, 63:86–7.

HAUCHECORNE, F. (1927). "*Studien über die wirtschaftliche Bedeutung des Maulwurfes (Talpa europæa).*" *Zeits. f. Morphol. Oekol. Tiere*, 9: 439–571.

HEIM DE BALSAC, H. (1951). "*Mycophagie méconnue de certains mammifères.*" *Revue de Mycologie*, 16:238–41.

KRISZAT, G. (1940). *"Untersuchungen zur Sinnesphysiologie, Biologie und Umwelt des Maulwurfes (Talpa europæa)."* Zeits. f. Morphol. Oekol. Tiere, 36:446–511.

LÖHNER, L. (1926). *"Untersuchungen über die geruschphysiologische Leistungsfähigkeit von Polizeihunden."* Pflügers Archiv., 212:84–94.

MATTHEWS, L. H. (1932). "Lobster krill, anomuran Crustacea that are the food of whales." *Discovery Reports*, 5:467.

MATTHEWS, L. H. (1939). "The bionomics of the spotted hyæna, *Crocuta crocuta* Erxl." *Proc. Zool. Soc. London*, A, 109:43–56, 4 pls.

MURIE, O. J. (1940). "Notes on the sea-otter." *Jour. Mammal.*, 21:119–31.

PEARSON, O. P. (1942). "On the cause and nature of a poisonous action produced by the bite of a shrew (*Blarina brevicauda*)." *Jour. Mammal.*, 23:159–66.

PORSCH, O. (1932). *"Crescentia, eine Fledermausblume."* Oesterr. Bot. Zeits., 80:31–44, pls. 9–10.

POULTON, E. B. (1929). "British insectivorous bats and their prey." *Proc. Zool. Soc. London*, 1929, 2:277–303.

ROONWAL, M. L. (1949). "Systematics, ecology and bionomics of mammals studied in connection with Tsutsugamushi disease (scrub typhus) in the Assam-Burma war theatre during 1945." *Trans. Nat. Inst. Sci. India*, 3:67–122, 6 pls.

SCHMIDT-NIELSEN, B., SCHMIDT-NIELSEN, K., BROKAW, A. and SCHNEIDERMAN, H. (1948). "Water conservation in desert rodents." *Jour. Cell. Comp. Physiol.*, 32:331–60.

SCOTT, T. G. (1943). "Some food-coactions of the Northern Plains red fox." *Ecol. Monogr.*, 13:427–79.

SHAW, W. T. (1934). "The ability of the giant kangaroo-rat as a harvester and storer of seeds." *Jour. Mammal.*, 15:275–86.

SHAW, W. T. (1936). "Moisture and its relation to the cone-storing habit of the western pine-squirrel." *Jour. Mammal.*, 17:337–49.

SOUTHERN, H. N. and WATSON, J. S. (1941). "Summer food of the red fox (*Vulpes vulpes*) in Great Britain: a preliminary report." *Jour. Anim. Ecol.*, 10:1–11.

TEVIS, L., JR. (1952). "Autumn foods of chipmunks and golden-mantled ground squirrels in the northern Sierra Nevada." *Jour. Mammal.*, 33:198–205.

VARLET, F. (1949). *"Les éléphants médecins."* Notes africaines, 1949, p. 100.

VELLARD, J. (1950). *"Résistance de la moufette andine au venin de serpent."* Travaux de l'Institut Français d'Études Andines, Lima, 2:19–38.

Chapter 3

ARLTON, A. V. (1936). "An ecological study of the mole." *Jour. Mammal.*, 17:349–71.

BARBOUR, T. (1932). "A peculiar roosting habit of bats." *Quart. Rev. Biol.*, 7:307–12.

BELA, B. (1934). *"Le Spalax de Hongrie (Spalax hungaricus)." Terre et Vie*, 4:323–33.

BLAIR, W. F. (1940). "A study of prairie deer-mouse populations in southern Michigan." *Amer. Midl. Natur.*, 24:273–305.

BLAIR, W. F. (1943). "Populations of the deer mouse and associated small mammals in the mesquite association of southern New Mexico." *Contr. Lab. Vert. Biol. Univ. Michigan*, 21:1–40.

BURT, W. H. (1940). "Territorial behavior and populations of some small mammals in southern Michigan." *Misc. Publ. Mus. Zool. Univ. Michigan*, 45:1–58, 2 pl.

BURT, W. H. (1943). "Territoriality and home range concepts as applied to mammals." *Jour. Mammal.*, 24:346–52.

CRIDDLE, S. (1930). "The prairie pocket gopher *Thomomys talpoides.*" *Jour. Mammal.*, 11:265–80.

DAVIS, D. E. (1945). "The home range of some Brazilian mammals." *Jour. Mammal.*, 26:119–27.

DAVIS, D. E., EMLEN, J. T., and STOKES, A. W. (1948). "Studies on home range in the brown rat." *Jour. Mammal.*, 29:207–25.

DIDIER, R. and MATHIAS, P. (1936). *"Le Hamster (Cricetus cricetus L.)." Mammalia*, 1:15–23.

EISENTRAUT, M. (1928). *"Ueber die Baue und den Winterschlaf des Hamsters (Cricetus cricetus L.)." Zeits. f. Säugetierkunde*, 3:142.

EISENTRAUT, M. (1933). *"Biologische Studien im bolivianischen Chaco. III. Beitrag zur Biologie der Säugetierfauna." Zeits. f. Säugetierkunde*, 8:47–69, 1 pl.

FENIUK, B. K. and KAZANTZEVA, J. M. (1937). "The ecology of *Dipus sagitta.*" *Jour. Mammal.*, 18:409–26.

HAYNE, D. W. (1949). "Calculation of size of home range." *Jour. Mammal.*, 30:1–18. (See also 31:26–39, 1950.)

GUIRAUD, M. (1948). *"Contribution à l'étude du Phacochoerus aethiopicus." Mammalia*, 12:54–66.

HEDIGER, H. (1949). *"Säugetier-Territorien und ihre Markierung." Bijdragen tot de Dierkunde*, 28:172–84.

HOWARD, W. E. (1949). "Dispersal, amount of inbreeding, and longevity in a local population of prairie deer mice on the George Reserve, southern Michigan." *Contr. Lab. vert. Biol.*, 43:1–50.

JETTMAR, H. M. (1926). *"Die Bauten einiger transbaikalischer Säugetiere in schematischer Darstellung."* Zeits. f. Säugetierkunde, 1:13–22.

KACHKAROV, D. N., and KOROVINE, E. P. (1942). *La Vie dans les déserts.* French edition by Th. Monod. Paris, Payot, 361 pp., 32 pls., 63 figs.

KOLOSOV, A. M. (1935). ("On the biology of the korsak fox and the fox of the steppes"). *Bull. Soc. Natur. Moscou, Ser. Biol.,* 44:165–77 (in Russian).

LAVAUDEN, L. (1933). *"Le Aye-aye."* Terre et Vie, 3:142–52.

MOHR, C. O. (1947). "Tables of equivalent populations of North American mammals." *Amer. Midl. Natur.,* 37:223–49.

REED, C. A. and CARR, W. H. (1949). "Use of cactus as protection by hooded skunk." *Jour. Mammal.,* 30:79–80 (see also Carr, *Nat. History,* 57:28–33, 1948).

REGNIER, R. and PUSSARD, R. (1926). *"Le Campagnol des champs (Microtus arvalis* Palbes) *et sa destruction."* Ann. Epiphyties, 12:385–522, 8 pl.

SALMAN, D. H. (1949). "On the home range of cottontails." *Physiol. Comp. Oecol.,* 1:95–109.

SCHMIDT-NIELSEN, B. and SCHMIDT-NIELSEN, K. (1950). "Evaporative water loss in desert rodents in their natural habitat." *Ecology,* 31: 75–85.

SHELDON, W. G. (1950). "Denning habits and home range of red foxes in New York State." *Jour. Wildlife Manag.,* 14:33–42.

SMITH, C. F. (1948). "A burrow of the pocket gopher (*Geomys bursarius*) in eastern Kansas." *Trans. Kansas Acad. Sci.,* 51:313–15.

TEVIS, L. (1950). "Summer behavior of a family of beavers in New York State." *Jour. Mammal.,* 31:40–65.

VESTAL, E. H. (1938). "Biotic relations of the wood rat (*Neotoma fuscipes*) in the Berkeley Hills." *Jour. Mammal.,* 19:1–36.

## Chapter 4

BENSON, S. B. (1939). "Concealing coloration among some desert rodents of the southwestern United States." *Univ. of Calif. Publ. in Zool.,* 40:1–70, 2 pls.

BRAESTRUP, F. W. (1941). "A study of the arctic fox in Greenland: immigrations, fluctuations in numbers, based mainly on trading statistics." *Medd. om Grönland,* 131:(4)1–101.

COTT, H. B. (1940). *Adaptive coloration in animals.* London: XXXII + 508 pp., 48 plates.

CUÉNOT, L. (1907). *"L'autotomie caudale chez quelques mammifères du groupe des rongeurs."* Comp. Rend. Soc. Biol., 62:174–6.

DEGERBÖL, M. (1940). *Mammalia,* in *Zoology of the Faroes.* Vol. 3, pt. 2, fasc. 65:1-133.

DEGERBÖL, M., and MÖHL-HANSEN, U. (1943). "Remarks on the breeding conditions and moulting of the collared lemming (*Dicrostonyx*)." *Medd. om Grönland,* 131:(11)1-40.

DICE, L. R. (1947). "Effectiveness of selection by owls of deer mice (*Peromyscus maniculatus*) which contrast in color with their background." *Contrib. Lab. Vert. Biol.,* 34:1-20.

GÖGL, H. (1930). "*Zur Frage der Schwanzautotomie bei Nagern.*" *Zeits. f. Morphol. Oekol Tiere,* 19:135-43.

HEIM DE BALSAC, H. (1936). "*Biogéographie des mammifères et des oiseaux de l'Afrique du Nord.*" *Bull. Biol. France Belgique,* Suppl. 21, 446 pp.

HOOPER, E. T. (1941). "Mammals of the lava fields and adjoining areas in Valencia County, New Mexico." *Misc. Publ., Mus. Zool. Univ. Michigan,* 51:1-47, 3 pls.

JOHNSON, C. E. (1921). "The 'hand stand' habit of the spotted skunk." *Jour. Mammal.,* 2:87-9.

MOHR, E. (1941). "*Schwanzverlust und Schwanzregeneration bei Nagetieren.*" *Zool. Anzeiger,* 135:48-65.

NOVIKOV, B. G., and BLAGODATSKIA, G. I. (1948). ("Mechanism of development of protective seasonal colorations"). *Doklad. Akad. Nauk. S. S. S. R.,* 61:577-80 (in Russian).

SHADLE, A. R., and PO-CHEDLEY, D. (1949). "Rate of penetration of a porcupine spine." *Jour. Mammal.,* 30:172-3.

SUMNER, F. R. (1932). "Genetic, distributional, and evolutional studies of the subspecies of deer mice (*Peromyscus*)." *Bibliog. Genetica,* 9:1-106.

### Chapter 5

ASDELL, S. A. (1946). *Patterns of Mammalian Reproduction.* Ithaca, Comstock, x + 437 pp., pl.

BEACH, F. A. (1939). "Maternal behavior of the pouchless marsupial, *Marmosa cinerea.*" *Jour. Mammal.,* 20:315-22, 1 pl.

BEACH, F. A. (1947). "Evolutionary changes in the physiological control of mating behavior in mammals." *Psychol. Reviews,* 54:297-315.

BURRELL, H. (1927). *The Platypus.* Sydney, Angus, vii-227 pp., pl.

CARPENTER, C. R. (1942). "Sexual behavior of free ranging rhesus monkeys (*Macaca mulatta*)." *Jour. Comp. Physiol.,* 33:133-62.

COURRIER, R. (1927). "*Étude sur déterminisme des caractères sexuels secondaires chez quelques mammifères à activité testiculaire periodique.*" *Arch. Biol.,* 37:173-334, pl.

FLEAY, D. (1944). "Observations on the breeding of *Platypus* in captivity." *Victorian Natur.*, 61:8–14, 29–37, 54–7, 74–8.

HARTMAN, C. G. (1920). "Studies in the development of the opossum, *Didelphys virginiana*. V. The phenomena of parturition." *Anat. Record*, 19:251–61.

HARTMAN, C. G. (1933). "On the survival of spermatozoa in the female genital tract of the bat." *Quart. Rev. Biol.*, 8:185–93.

HEDIGER, H. (1940). "*Zum Verhalten des amerikanischen Bisons bei der Geburt.*" *Verhandl. schweiz. naturforsch. Ges.*, 120:174–6.

HEDIGER, H. (1948). "*Die Zucht des Feldhasen (Lepus europæus Pallas) in Gefangenschaft.*" *Physiol. comp. Oecol.*, I:46–62.

HEDIGER, H. (1952). "*Brutpflege bei Säugetieren.*" *Ciba-Zeitschrift*, no. 129:4749–4758.

HERLANT, M. (1934). "*Recherches sur les potentialités de développement des oeufs obtenus par ovulation provoquée chez la chauve-souris en hibernation.*" *Bull. Acad. Roy. Belgique*, (5), 20:359–66.

LATASTE, F. (1887). "*Documents pour l'éthologie des mammifères.*" Bordeaux, 659 pp. Reprinted from: *Actes Soc. Linn. Bordeaux*, Vols. 40, 41, 43.

MATTHEWS, L. H. (1944). "Parturition in the kangaroo." *Proc. Zool. Soc. London*, 113:117–20, fig.

MINCHIN, K. A. (1937). "Notes on the weaning of a young koala (*Phascolarctus cinereus*)." *Records S. Austral. Mus.*, 6:1–3, pl.

PEARSON, O. P. (1944). "Reproduction in the shrew (*Blarina brevicauda* Say)." *Amer. Jour. Anat.*, 75:39–93.

PETZSCH, H. (1936). "*Beiträge zur Biologie, inbesondere Fortpflanzungsbiologie des Hamsters (Cricetus cricetus L.)*," Leipzig, 83 pp., fig.

RAMAKRISHNA, P. A. (1950). "*Parturition in certain Indian bats.*" *Jour. Mammal.*, 31:274–8.

RASPOPOV, M. P., and ISSAKOV, U. A. (1934). "On the biology of the squirrel." In *The biology of hares and squirrels: their diseases.* Moscow, 140 pp. (in Russian).

REED, C. E. (1946). "The copulatory behavior of small mammals." *Jour. Comp. Psychol.*, 39:185–206.

SCHNEIDER, K. M. (1930). "*Einige Boebachtungen über das Geschlechtleben des indischen Elefanten.*" *Zool. Garten*, 3:305–14.

SHADLE, A. R. (1946). "Copulation in the porcupine." *Jour. Wildlife Manag.*, 10:159–62, 1 pl.

SHADLE, A. R., SMELZER, M., and METZ, M. (1946). "The sex reactions of porcupines (*Erethizon d. dorsatum*) before and after copulation." *Jour. Mammal.*, 27:116–21.

SLIJPER, E. J. (1949). "On some phenomena concerning pregnancy and parturition of the Cetacea." *Bijdragen tot de Dierkunde*, 28:416–28, pl.

THOMPSON, W. K. (1949). "Observations of moose courting behavior." *Jour. Wildlife Manag.*, 13:313.

WELLS, L. J. (1935). "Seasonal sexual rhythm and its experimental modification in the male of the thirteen-lined ground squirrel (*Citellus tridecemlineatus*)." *Anat. Record*, 62:409–47.

WIMSATT, W. A. (1945). "Notes on breeding behavior, pregnancy, and parturition in some vespertilionid bats of the eastern United States." *Jour. Mammal.*, 26:23–33.

WUNDER, W. (1937). "*Brutpflege und Nestbau bei Säugetieren.*" *Ergebnisse der Biol.*, 14:280–348.

YOUNG, W. C. (1941). "Observations and experiments on mating behavior in female mammals." *Quart. Rev. Biol.*, 16:135–56, 311–55.

### Chapter 6

ADOLPH, E. F. (1948). "Tolerance to cold and anoxia in infant rats." *Amer. Jour. Physiol.*, 155:266–77.

BEACH, F. A. (1945). "Current concepts of play in animals." *Amer. Nat.*, 79:523–41.

BODENHEIMER, F. S. (1949). "Ecological and physiological studies on some rodents." *Physiol. Comp. Oecol.*, 1:376–89.

BOURLIÈRE, F. (1947). "*Le longévité des petits mammifères sauvages.*" *Mammalia*, 11:111–15.

BOURLIÈRE, F. (1948). "*Sur le reproduction et la croissance de Cricetomys gambianus.*" *Terre et Vie*, 1948:65–8, pl. IV.

BURBANK, R. C., and YOUNG, J. Z. (1934). "Temperature changes and winter sleep of bats." *Jour. Physiol.*, 82:459–67.

DAVIS, M. (1949). "Parturition in the Nubian giraffe (*Giraffa camelopardalis*)." *Jour. Mammal.*, 30:306–7.

EIBL-EIBESFELDT, I. (1950). "*Ueber die Jugendentwicklung des Verhaltens eines männlichen Daches (Meles meles L.) unter besonderer Berücksichtigung des Spieles.*" *Zeits. f. Tierpsychol.*, 7:327–55.

EIBL-EIBESFELDT, I. (1951a). "*Beobachtungen zur Fortpflanzungsbiologie und Jugendentwicklung des Eichhörnchens.*" *Zeits. f. Tierpsychol.*, 8:370–600.

EIBL-EIBESFELDT, I. (1951b). "*Gefangenschaftsbeobachtungen an den persischen Wüstenmaus (Meriones persicus persicus Blanford): Ein Beitrag zur vergleichenden Ethologie der Nager.*" *Zeits. f. Tierpsychol.*, 8:400–23.

EISENTRAUT, M. (1934). *"Der Winterschlaf der Fledermäuse mit besonderer Berücksichtigung der Wärmregulation."* Zeits. f. Morphol. Oekol. Tiere, 29:231–67.

FAIRFIELD, J. (1948). "Effects of cold on infant rats: body temperatures, oxygen consumption, electrocardiograms." *Amer. Jour. Physiol.,* 155:355–65.

FISHER, E. M. (1940). "Early life of a sea otter pup." *Jour. Mammal.,* 21:132–7.

FLOWER, S. S. (1931). "Contributions to our knowledge of the duration of life in vertebrate animals. V. Mammals." *Proc. Zool. Soc. London.* 1931:145–234.

FLOWER, S. S. (1948). "The alleged and actual ages to which elephants live." *Proc. Zool. Soc. London,* 117:680–8.

GEYER, R. P., GEYER, B. R., DERSE, P. H., ZINKIN, T., ELVEHJEM, C. A., and HART, E. B. (1947). "Growth studies with rats kept under conditions which prevent coprophagy." *Jour. Nutrition,* 33:129–42.

GRETER, W. F., and YERKES, R. M. (1940). "Weight norms and relations for chimpanzee." *Amer. Jour. Phys. Anthropol.,* 27:181–97.

HEYERDAL, E. F. (1930). Cited by Sivertsen.

HORNER, B. ELIZABETH (1947). "Paternal care of young mice of the genus *Peromyscus.*" *Jour. Mammal.,* 28:31–6.

KAYSER, C. (1950). *"Le sommeil hibernal."* Biol. Rev. 25:255–82. Contains a very complete bibliography of the physiological side of the problem.

MCBRIDE, A. F., and KRITZLER, H. (1951). "Observations on pregnancy, parturition and post-natal behavior in the bottlenose dolphin." *Jour. Mammal.,* 32:251–66.

RAND, A. L. (1935). "On the habits of some Madagascar mammals." *Jour. Mammal.,* 16:89–104.

SEITZ, A. (1950). *"Untersuchungen über angeborene Verhaltensweisen bei Caniden."* Zeits. f. Tierpsychol., 7:1–46.

SHADLE, A. R. (1944). "The play of American porcupines (*Erethizon d. dorsatum* and *E. epixanthum*)." *Jour. Compar. Psychol.,* 37:145–9.

SIVERSTEN, E. (1941). "On the biology of the harp seal *Phoca grœnlandica* Erxl." *Hvalradets Skrifter,* No. 26, ix plus 166 pp., 11 pl.

WAHLSTROM, A. (1929). *"Beitrage zur Biologie von Crocidura leucodon (Herm.)."* Zeits. f. Säugetierkunde, 4:157–185. For *Sorex vulgaris* see, *Ibid.,* 3:284–94, 1928.

ZIPPELIUS, H. M., and GOETHE, F. (1951). *"Ethologische Beobachtungen an Haselmäusen (Muscardinus a. avellanarius L.)."* Zeits. f. Tierpsychol., 8:348–67.

### Chapter 7

BELS, L. (1939). *"Leven en Trek van de Rosse Vleermuis (Nyctalus noctula Schreb)." De Levende Natuur*, 1939, pp. 289–99.

BURESCH, I. (1941). *"Die Fledermäuse ziehen wie die Zugvögel." Schr. Bulgar. Akad. Wiss.*, 61:51–72.

CASTERET, N. (1938). *"Observations sur une colonie de Chauves-souris migratrices." Mammalia*, 1938, pp. 29–34; see also *Ibid.*, 1939, pp. 1–9.

CLARKE, C. H. D. (1940). "A biological investigation of the Thelon game sanctuary." *National Museum of Canada, Bull.* 96, iv + 135 pp.

EISENTRAUT, M. (1934). *"Markierungs-versuche bei Fledermäusen." Zeits. f. Morphol. Oekol. Tiere*, 28:553–560.

EISENTRAUT, M. (1943). *"Zehn Jahre Fledermausberingung." Zool. Anz.*, 144:20–32.

GRIFFIN, D. R. (1945). "Travels of banded cave bats." *Jour. Mammal.*, 26:1–15.

HAMILTON, W. J., Jr. (1937). "Activity and home-range of the field mouse, *Microtus pennsylvanicus pennsylvanicus* (Ord.)." *Ecology*, 18:255–63.

HILZHEIMER, M. (1929). *"Die Wanderungen der Säugetiere." Ergebnisse der Biologie*, 5:219–89.

HOARE, W. H. B. (1930). *Notes on the muskox and the caribou.* Ottawa. Cited from Clarke.

MURIE, O. J. (1935). "Alaska-Yukon Caribou." *U. S. Dept. Agric., North Amer. Fauna*, 54; 93 pp.

MURIE, O. J., and MURIE, A. (1931). "Travels of *Peromyscus*." *Jour. Mammal.*, 12:200–9.

RAYNER, G. W. (1940). "Whale marking. Progress and results to December, 1939." *Discovery Reports*, 19:245–84, pl. 43–68.

RUSSELL, C. P. (1932). "Seasonal migration of mule deer." *Ecological Monographs*, 2:1–46.

SCHLEIDT, W. M. (1951). *Orientierende Versuche über die Heimkehrfähigkeit der Rötelmaus (Evotomys glareolus ruttneri)." Zeits. für Tierpsychol.*, 8:132–7.

SIVERSTEN, E. (1941). See the bibliography for the preceding chapter.

STICKEL, L. F. (1949). "An experiment on *Peromyscus* homing." *Amer. midland. Natur.*, 41:659–64.

### Chapter 8

ALLEE, W. C. (1938). *The Social Life of Animals.* New York, Norton.

ALLEE, W. C. (1950). "Dominance and Hierarchy in Societies of Vertebrates." In *Structure et physiologie des sociétés animales.* Paris, March 1950 (1952), pp. 157–81, pls. IV–VII.

ALTMANN, M. (1952). "Social behavior of elk, *Cervus canadensis nelsoni*, in the Jackson Hole area of Wyoming." *Behaviour*, 4:115–43.

ANTONIUS, O. (1937). "*Ueber Herdenbildung und Paarungseigentümlichkeiten der Einhufer.*" *Zeits. für Tierpsychol.*, 1:259–89.

ANTONIUS, O. (1939). "*Ueber Symbolhandlungen und Verwandtes bei Säugetieren.*" *Zeits. für Tierpsychol.*, 3:263–78.

BOURLIÈRE, F. (1950). "*Classification et caractéristiques des principaux types de groupements sociaux chez les Vertébrés sauvages.*" In *Structure et physiologie des sociétés animales*. Paris, March 1950 (1952), pp. 71–9.

BRADT, G. W. (1938). "A study of beaver colonies in Michigan." *Jour. Mammal.*, 19:139–52.

BUXTON, A. P. (1952). "Observations on the diurnal behavior of the redtail monkey (*Cercopithecus ascanius schmidti*) in a small forest in Uganda." *Jour. Animal Ecol.*, 21:25–58.

CARPENTER, C. R. (1942). "Societies of monkeys and apes." *Biological Symposia*, 8:177–204. See also the general bibliography, pp. 337–8.

CARPENTER, C. R. (1950). "Social behavior of non-human Primates." In *Structure et physiologie des sociétés animales*. Paris, March 1950 (1952), pp. 227–45, pls. VIII–XIII.

DARLING, F. (1950). "Social life in Ungulates." In *Structure et physiologie des sociétés animales*. Paris, March 1950 (1952), pp. 221–5. See also the general bibliography, pp. 337–8.

DAVIES, J. L. (1948). "Observations on the grey seal (*Halichœrus grypus*) at Ramsey Island, Pembrokeshire." *Proc. Zool. Soc. London*, 119:673–92, 2 pls.

HAMILTON, J. E. (1932). "The southern sea lion, *Otaria byronia* (de Blainville)." *Discovery Reports*, 8:269–318, pls. 1–13.

HEDIGER, H. (1950). "*Beiträge zur Säugetier-Sociologie.*" In *Structure et physiologie des sociétés animales*. Paris, March 1950 (1952), pp. 297–321, pls. XIV–XVI.

KATZ, I. (1949). "Behavioral interactions in a herd of Barbary sheep (*Ammotragus lervia*)." *Zoologica*, 34:9–18.

KRITZLER, H. (1952). "Observations on the pilot whale in captivity." *Jour. Mammal.*, 33:321–34.

MATTHEWS, L. H. (1929). "The natural history of the elephant seal." *Discovery Reports*, 1:233–56, pls. 19–24.

PEARSON, O. P. (1948). "Life history of mountain viscachas in Peru." *Jour. Mammal.*, 29:345–73

POCOCK, R. I. (1910). "On the specialized cutaneous glands of ruminants." *Proc. Zool. Soc. London*, 1910:840–985.

POCOCK, R. I. (1915). "On the feet and glands and other external characters of the Viverrinæ." *Proc. Zool. Soc. London,* 1915:131–49.

SAUVEL, R. (1949). "*Le kou-prey ou boeuf gris du Cambodge.*" *Terre et Vie,* 1949:89–109.

SCHAFFER, J. (1940). *Die Hautdrüsenorgane der Säugetiere.* Wien und Berlin, 1940.

SCHEVILL, W. E., and LAWRENCE, B. (1949). "Underwater listening to the white porpoise." *Science,* 109:143–4.

SCHENKEL, R. (1947). "*Ausdrucks-Studien an Wölfen.*" *Behaviour,* 1:81–129.

SOUTHERN, H. N. (1948). "Sexual and aggressive behaviour in the wild rabbit." *Behaviour,* 1:173–94.

YERKES, R. M., and LEARNED, B. W. (1925). *Chimpanzee Intelligence and its Vocal Expressions.* Baltimore.

### Chapter 9

ADOLPH, E. F. (1947). *Physiology of Man in the Desert.* New York, xiii + 357 pp., figs.

BAKER, J. R., and RANSON, R. M. (1932). "Factors affecting the breeding of the field mouse (*Microtus agrestis*) I. Light." *Proc. Roy. Soc.* (B) 110:313–22.

BISSONNETTE, T. H. (1936). "Sexual periodicity." *Quart. Rev. Biol.,* 11:371–86.

BISSONNETTE, T. H. (1941). "Experimental modifications of the breeding cycles in goats." *Physiol. Zool.,* 14:379–83.

BISSONNETTE, T. H., and BAILEY, E. E. (1944). "Experimental modification and control of moults and changes in coat color in weasels by controlled lighting." *Ann. N. Y. Acad. Sci.,* 45:221–60, pls.

BRITTON, S. W., and ATKINSON, W. E. (1938). "Poikilothermism in the sloth." *Jour. Mammal.,* 19:94–9.

DAVIS, W. B. (1938). "Relation of size of pocket gophers to soil and altitude." *Jour. Mammal.,* 19:338–42.

ELLISON, L. (1946). "The pocket gopher in relation to soil erosion on mountain range." *Ecology,* 27:101–14.

FORMOSOV, A. N. (1928). "Mammalia in the steppe biocenose." *Ecology,* 9:449–60.

FORMOSOV, A. N. (1946). "*La couverture de neige comme facteur intégrant du milieu et son importance dans l'écologie des mammifères et des oiseaux.*" *Mater. Flore Faune U. R. S. S.,* ser. Zool., 5:1–141, figs. In Russian with French summary.

GIAJA, J. (1938). "*L'homéothermie.*" Paris, *Actualités scient. industr.,* No. 576, 70 pp.

GRINNELL, J. (1923). "The burrowing rodents of California as agents in soil formation." *Jour. Mammal.*, 4:137–49.

GROOME, J. R. (1940). "The seasonal modification of the interstitial tissue of the fruit-bat (*Pteropus*)." *Proc. Zool. Soc. London*, (A), 110:37–42.

HALL, F. G., DILL, D. B., and GUZMAN BARRON, E. S. (1936). "Comparative physiology in high altitudes." *Jour. Cell. Comp. Physiol.*, 8:301–13.

HARRIS, V. T. (1952). "An experimental study of habitat selection by prairie and forest races of the deermouse *Peromyscus maniculatus.*" *Contrib. Lab. Vertebr. Biol. Univ. Michigan*, 56:1–53, 2 pls.

HARRISON, J. L. (1952). "Moonlight and the pregnancy of Malayan forest rats." *Nature*, 170:73–4.

HERTER, K. (1936). "*Das thermotaktische Optimum bie Nagetieren, ein mendelndes Art- und Rassenmerkmal.*" *Zeits. vergl. Physiol.*, 23:605–50.

HUBERT, E. (1947). *La faune des grands Mammifères de la plaine Rwindi-Rutshuru (Lac Edouard). Son évolution depuis sa protection totale.* Brussels. 84 pp., 25 pls., chart.

INGLES, L. G. (1949). "Ground water and snow as factors affecting the seasonal distribution of pocket gophers, *Thomomys monticola.*" *Jour. Mammal.*, 30:343–50.

KALABUCHOV, N. J. (1937). "Some physiological adaptations of the mountain and plain forms of the wood-mouse (*Apodemus sylvaticus*) and other species of mouse-like rodents." *Jour. Animal Ecol.*, 6:254–72.

LYMAN, C. P. (1942). "Control of coat color in the varying hare by daily illumination." *Proc. New Eng. Zool. Club*, 19:75–8.

MIDDLETON, A. D. (1930). "The ecology of the American gray squirrel (*Sciurus carolinensis*) in the British Isles." *Proc. Zool. Soc. London*, 1930:809–43, 6 pls.

MILLS, C. A. (1945). "Influence of environmental temperatures on warm-blooded animals." *Ann. N. Y. Acad. Sci.*, 46:97–105.

NERINCX, E. (1944). "*Notes sur l'éthologie et l'écologie des Cheiroptères de Belgique.*" *Bull. Mus. Roy. Hist. Nat. Belgique*, 20, Art. 19, 24 pp.

PAVLININE, V. N. (1948). ("Marking the European mole (*Talpa europæa* L.) in the Ural Mountains"). *Zool. Zjur.*, 27:555–62. In Russian.

SCHAERFFENBERG, B. (1939). "*Haltung und Pflege des Maulwurfs (Talpa europæa L.*)." *Zool. Garten*, 11:107–9.

SCHMIDT-NIELSEN, B., SCHMIDT-NIELSEN, K., BROKAW, A., and SCHNEIDER-

MAN, H. (1948). "Water conservation in desert rodents." *Jour. Cell. Comp. Physiol.*, 32:331–60.

SCHOLANDER, P. F., HOCK, R., WALTERS, V., and IRVING, L. (1950). "Adaptation to cold in arctic and tropical mammals and birds in relation to body temperature-insulation and basal metabolic rate." *Biol. Bull.*, 99:259–71 (See also other papers by the same authors in the same volume, pp. 229, 258).

SHORTEN, M. (1946). "A survey of the distribution of the American grey squirrel (*Sciurus carolinensis*) and the British red squirrel (*S. vulgaris leucorus*) in England and Wales in 1944–5." *Jour. Anim. Ecol.*, 15:82–92.

SUMMERHAYES, V. S. (1941). "The effect of voles (*Microtus agrestis*) on vegetation." *Jour. Ecol.*, 29:14–48.

STEIN, G. H. W. (1950). "*Grössenvariabilität und Rassenbildung bei Talpa europæa.*" *Zool. Jahrb.*, (Syst.), 79:321–49.

THOMAS, A. S. (1943). "The vegetation of the Karamoja district, Uganda." *Jour. Ecol.*, 31:149–78.

VORHIES, C. T. (1945). "Water requirements of desert animals in the Southwest." *Univ. Arizona Tech. Bull.*, No. 107 (cited by Schmidt-Nielsen *et al.*).

## Chapter 10

BLAIR, W. F. (1948). "Population density, life span, and mortality rates of small mammals in the bluegrass meadow and bluegrass field associations of southern Michigan." *Amer. Midl. Natur.*, 40:395–419.

BLAIR, W. F. (1950). "Ecological factors in speciation of *Peromyscus.*" *Evolution*, 4:253–75.

BODENHEIMER, F. S. (1949). "Problems of vole populations in the Middle East. Report on the population dynamics of the Levant vole (*Microtus guentheri* D. and A.)." Jerusalem, *Research Council of Israel*, 77 pp., fig.

BODENHEIMER, F. S., and DVORETZKY, A. (1952). "A dynamic model for the fluctuation of populations of the Levant vole (*Microtus guentheri* D. A.)." *Bull. Res. Council Israel*, 1:62–80.

BRAESTRUP, F. W. (1941). "A study on the arctic fox in Greenland: immigrations, fluctuations in numbers, based mainly on trading statistics." *Meddelelser om Grönland*, 131, No. 4, pp. 1–101.

BURT, W. H. (1940). "Territorial behavior and populations of some small mammals in southern Michigan." *Mus. Zool., Univ. Michigan, Misc. Publ.*, No. 45, pp. 1–58, 2 pls.

CALHOUN, J. B. (1948). "Mortality and movement of brown rats (*Rattus *norvegicus*) in artificially supersaturated populations." *Jour. Wildlife Manag.*, 12:167–72.

CALHOUN, J. B. (1952). "The social aspects of population dynamics." *Jour. Mammal.*, 33:139–59.

CHRISTIAN, J. J. (1950). "The adreno-pituitary system and population cycles in mammals." *Jour. Mammal.*, 31:247–59.

COLLETT, R. (1911–12). *Norges Pattedyr.* Oslo.

CURRIER, W. W. (1949). "The effect of den flooding on woodchucks." *Jour. Mammal.*, 30:429–30.

DAVIS, D. E. (1948). "The survival of wild brown rats on a Maryland farm." *Ecology*, 29:437–48.

DEEVEY, E. S. (1947). "Life tables for natural populations of animals." *Quart. Rev. Biol.*, 22:283–314.

EISENTRAUT, M. (1947). *"Die mit Hilfe der Beringungsmethode erzielten Ergebnisse über Lebensdauer und jährliche Verlustziffern bei Myotis myotis Borkh."* *Experientia*, 3:157.

ELTON, C. (1942). *Voles, Mice and Lemmings: Problems in Population Dynamics.* Oxford, 496 pp.

ELTON, C., and NICHOLSON, M. (1942). "The ten-year cycle in numbers of the lynx in Canada." *Jour. Anim. Ecol.*, 11:215–44.

ELTON, C., and NICHOLSON, M. (1942). "Fluctuations in numbers of the muskrat in Canada." *Jour. Anim. Ecol.*, 11:96–126.

ELTON, C., FORD, E. B., BAKER, J. R., and GARDNER, A. D. (1931). "The health and parasites of a wild mouse population." *Proc. Zool. Soc. London*, 1931:657–721.

ERRINGTON, P. L. (1946). "Predation and vertebrate populations." *Quart. Rev. Biol.*, 21:144–77, 221–45.

ERRINGTON, P. L. (1951). "Concerning fluctuations in populations of the prolific and widely distributed muskrat." *Am. Nat.*, 85:273–92.

FINDLAY, G. M., and MIDDLETON, A. D. (1934). "Epidemic disease among voles (*Microtus*) with special reference to *Toxoplasma*." *Jour. Anim. Ecol.*, 3:150–60.

FRILEY, C. E., JR. (1949). "Age determination, by use of the baculum, in the river otter, *Lutra c. canadensis* Schreber." *Jour. Mammal.*, 30:102–10.

FRILEY, C. E., JR. (1949). "Use of the baculum in age determination of Michigan beaver." *Jour. Mammal.*, 30:261–7.

GREEN, R. G., and EVANS, C. A. (1940). "Studies on a population cycle of snowshoe hares on the Lake Alexander area." *Jour. Wildlife Manag.*, 4:220–38, 267–78, 347–58. See also *Amer. Jour. Hygiene* (1938), 28:190–212 and (1939), 30:83–102.

HAYNE, D. W. (1949). "Two methods for estimating population from trapping records." *Jour. Mammal.*, 30:399–411.

HAMILTON, W. J., JR. (1937). "The biology of microtine cycles." *Jour. Agric. Research*, 54:779–790.

JACKSON, C. H. N. (1939). "The analysis of an animal population." *Jour. Anim. Ecol.*, 8:238–46.

KALABUCHOV, N. J. (1933). ("Marking of *Citellus pygmaeus* Pall. in order to study their length of life in natural conditions.") *Rec. Trav. Sci. Univ. Moscou*, 1:29–33. In Russian.

KALELA, O. (1949). "*Über Fjeldlemming-Invasionen und andere irreguläre Tierwanderungen.*" *Ann. Soc. Zool. Bot. Fennicae, Vanamo*, Vol. 13, No. 5, iv–90 pp.

LAURIE, E. M. O. (1946). "The reproduction of the house-mouse (*Mus musculus*) living in different environments." *Proc. Roy. Soc. Biol.*, 133:248–81.

LESLIE, P. H., and RANSON, R. M. (1940). "The mortality, fertility and rate of natural increase of the vole (*Microtus agrestis*) as observed in the laboratory." *Jour. Anim. Ecol.*, 9:27–52.

LINDUSKA, J. P. (1947). "Longevity of some Michigan farm game animals." *Jour. Mammal.*, 28:126–9.

MacLULICH, D. A. (1937). "Fluctuations in the numbers of the varying hare (*Lepus americanus*)." *Univ. Toronto Stud., Biol. Ser.*, 43:136 pp.

MAXIMOV, A. A. (1948). ("Fecundity and population dynamics of *Microtus arvalis* Pall.") *Izvestia Akad. Naouk SSSR*, 1948:73–81. In Russian.

MILLER, W. C. (1932). "A preliminary note upon the sex-ratio of Scottish red deer." *Proc. Roy. Phys. Soc.*, 22:99–101.

PALMGREN, P. (1949). "Some remarks on the short-term fluctuations in the numbers of northern birds and mammals." *Oikos*, 1:114–21.

POPOV, V. A. (1943). "A new age index in Mustelidae." *C. R. Acad. Sci. URSS*, 38:258–60.

RANSON, R. M. (1941). "Pre-natal and infant mortality in a laboratory-population of voles (*Microtus agrestis*)." *Proc. Zool. Soc. London*, (A) 111:45–57.

RUUD, J. T. (1940). "The surface structure of the baleen plates as a possible clue to age in whales." *Hvalrad. Skr.*, No. 23. See also No. 29, 1945.

SCHEFFER, V. B. (1951). "The rise and fall of a reindeer herd." *Sci. Monthly*, 73:356–62.

SCHEIN, M. W. (1950). "The relation of sex-ratio to physiological age in the wild brown rat." *Am. Nat.*, 84:489–96.

SEVERINGHAUS, C. W. (1949). "Tooth development and wear as criteria of age in white-tailed deer." *Jour. Wildlife Manag.*, 13:195–216. 4 pls.

SIIVONEN, L. (1948). "Structure of short-cyclic fluctuations in numbers of mammals and birds in the northern parts of the Northern Hemisphere." Helsinki, *Papers on game research*, No. 1, 166 pp.

SPERBER, I. (1948). "On the growth of rootless molars, particularly in the field-vole (*Microtus agrestis. L.*)." *Archiv för Zoologi*, 40 A:1–12.

STICKEL, L. F. (1948). "Observations on the effect of flood on animals." *Ecology*, 29:505–7.

WIESNER, B. P., and SHEARD, N. M. (1934). "The duration of life in an albino rat population." *Proc. Roy. Soc. Edinburgh*, 55:1–22.

ZIMMERMANN, K. (1937). *"Die märkische Rötelmaus. Analyse einer Population."* *Märkische Tierwelt*, 3:24–40.

# A Note on the Type

*The text of this book was set on the Linotype in Janson,
a recutting made direct from the type cast from matrices
(now in possession of the Stempel foundry, Frankfurt am
Main) made by Anton Janson some time between 1660
and 1687.*

*Of Janson's origin nothing is known. He may have
been a relative of Justus Janson, a printer of Danish birth
who practiced in Leipzig from 1614 to 1635. Some time
between 1657 and 1668 Anton Janson, a punch-cutter and
type-founder, bought from the Leipzig printer Johann
Erich Hahn the type-foundry that had formerly been a
part of the printing house of M. Friedrich Lankisch.
Janson's types were first shown in a specimen sheet issued
at Leipzig about 1675. Janson's successor, and perhaps his
son-in-law, Johann Karl Edling, issued a specimen sheet
of Janson types in 1689. His heirs sold the Janson matrices
in Holland to Wolffgang Dietrich Erhardt of Leipzig.*

*Composed, printed, and bound by* KINGSPORT PRESS,
INC., *Kingsport, Tennessee.*

*Designed by* HARRY FORD.